# The Dentist's Handbook
## on Law and Ethics

# The Dentist's Handbook on Law and Ethics

### WITH SECTIONS ON
### FORENSIC DENTISTRY, INCOME TAX
### AND SUPERANNUATION

*by*

## W. R. TATTERSALL
**F.D.S., H.D.D.R.C.S.EDIN., L.D.S.U.ST.AND.**

*Lecturer and Examiner in Dental Jurisprudence, formerly
Lecturer and Examiner in Dental Surgery, University of
St. Andrews, Vice-Chairman of Council of the Medical and Dental
Defence Union of Scotland*

## H. D. BARRY
*of the Middle Temple, Barrister-at-Law,
formerly Deputy Secretary,
British Dental Association*

*and*

## E. EDEN, M.A. (OXON)
*of the Inner Temple, Barrister-at-Law, Assistant
Secretary, British Dental Association*

### With a Section on Income Tax by

## W. DONALD, C.A.
*Accountant to the British Dental Association*

### and a Foreword by

### SIR E. WILFRED FISH
**C.B.E., M.D., D.SC., D.D.SC., F.D.S.R.C.S.**
*President of the General Dental Council*

1962
## EYRE & SPOTTISWOODE
LONDON

Dedicated to

the late

DR LILIAN LINDSAY

*who first inspired the authors*

*to undertake this work*

First published 1953
Second edition 1962
© 1962 by W. R. Tattersall, H. D. Barry and E. Eden
Printed in Great Britain
for Eyre & Spottiswoode (Publishers) Ltd
22 Henrietta Street, London, W.C.2,
by The Camelot Press, Southampton
Catalogue No. 6/6050

# Contents

## Part I. LAW AND ETHICS IN THE CONDUCT OF DENTAL PRACTICE

### A. *The Dentist and the State*

## B. *The Dentist in the Organized Dental Services*

## C. *The Dentist and the Public*

# APPENDICES

# Foreword

That "ignorance of the law excuses no man" is a maxim which has received wide acceptance since the days of Justinian, and even in the modern highly organized state a citizen is expected to have knowledge of the law, despite its growing complexity, whenever he comes into contact with it. This considerable obligation weighs particularly heavily upon the professional man, who, by definition, incurs special responsibilities towards those who consult him, towards his colleagues and towards the State. Such a one must have a more than passing acquaintance not only with those Acts of Parliament and regulations which expressly order the conduct of his profession but also with such aspects of more general laws as may affect him in practice—aspects in which the law is by no means always clearly defined.

The introduction of the National Health Service has greatly augmented the body of specialized law which dentists are required to assimilate. Henceforward jurisprudence must occupy a position of increased importance in the curriculum of the dental student, and even the most seasoned practitioner will find many occasions on which he needs to seek information or refresh his memory from an authoritive source.

Moreover, as a profession grows in self-awareness and public recognition, so of itself it evolves rules of conduct for its members. By the ethical content of such rules and by the extent to which they are observed the profession will ultimately come to be judged, and it is therefore of great concern to the members thereof that at the proper time the rules should be codified and thereafter consciously studied by all who practise upon the public. Dentistry is a young profession, and the ethics of dental practice are as yet neither as fully developed nor as widely understood and observed as those of older professions, but development and appreciation are today proceeding apace, and whatever furthers the process and helps to ensure that it follows the right lines must be warmly welcomed.

It is therefore a reason for much satisfaction that the authors of this handbook should have combined their wide experience, both theoretical and practical, of the impact of the law and of professional ethics upon dental practitioners to produce a work which is at once comprehensive and stimulating. They have given real assistance to many generations of students and, by their most valuable contribution to the promotion of high standards of professional conduct among dentists, have earned the gratitude of the whole profession.     E. W .F.

# Preface to First Edition

This book, as the title implies, has been written for the practical purpose of providing students and practitioners with a concise account of those legal, ethical and financial problems which surround the practice of dentistry.

Its arrangement into three parts will, we hope, assist the student and practitioner reader alike, the former in preparing for examination in the subject of Dental Jurisprudence, now required in our Dental Schools, and the latter in gaining guidance in problems which beset him in the course of his professional work. In the chapters in Part I dealing with the Dentist and the State there is a certain amount of repetition which has been introduced purposely to aid the student reader in the assimilation of facts. The chapters in Part III are included in the belief that they will provide the practitioner with useful information on the complicated subjects of Income Tax and Superannuation. The inclusion of a number of appendices will, we think, enhance the usefulness of the volume as a book of reference.

The chapter on Superannuation for the Dentist was originally written by one of us at the request of the British Dental Association for the benefit of its members. We acknowledge our indebtedness to the Council of the Association for permission to incorporate the chapter here and also for permission to include as an appendix the British Dental Association's Guidance for Professional Conduct.

By footnotes throughout the text, we have endeavoured to acknowledge our sources of information but we must specially record our thanks to Miss Christian J. Bisset, Lecturer in Evidence and Procedure in the University of St. Andrews and to Mr. James Clark, Procurator-Fiscal, Dundee, for their assistance in matters relating to Courts of Law and Legal Procedure in Scotland. Mr. John Riddell, Solicitor, Dundee, also deserves our thanks for his guidance regarding the legal position in Scotland of married women and persons under age.

In our search for references we have been greatly assisted by the Librarian and Staff of the British Dental Association, of the University College, Dundee, and of the Perth and Kinross County, to all of whom we tender our grateful thanks. For assistance in preparing illustrations we are indebted to Mr. J. Grierson of the Dundee Dental School.

The important task of reading proofs was kindly undertaken by

Mr. D. Hindley Smith, Registrar of the Dental Board of the United Kingdom, and for this, as well as for much helpful advice which he has given, we are greatly indebted and most grateful.

Finally, we cordially thank our publishers for the help they have given us and the care they have bestowed in the production of this book.

W. R. T.
H. D. B.

1953

# Preface to Second Edition

The authors believe that this handbook, designed to serve students and practitioners of dentistry, has been of some assistance, but its usefulness as a guide to the legal problems which may arise in everyday practice depends upon its being kept up to date.

Since its publication there have been two major alterations in the law. The Dentists Act of 1957 has amended the law relating to the practice of dentistry and the control of the profession and this has called for a complete revisal of the first five chapters. Decisions in the Courts have clarified the position regarding the vicarious liability of Hospital Authorities and this important change has been incorporated in the chapter on Negligence. The section on Income Tax has also been brought up to date by Mr Donald. To him and to Mr E. Eden, who has assisted in the general revision of the text for this new edition, we express our indebtedness.

W. R. T.
H. D. B.

# Law and Ethics in the
# Conduct of Dental Practice

# A. The Dentist and the State

# CHAPTER I

# Introductory

## I. HISTORICAL

Control of dentists by the State, brought about by the Dentists Acts, passed between 1878 and 1957, is of recent origin though *recognition* of persons entitled to practise dentistry dates back to the days when there were three types of practitioners of the healing art, namely the learned physicians, the apothecaries and the surgeons. The surgeons combined their art with the humbler craft of the barbers and the Guild of Barber-Surgeons was a flourishing body in London in the fifteenth century. A smaller Guild of Surgeons also existed and the two were incorporated as one Company in 1540, but the Act of Parliament[1] which united them kept separate the functions of each, the barbers being permitted to practise no surgery except blood-letting and the drawing of teeth.

While there was recorded in 1551 the admission to the Barber-Surgeons of John Brychett, 'toothe-drawer', it was not till six years later, as stated by Lindsay,[2] that the first licence in dentistry was granted. In that year (1557) William Tomlyn was permitted to 'draw teethe and to make clean teethe and no more'.

In those days and for a long period afterwards the majority of persons undertaking dental operations were itinerant tooth-drawers without training, many of whom combined tooth drawing with other occupations. There were some legitimate practitioners, often surgeons, styling themselves 'operators for the teeth' who employed a fair degree of skill and from among whom royal appointments were made, namely Middleton in 1671, Green in 1756 and Berdmore in 1766.

Berdmore it was who published one of the first books on dentistry. His *Treatise on the Disorders and Deformities of the Teeth and Gums* in 1768 was preceded by Charles Allen's *The Operator for the Teeth* in

---

[1] 32 Henry 8, c. 42.
[2] LINDSAY, LILIAN (1931), *A Short History of Dentistry*, London, Bale.

1685 and succeeded by John Hunter's *Natural History of the Human Teeth* in 1771.[1]

The honour of instituting the first lectures in dental surgery in Britain goes to James Rae, a prominent surgeon in Edinburgh who gave a course there in 1764 on Diseases of the Teeth.[2] His son William Rae was the pioneer in England, having delivered in 1782 the first lectures in dentistry which he gave in Hunter's house in London.

The Surgeons broke away from the Barbers in 1745 and the Company of Surgeons was reconstituted by Royal Charter in 1800 under the name of the Royal College of Surgeons of London to become in 1843 the Royal College of Surgeons of England.[3] By the Medical Act of 1858 the Royal College became entitled to institute and hold examinations for the purpose of testing the fitness of persons to practise as dentists, who desired to be examined. In 1860 the first forty-three dentists, already in practice, who presented themselves passed the examination and were granted certificates by the College. The first List of Licensed Dentists was published in 1865 as part of the unofficial Medical Directory. In Scotland, the Royal College of Surgeons of Edinburgh received its Charter in 1778 but did not institute examinations in dentistry until the Dentists Act was passed in 1878.

In 1858 the first dental hospital and school opened in London and was followed in 1860 by the Edinburgh Dental Dispensary which was to become the pioneer dental hospital and school in Scotland.

Meantime, the Odontological Society was founded by Tomes and others in 1855 and the College of Dentists by Rymer and others two years later. The Odonto-chirurgical Society of Scotland came into being in 1867 and the British Dental Association was incorporated in 1880. There was thus a long interval between the development of the art of dentistry and its organization into any semblance of a profession.

The transition from the craft to the profession of dentistry, according to some, occurred at the time when organized bodies came into existence, but whether professional status was reached at that stage, or indeed for many years later, may be doubted. Certain it is that dentistry continued to be carried on more as a craft than as a profession, due doubtless to the fact that those practising it fell into two distinct groups. A few men with medical and surgical qualifications specialized

[1] CAMPBELL, J. M. (1951), *18th Century Dentistry*, London, Gale & Polden.
[2] HUTCHINSON, A. C. W. (1952), 'The History of Dentistry in Edinburgh', *Brit. dent. J.*, **93**, 36.
[3] ROWLETT, A. E. (1945), *The Royal College of Surgeons and its Connection with Dentistry*, Leicester, Thornly.

in dentistry and a small number, which by 1870 did not exceed three hundred, practised by virtue of a certificate of fitness granted by the Royal College of Surgeons of England. By far the larger group consisted of unqualified individuals who attracted patients by blatant advertising and whose self-praises were generally in inverse ratio to their knowledge and skill. Moreover, the public had no means of distinguishing the qualified from the unqualified practitioner and unwittingly placed themselves in unskilled hands, often with unfortunate results. In an endeavour to remedy this state of affairs, there was set up in 1875 a Dental Reform Committee, having for its object 'the promulgation of legislation to amend the law relating to persons practising dentistry'.[1] The Work of this Committee prepared the way for the Dentists Act, 1878 which can be regarded as the first legislative attempt to control the practice of dentistry. That the Act failed to effect any real control soon became apparent but the public remained unprotected from the evils of unregistered practice until 1922 when the Dentists Act of the previous year became operative. The Act of 1921, though perhaps not an ideal measure, largely restricted the practice of dentistry to registered practitioners, and was, on that account, a landmark in the history of dentistry in this country. So also was the Dentists Act, 1956 which included in its provisions the establishment of the General Dental Council to give for the first time self-government to the profession. The Dentists Act, 1957 is a consolidating measure which incorporates into one Act the law relating to dentistry.

Between 1911 and 1936 a number of National Health Insurance Acts were passed, by some of which certain wage earners who were compulsorily insured became entitled to 'dental benefit'. These Acts, now repealed, are of historical interest for they paved the way for a state dental service which was introduced on a comprehensive basis by the National Health Service of 1946 and the National Health Service (Scotland) Act of 1947.

## 2. ACTS GOVERNING DENTAL PRACTICE

While the Medical Act, 1858 affects to some extent the practice of dentistry in that section 48 empowers the Royal College of Surgeons of England to institute and conduct examinations for the purpose of 'testing the fitness of persons to practise as dentists and to grant

---

[1] HILL, A. (1877), *History of the Reform Movement of the Dental Profession in Great Britain*, London, Trübur.

BDH

certificates of such fitness', the Dentists Act of 1878 was the first legislative measure designed to control the practice of dentistry and the conduct of dentists.

The main features of this Act and subsequent Acts are mentioned in this chapter but only briefly because such important matters as the bodies concerned with the administration of the Dentists Acts, registration of dentists, the Dentists Register and discipline of the profession are dealt with in detail in the chapters which follow. Details concerning the National Health Service Acts are included in Chapter VII. Other Statutes which govern the practice of dentistry are also briefly considered here except those which control the dentist in his use of dangerous drugs and poisons. The Dangerous Drugs Act, 1951 and the Pharmacy and Poisons Act, 1933 are considered in more detail for they are not dealt with elsewhere in this volume.

## A. Dentists Act, 1878

Modelled on the Medical Act, 1858, the Dentists Act, 1878 was passed to make provision for the registration of persons specially qualified to practise as dentists in the United Kingdom and to amend the law relating to persons practising as dentists.

Having been repealed almost entirely by the Dentists Act, 1957 the 1878 Act is now only of historical interest.

i] *Main Features.* The Act established the Dentists Register, to be kept by the General Medical Council, and gave the right to be registered to *a)* those already practising dentistry at the time of the passing of the Act and *b)* for the future, only those possessing appropriate academic qualifications.

To those who were registered it gave the right to use the title 'dentist' or 'dental practitioner' or any other title which implied registration and prohibited the taking or using of any such titles by persons who were not registered.

It conferred on those who were registered the right to practise dentistry in any part of Her Majesty's dominions (subject outside the United Kingdom to any local rule in force). It did *not* prohibit the practice of dentistry by unregistered persons.

Until 1878 the Royal College of Surgeons of England was the only body authorized to conduct examinations and grant certificates of fitness for the practice of dentistry. By section 18 of the 1878 Act this power was extended to all those medical authorities entitled to grant surgical degrees or diplomas.

The duty of superintending examinations and the courses of study preparatory to them was given to the General Medical Council who appointed Visitors or Deputy Visitors for the purpose, and power was given to rectify examinations or courses of study which might be found defective.

ii] *Defects of the Act.* Although the Act did much to raise the status of dentistry by establishing the Dentists Register and by granting certain privileges to registered dentists, that was not its main object. It was designed to protect the public from the evil effects of haphazard practice by untrained and unskilled persons. Adequate protection, it was hoped, would be achieved by the restriction of the use of title to those who were registered so that the public could distinguish the trained and skilful registered dentist from the untrained, unskilled and often unscrupulous 'quack'. But the privilege of title for the registered dentist proved to be worthless, for in the case of *Bellerby* v. *Heyworth*[1] the House of Lords ruled that the words 'specially qualified to practise dentistry' in section 3 meant only that the person using them was entitled to be registered and not that he was specially skilful or competent. By this decision it became lawful for any unregistered person to represent himself as competent so long as he did not use the forbidden title of 'dentist' or 'dental practitioner', etc. Indeed, after this, unregistered persons in increasing numbers described themselves as 'dental consultants', 'dental experts' and the like so that the public were unable to distinguish the registered from the unregistered practitioner.

Furthermore, the provision in section 5 of the Act whereby an unregistered person was prohibited from recovering in any court any fee or charge 'for the performance of any dental operation or for any dental attendance or advice' did not act as a deterrent to the unregistered, for it was decided that this prohibition did not extend to the recovery of charges for supplying artificial dentures[2] and the supplying of such dentures constituted the main activity in unregistered practices.

The Act, failing as it did to place any restriction upon unregistered practice, permitted the springing up and multiplication of Dental Companies so long as they conformed to the requirements of the Companies Act. There was also an increase in the number of individual unregistered practitioners, many of whom brought little skill and doubtful ethics into the conduct of their calling. They were not all quacks and charlatans: the more skilful and ethical unregistered practitioners in 1893 formed themselves into the 'Society of Extractors and

[1] (1910), A.C. 377.    [2] *Hennan* v. *Duckworth*, 20 T.L.R. 436.

Adapters' which later became the respected and important 'Incorporated Dental Society'.

Nevertheless, the public continued to be subjected to the evils of unregistered practice and so serious did the situation become that in 1918, largely as a result of the efforts of the British Dental Association, there was set up a Government Departmental Committee to inquire into 'the extent and gravity of the evils of dental practice by persons not qualified under the Dentists Act'. The Report of this Committee[1] revealed that:

 *a*) Under the existing law any person, however ignorant, unskilled or untrained, could practise dentistry and inform the public that he did so.

 *b*) The public had no protection except an action for damages in case of injury or the fear on the part of the operator of a possible prosecution for manslaughter in the case of death.

 *c*) The law which permitted unregistered practice produced among other evils, a lowering of social status and public esteem of the profession and a consequent shortage of registered dentists owing to the unattractiveness of the profession.

The Committee emphasized the urgent need to protect the public against the evils of unregistered practice and to protect the registered dentist from unfair competition. Its Report did much to facilitate the passing of the Dentists Act, 1921.

### B. Medical Act, 1886

In its bearing on the Dentists Act, 1878 the Medical Act of 1886 is of minor importance only.

It enacts that persons who, by virtue of section 5 of the Dentists Act, 1878, practise in any of Her Majesty's dominions other than the United Kingdom shall be subject to any local law in force in that part. This means that a qualification which entitles a person to be registered in the Dentists Register and to practise in this country may not, *ipso facto*, confer similar rights in British territory overseas.

It also amended the Dentist Act, 1878 by placing further restrictions on the use of title by the unregistered and by permitting any private individual to institute a prosecution for an offence against the Act. That part of the section dealing with these points was repealed by the Dentists Act, 1921.

---

[1] Report of the Departmental Committee on the Dentists Act, 1878 (1919).

## C. Dentists Act, 1921

The Dentists Act, 1921, though repealed by the Act of 1957, was an important measure for it prohibited the practice of dentistry by unregistered persons (with a few exceptions) and transferred to the Dental Board of the United Kingdom, which it established, some of the duties of governing the profession which had formerly been undertaken by the General Medical Council.

i] *Main Features.* The Act laid down that 'no person shall, unless he is registered in the dentists register under the Dentists Act, 1878 . . . practise, or hold himself out, whether directly or by implication, as practising or as being prepared to practise dentistry'. The practice of dentistry was defined in section 14(2), as follows: 'For the purpose of this Act, the practice of dentistry shall be deemed to include the performance of any such operation and the giving of any such treatment, advice, or attendance as is usually performed or given by dentists, and any person who performs any operation or gives any treatment, advice, or attendance on or to any person as preparatory to or for the purpose of or in connexion with the fitting, insertion, or fixing of artificial teeth shall be deemed to have practised dentistry within the meaning of this Act.'

The Dental Board was empowered to institute prosecutions for offences against the Dentists Acts, though not in Scotland where prosecutions for such offences are undertaken by the Procurator-Fiscal. Any person contravening section 1 of the Act was liable, on summary conviction, to a fine not exceeding £100 for each offence.

The only exceptions[1] to the prohibition upon unregistered practice are:

*a)* A registered medical practitioner may carry on dental practice to any extent.

*b)* A registered pharmaceutical chemist or registered chemist and druggist may, in urgent circumstances and when no registered medical or dental practitioner is available, extract a tooth provided no local or general anaesthetic is employed.

*c)* A person may undertake 'minor dental work' in any public dental service provided he or she does so under the personal supervision of a registered dentist and in accordance with conditions approved by the Minister of Health after consultation with the Dental Board.

---

[1] These exceptions were re-enacted by the Dentists Act, 1957, s. 34.

The establishment of a Dental Board and the appointment of a Registrar were important provisions in the Act, for they allowed of the transference of certain duties relating to the discipline of the dental profession and to registration of dentists which were formerly undertaken by the General Medical Council. By these provisions the Act gave to the dental profession some measurement of control of its own affairs.

The Act entitled certain persons to be admitted to the Dentists Register in addition to those already entitled to be registered in virtue of the Dentists Act, 1878 (for details see page 35).

The Act permitted, subject to conditions, the carrying on of dental practice by limited companies and provided for their registration in a separate list in the Dentists Register.

ii] *Defects of the Act.* Though the Act intended to prevent anyone from practising dentistry who was not registered in the Dentists Register (with the exceptions already noted) it was not altogether successful in this. Many dental mechanics or persons calling themselves dental mechanics carried on the business of 'denture repair shops' ostensibly for the repair of artificial dentures. So long as a person merely repaired a broken denture he was not in breach of the Act but only in a minority of instances can an artificial denture be repaired satisfactorily *without taking an impression of the mouth.* If, therefore, a person working in a denture repair shop did the work satisfactorily he had to take an impression of the mouth in most cases and by so doing he contravened section 14(2) of the Act.

The Act stated[1] that 'nothing shall operate to prevent the practice of dentistry by a registered medical practitioner' who might, therefore, perform any dental operation. In rural areas without a resident dentist it is customary for medical practitioners to extract teeth for the relief of pain. That they should do so in such circumstances is obviously in the public interest but it is questionable whether the possession of a medical qualification alone can fit a person to perform satisfactorily those operations in the mouth for which the dentist is required to devote years of study and training. It might have been more logical to have curtailed the privileges of medical practitioners so far as dental practice was concerned to emergency operations for the relief of pain.

While the Act did much to raise the status of the profession by establishing the Dental Board of the United Kingdom and allotting to it certain administrative duties formerly undertaken by the General

[1] Dentists Act, 1921, s. 1 (3) (*a*).

Medical Council, dentists were not given full control of their affairs. Of the thirteen members constituting the Dental Board only six were required to be registered dental practitioners, and the Chairman, who did not need to be a dentist, was appointed by the Privy Council. Furthermore, the Dental Board could only *recommend* cases for disciplinary action by the General Medical Council and had no control over dental education and examinations, which remained the function of the General Medical Council.

To many, the chief defect of the Act was that it permitted limited companies to carry on the business of dentistry. The Act laid down the conditions under which a body corporate could carry on the business of dentistry but these were found in some instances to provide less adequate safeguards than were intended. Even if the safeguards had been found to be satisfactory, there remained the undesirable feature that dentists employed by such companies had to share with laymen the professional fees which they earned.

## D. Dentists Act, 1923

Section 3 of the Dentist Act, 1921 conferred on certain persons who possessed no registerable qualification, the right to be admitted to the Dentists Register, provided that, *inter alia*, they applied for registration within the stipulated period and passed the prescribed examination in dentistry within ten years from the passing of the Act.

Because of their service in His Majesty's Forces during the war, 1914–18, some persons were unable to comply with these requirements and the Dentists Act, 1923, was passed to permit of the possibility of their being registered. In particular, the Act extended the period during which application had to be made and, at the discretion of the Dental Board, the period during which the prescribed examination had to be passed.

## E. Medical and Dentists Acts Amendment Act, 1927

As a consequence of the establishment of an independent Irish Free State, it became expedient that there should be an agreement between Great Britain, the Irish Free State and Northern Ireland in matters relating to the registration and control of dentists in these countries.

The agreement relating to dentists is set forth in Part II of the Schedule to the Act and confirmed by section 2 of the Act. Where reference is made to the Dental Board of the United Kingdom the body now concerned is the General Dental Council. The Act entitles, with certain provisos, a person registered in the Dentists Register of the United Kingdom to be registered in the corresponding register in what is now the Republic of Ireland: but this privilege no longer applies to those whose names appear in the Commonwealth or Foreign List of the United Kingdom Register.[1]

## F. Dentists Act, 1956

The provision of this important measure can be summarized thus:

1) The Act dissolved the Dental Board of the United Kingdom and established in its place the General Dental Council which is now responsible for carrying out the duties formerly undertaken by the Dental Board in respect of the registration of dentists and by the General Medical Council in matters relating to dental education and examinations. The General Dental Council is wholly responsible for the discipline of the profession.
2) The Act put a further curb on practice by unregistered persons by extending the definition of the practice of dentistry and thus facilitating prosecutions for infringement of the Dentists Acts.
3) The Act placed severe restrictions upon the conduct of the business of dentistry by limited companies and by lay persons.
4) The Act permitted anyone in the Dentists Register to use the title of 'Dental Surgeon'.
5) The Act gave the General Dental Council power to introduce ancillary dental workers to perform a wide range of dental operations.

The Dentists Act, 1957 repealed the 1956 Act almost entirely but re-enacted all the provisions summarized above.

## G. Dentists Act, 1957

The Dentists Act, 1957 which came into force on 1 September of that year made no new law: it merely consolidated into one Act the law relating to the practice of dentistry. It should be regarded as the dentists' 'bible' and should be in the possession of every practitioner and student of dentistry. In the next four chapters which follow, the 1957 Act rather than the 1956 Act, will be constantly referred to.

## H. National Health Insurance Acts

Between 1911 and 1936 there were passed a number of Acts having for their object the provision of an insurance scheme and health service for those, having an income less than a stated amount, who were

---

[1] Dentists Act, 1956, s. 16 (9).

compelled to insure themselves and for a small number of persons, with an income greater than the stated amount, who volunteered to do so.

The scheme was administered by Friendly Societies approved under the Acts and these 'Approved Societies', as they were called, organized certain statutory benefits for their members. By the Act of 1924, the Approved Societies were required to have their assets valued periodically by the Government Actuary, and if an Approved Society possessed a sufficiently large surplus it could submit to the Minister of Health a plan for distributing additional benefits out of the surplus. One of the additional benefits which might be chosen by the members of an Approved Society and submitted for the Minister's approval was the payment of the whole or part of the cost of dental treatment.

Those dental practitioners who undertook to provide treatment for insured persons were subject to conditions of service and were remunerated on a scale of fees determined by Regulations made under the Acts from time to time.

## I. The Education Acts

Some of the Education Acts passed in England and Wales and corresponding Acts passed in Scotland are of interest to the dental profession for they have enabled provision to be made for the State-aided dental care of school children.

The Education Act, 1907 was the first to *permit* school boards to make arrangements for the medical inspection of the children under their care and to appoint School Medical Officers and School Dental Officers. Under the powers conferred by the Act, a few school dental clinics were established in England. The Education (Scotland) Act, 1908 contained no financial provision for the institution of medical or dental clinics in schools but a Treasury grant was made which enabled school clinics to be opened later in some of the large cities.[1]

By sections 48 and 79 of the Education Act, 1944 and section 51 of the Education (Scotland) Act, 1946 local education authorities are obliged to provide facilities for the dental inspection of children attending their schools. The Acts also require them to make arrangements for securing that free dental treatment is available for such children through the school dental service or otherwise. The Acts make inspection compulsory, but where treatment is concerned the parent is given the right to object to the child availing himself of any treatment provided by the education authority. If the parent makes such

[1] *Brit. dent. J.*, **34**, pp. 49 and 415.

an objection, the child must not be encouraged or assisted to have that treatment.

The Education (Miscellaneous Provisions) Act, 1953 and the Education (Scotland) Act, 1956 place a more direct duty upon education authorities with regard to the provision of dental treatment. They make it a duty of such authorities to provide free dental treatment for their pupils: 'either

i] by persons employed or engaged by, and at the expense of, the authority, either regularly (whether whole-time or part-time) or for the purposes of particular cases; or

ii] under arrangements made by a Regional Hospital Board or the Board of Governors of a teaching hospital. . . .'

## J. The National Health Service Acts

The National Health Service Act, 1946 and the National Health Service (Scotland) Act, 1947 became operative on 5 July 1948. Designed to provide a comprehensive health service for everyone, they have an important bearing on dental practice in this country. They affect dentists who treat patients in State hospitals; dentists who teach students in dental schools; dentists who provide specialist services and dentists who are employed by a local authority to undertake the care of expectant and nursing mothers and pre-school children. The Acts affect profoundly the practitioners who participate in the General Dental Services and they constitute the great majority of dentists in the country.

As the main features of the Acts are dealt with in some detail in Chapter VII, it is necessary here only to mention the Amending Acts which have been passed since 1948.

i] *The National Health Service (Amendment) Act, 1949.* This Act amends slightly both the English and the Scottish Health Service Acts. Its first part, dealing with matters relating to partnerships in medical practice, is not of interest to dental practitioners because they are not restricted by the original Acts, as are medical practitioners, in partnership arrangements or in the selling of practices.

In the second part the Act contains sections which are of importance to the dental practitioner. Thus section 11 adds certain words to the appropriate sections of the Principal Acts and provides that, save in special circumstances, a dentist shall not be paid on a salary basis for the general dental services he provides anywhere except in a health centre.

Section 12 stipulates that no regulation shall be introduced which contains any requirement that 'all specialists employed for the purpose of hospital and specialist services shall be employed whole-time'.

Section 14 permits regulations to be made for the removal from the list of a local executive council of the name of any dental practitioner who has never provided or who has ceased to provide general dental services for persons in the area.

Sections 18 and 19 relate to superannuation benefits and section 20 modifies slightly the manner in which the Minister shall appoint the practitioner member of the Tribunal.

In the Schedule to the Act it is laid down that a dental practitioner shall have equal rights with a medical practitioner in treating his patients in pay-beds in a hospital of which he is a member of the staff.

The schedule also permits a Local Executive Council, at the request of a Local Dental Committee, to deduct money from the remuneration of general dental practitioners in the area and to allot it to the Committee to meets its administrative expenses (including the travelling expenses of its members).

ii] *The National Health Service Act*, 1951. This Act provides, among other things, that a person supplied with an artificial denture under the General Dental Service arrangements shall contribute towards the cost of the denture in accordance with the scale set forth in the Schedule to the Act. Persons who are in-patients in a hospital are exempt from the charges.

iii] *The National Health Service Act*, 1952. Like the Act of 1951, this Act was passed for reasons of national economy. It provides that persons over twenty-one years of age who obtain treatment under the General Dental Services arrangement shall pay 20s. (or the whole charge if less than 20s.) towards the cost of most kinds of dental treatment other than the supply of artificial dentures. Expectant and nursing mothers are exempt from these charges.

iv] *The National Health Service Act*, 1961. This Act amends the 1951 and 1952 Acts. It provides for an increase in the charges which a person must pay for artificial dentures supplied under the General Dental Service arrangements. It specifies that no charge shall be made to expectant and nursing mothers and children under the age of sixteen (or above that age if receiving full-time school education) for the provision or repair of a denture.

The Act also empowers the Minister of Health in England and Wales and the Secretary of State for Scotland to vary by regulation the charges for dental appliances payable by the patient and this power to vary a charge includes the power to abolish it.

## K. Dangerous Drugs Act, 1951

This Act regulates the importation, manufacture, sale and use of certain drugs of addiction with the object of preventing illicit traffic in them. Drugs specified in the Acts include opium, Indian hemp, morphine and cocaine, and their salts and derivatives.

The Act affects the dentist in four ways:

i] he must comply with certain requirements when ordering the drugs;

ii] he must keep a record of the drugs which he obtains;

iii] he must comply with certain requirements when prescribing the drugs for patients; and

iv] he must keep the drugs, when not in use, in a locked receptacle.

i] *Ordering*. The dentist must either be known to the supplier from whom he orders the drugs or must be introduced by someone known to the supplier. When ordering he must either sign the Poison Book in person or send a written and signed order stating his name and address and the name and quantity of the article required.

In the case of emergency, drugs may be supplied to the dentist without the Poison Book being signed or the written order given, provided that the dentist furnishes a signed order within twenty-four hours of the supply.

ii] *Records*. A register must be kept of the drugs which the dentist obtains and it must be in the following form:

| Date on which supply received | Name  \|   Address of person or firm from whom obtained | Amount obtained | Form in which obtained |
|---|---|---|---|
| | | | |
| | | | |

The Register must be kept for not less than two years after the date of the last entry and must be produced when required for inspection by an Inspector.

iii] *Prescribing*. Any prescription for dangerous drugs must:

a) be in writing and be dated;

b) be signed with the usual signature of the dentist;

*c*) bear the address of the dentist, except in the case of prescriptions given under the General Dental Services;

*d*) state the name and address of the patient;

*e*) specify the total amount of the drug to be supplied;

*f*) be marked 'For local dental treatment only'.

In contrast to a doctor, who may dispense dangerous drugs himself for the use of his patients, a dentist must not personally supply drugs or preparations unless they are administered by him or under his direct supervision and in his presence to persons receiving treatment from him.

iv] *Storage.* When any dangerous drugs are not in use the dentist must keep them in a locked receptacle. A locked motor-car is not a 'locked receptacle'.[1]

## L. Pharmacy and Poisons Act, 1933

The sale of poisons is governed by the Pharmacy and Poisons Act, 1933, and the Poisons Rules, 1952, made by the Poisons Board established by the Act. A poison, for the purposes of the Act and Rules, is any substance contained in the Poisons List drawn up by the Poisons Board. The Poisons List is in two parts. In Part I are those substances which may be sold only by pharmacists. In Part II are those substances which may be sold by pharmacists and persons whose names appear on a list kept by the local authority.

Appended to the Poisons Rules are several Schedules, of which I and IV are of interest to the dental practitioner. Schedule I contains the list of substances which in the opinion of the Poisons Board require to be most strictly controlled. In Schedule IV there are listed those substances which may be sold to the public only on the written prescription of a doctor, dentist or veterinary surgeon.

i] *Rules concerning Schedule I poisons.* When a dental practitioner purchases a Schedule I poison he must:

*a*) Be known to the seller;

or

Produce a certificate signed by a householder in the approved form.

*b*) Give a written order, duly signed by himself, containing his name and address, his profession, the name and quantity of the

---

[1] *Kameswara Rao* v. *Wyles* (1949), 2 A.E.R. 685.

substances required and the purpose for which they are required; or

Sign the Poison Book of the seller.

*c*) In cases of emergency, the requirement *b*) may be relaxed if the dentist undertakes to supply a written order within twenty-four hours after purchase.

When a dental practitioner supplies a First Schedule poison for the use of his patients, he must:

*a*) label the container distinctly with his name and address;

*b*) add to the label 'For external use only' when the substance is for external application; and

*c*) on the day when he supplies the poison (or within twenty-four hours) enter in a book the date when the medicine was supplied, its ingredients and quantity, and the name of the person supplied.

ii] *Rules concerning Schedule IV poisons.* The prescription required to enable a patient to obtain any substance included in the Fourth Schedule must:

i] be in writing and signed by the practitioner and dated by him;

ii] specify the address of the practitioner;

iii] specify the name and address of the patient;

iv] bear the words 'For dental treatment only';

v] indicate the total amount of the medicine to be supplied and the dose to be taken.

A prescription for a Fourth Schedule poison may not be prescribed more than once unless it so directs but a prescriber may direct it to be dispensed any number of times without limit. It is preferable that the prescriber should indicate the number of times a prescription is to be repeated and possibly the dates of repetition.

Contravention of the Dangerous Drugs Acts or the Pharmacy and Poisons Act, or of the Regulations or Rules made under them, are punishable by heavy penalties. The Dental Board have also drawn attention to the fact that removal from the Register may follow any abuse by the dentist of the privileges conferred on him by the Dangerous Drugs Acts and Regulations, even if no criminal prosecution has resulted. Practitioners are therefore advised to familiarize themselves with the details of the requirements placed upon them and for this purpose should obtain from H.M. Stationery Office two leaflets:

i) Dangerous Drugs Acts. Memorandum as to the Duties of Doctors and Dentists (D.D. 101); and ii] Memorandum on the Provisions of the Pharmacy and Poisons Act affecting Medical, Dental and Veterinary Practitioners . . . (Poisons No. 3).

## M. The Therapeutic Substances Act, 1956

This Act consolidates previous Acts including the Penicillin Act, 1947.

Part I controls the manufacture and importation of vaccines, sera, toxins and antitoxins, insulin, etc.

Part II prohibits the sale or administration, or the dispensing of certain substances such as penicillin, streptomycin, aureomycin, cortisone, etc. The regulations made under the Act decree that these substances may be prescribed or administered only by registered medical, dental, or veterinary practitioners.

## N. Radioactive Substances Act, 1948

The Radioactive Substances Act is designed to control the manufacture, supply and use of radioactive substances and certain apparatus producing radiation. It also authorizes the making of safety regulations to prevent injury to those engaged in manufacture or to anyone from the waste products of manufacture.

No one may sell or supply for administration to a human being any substance which contains more than the prescribed quantity of a radioactive chemical element, unless:

*a*) that person is a duly qualified medical practitioner or a person registered in the Dentists Register, who is licensed under the 1948 Act, or a person acting in accordance with the directions of such a practitioner.

The duly qualified medical practitioner or registered dentist must apply for his licence in writing to the Minister of Health, the Secretary of State for Scotland or the Ministry of Health and Local Government for Northern Ireland respectively; or

*b*) that person is a registered pharmacist or an authorized seller of poisons who may sell or supply only on the prescription of a licensed medical or dental practitioner.

# CHAPTER II

# Bodies Concerned with the Administration of the Dentists Acts

## 1. THE PRIVY COUNCIL

The Privy Council was once the Private Council of the Sovereign. During the past century it has been the custom of the Sovereign to nominate the Council on the advice of the Ministers of the Crown. There is no limit to the numbers of Privy Councillors, who include the royal princes, the archbishops, the officers of state and of the royal household along with certain judges, colonial governors and members of political parties.

The executive functions of the Privy Council are nowadays largely formal and it is used principally as an instrument for confirming certain decisions taken by the Government of the day. For example, a decision of the Privy Council in a matter relating to the Dentists Acts will for all practical purposes be a decision of the Minister of Health with the concurrence of any other Minister concerned. The function remaining to it which is of most importance is the judicial function which is exercised by a Judicial Committee, composed mainly of the Lord Chancellor and the Lords of Appeal in Ordinary. Except for the judicial function of hearing appeals in registration matters, the functions assigned to the Privy Council by the Dentists Acts may be exercised by any two or more of the members of the Council (Dentists Act, 1957, s. 47).

The functions of the Privy Council in respect of the Dentists Acts are:

### Concerning Dental Education and Examinations

1) The Privy Council may issue directions to the General Dental Council regarding the visitation of Dental Schools and shall receive from the General Dental Council any report on these visitations, together with the General Dental Council's observations thereon (Dentists Act, 1957, s. 9).

2) On receiving from the General Dental Council a report of defects

in the courses of study or examinations conducted by a Dental Authority, the Privy Council may order that the degree or licence granted by that Authority shall not entitle the holder to be registered in the Dentists Register (Dentists Act, 1957, s. 10).

3) The Privy Council must approve fees payable to visitors to Dental Schools appointed by the General Dental Council (Dentists Act, 1957, s. 5).

4) The Privy Council may prohibit attempts on the part of a Dental Authority to impose restrictions as to any theory of dentistry (Dentists Act, 1957, s. 11).

## Concerning Registration of Dentists

5) The Privy Council must approve the regulations made by the General Dental Council prescribing fees for registration or dealing with the erasure of names from the Register because of non-payment of a fee (Dentists Act, 1957, s. 18(5)).

6) The Privy Council must approve rules made by the General Dental Council for proceedings of the Disciplinary Committee in cases where it is alleged that an entry in the Register has been made fraudulently (Dentists Act 1957, 1st Sch. 9(2)).

7) The Privy Council must approve regulations made by the General Dental Council for the examination of Commonwealth and Foreign dentists who apply for registration in the Dentists Register (Dentists Act, 1957, s. 12(4)).

8) The Privy Council must approve rules made by the General Dental Council in respect of procedure in disciplinary cases (Dentists Act, 1957, s. 27(3)).

9) The Privy Council must approve the remuneration to be paid to assessors appointed to advise the Disciplinary Committee of the General Dental Council (Dentists Act, 1957), s. 28(5)).

10) Through its Judicial Committee, the Privy Council hears appeals against decisions of the Disciplinary Committee to erase a name from the Dentists Register on disciplinary grounds; or to take from a body corporate the right to carry on the business of dentistry (Dentists Act, 1957, s. 29(1) and s. 40(3)).

## Concerning Ancillary Dental Workers

11) The Privy Council must appoint four persons to serve on the committee of the General Dental Council entrusted with carrying out the experimental scheme for training ancillary dental workers in filling and extracting teeth (Dentists Act, 1957, 1st Sch. 13(3).

CDH

12) The Privy Council has various duties in connexion with the initiation, progress and termination of that experimental scheme and may ultimately require the General Dental Council to make regulations establishing a class of ancillary dental workers to perform those operations (Dentists Act, 1957, ss. 43 and 44).

13) The Privy Council may approve regulations made by the General Dental Council for the establishment of classes of ancillary dental workers and prescribing the fees to be charged for their entry and retention on a roll of such workers (Dentists Act, 1957, s. 41(9)).

14) The Privy Council is required to advise the Crown regarding the appointment of certain members of the General Dental Council (Dentists Act, 1957, 1st Sch. 2(2)).

15) The Privy Council must prescribe the manner in which the accounts of the General Dental Council shall be audited (Dentists Act, 1957, 1st Sch. 8(2)).

## 2. THE GENERAL MEDICAL COUNCIL

The General Medical Council was created by the Medical Act, 1858 and its constitution was amended by the Medical Council Act, 1862 and the Medical Acts of 1886 and 1950.

Existing as it does for the protection of the public, its main function is to keep the medical register, to ensure that no name is entered therein unless the person has been adequately examined by a medical authority and to erase from the register the name of any person deemed to be no longer entitled to public confidence. It has the additional important duty of providing for the publication of the British Pharmacopoeia.

By the Dentists Act, 1878 the General Medical Council was given the sole responsibility of governing the dental profession. By the Dentists Act, 1921 some of its duties in this connexion were transferred to the Dental Board of the United Kingdom and by the Dentists Act, 1956 the profession became self-governing through the aegis of the General Dental Council.

The only function relating to dentistry which the General Medical Council still retains concerns dental education and examinations: to assist in these matters the General Medical Council appoints six of its members as additional members of the General Dental Council.

## 3. THE DENTAL BOARD OF THE UNITED KINGDOM

This important body was established by the Dentists Act, 1921 and dissolved by the Dentists Act, 1956. It consisted of six elected and seven appointed members. Only the elected members had to be registered dentists who might therefore be in a minority if the chairman appointed by the Privy Council was a layman (as was the case when the first chairman was appointed).

The duties of the Dental Board were:

1) It had to keep the Dentists Register.

2) It had to inquire into alleged misconducts of a dentist.

3) After such inquiry it had to report its findings to the General Medical Council and only that Council had the power to order the erasure of a name from the Register.

4) It had to report to the General Medical Council on any case where a dentist, having been struck off the Register, applied to be readmitted and again it was the Council and not the Board which had the power to readmit.

5) Subject to the approval of the General Medical Council, the Board had to spend its surplus funds on dental education, research and dental health propaganda.

## 4. THE GENERAL DENTAL COUNCIL

Originally established by the Dentists Act, 1956, the General Dental Council is the governing body of the profession. It undertakes those duties which were formerly shared by the General Medical Council and the Dental Board of the United Kingdom.

## A. Constitution

In accordance with the 1st Schedule of the Dentists Act, 1957, the General Dental Council consists of eleven elected members and a number of appointed members:

*Elected members*

Seven elected by dentists whose addresses in the Dentists Register are in England[1]

One elected by dentists whose addresses in the Dentists Register are in Wales[2]

---

[1] Including the Isle of Man and the Channel Islands.    [2] Including Monmouthshire.

| Two elected by | dentists whose addresses |
| | in the Dentists Register are | in Scotland |
| One elected by | dentists whose addresses |
| | in the Dentists Register are | in Ireland |

### Appointed members

Three registered dentists nominated by Her Majesty on the advice of the Privy Council.

Three persons, not registered dentists, nominated by Her Majesty on the advice of the Privy Council.

One person, not a registered dentist, nominated by the Governor of Northern Ireland.

A number of persons[1] who are registered dentists, one nominated by each of the Dental Authorities[2] except the University of London which nominates two.

### Additional members

Six persons, who are members of the General Medical Council, nominated by that Council to act as members of the General Dental Council only in connexion with matters relating to dental education and examinations.

### Tenure of Office of Members

Elected members serve for a period of five years. Appointed members serve for a like period except those nominated to serve on the General Dental Council at its inception: they served for three years only. All members are eligible for re-election or reappointment.

### President of the Council

The Council elects its President from among its members who are registered dentists (whether elected or appointed members). The President holds office until he retires from membership of the Council. He is eligible for re-election (Dentists Act, 1957, 1st Sch. 5).

### Casual Vacancies

A casual vacancy among the elected members shall be filled by election if the vacancy occurs more than twelve months before the beginning of the next five-year period. A casual vacancy among the appointed members shall be filled whenever it occurs.

[1] When the Dentists Acts were passed in 1956 and 1957 there were eighteen Dental Authorities in the United Kingdom and Ireland.

[2] 'Medical Authorities' are defined as bodies and universities who choose members of the General Medical Council and 'Dental Authorities' as those Medical Authorities who grant diplomas in dentistry (Dentists Act, 1957 s. 2).

In the event of a new Dental Authority coming into existence during the three- or during a five-year period, it may not nominate a member to serve on the General Dental Council until the end of the period (1957 Act, 1st Sch. 4(4)).

## B. Payments to Members

The Council has the power to pay its members (including the additional members nominated from the General Medical Council) for attendance at its meetings or meetings of its committees and travelling and subsistence allowances; but it is debarred from paying attendance fees to any member who is also a member of the House of Commons or a member of the Senate or House of Commons of Northern Ireland. The Council is, however, not empowered to pay any member for doing the business of the Council (Dentists Act, 1957, 1st Sch. 7(2)).

## C. Committees of the Council

While the Council may set up any committee or sub-committee to assist in the carrying out of its functions, it *must* set up 1) an Education Committee, 2) a Preliminary Proceedings Committee, 3) a Disciplinary Committee, 4) a committee to carry out the experimental scheme for training ancillary dental workers, and 5) an Ancillary Dental Workers Committee.

1) *Education Committee.* This consists of the President, eight other members of the Council who are registered dentists and the six additional members nominated by the General Medical Council. The Committee appoints its own Chairman who must be a registered dentist (Dentists Act, 1957, 1st Sch. 10).

2) *Preliminary Proceedings Committee.* On this Committee sits the President and five other members of the Council of whom one must be a person who is not a registered dentist. For the consideration of any particular case, the President has the right to appoint one or two other members to serve on the Committee (Dentists Act, 1957, 2nd Sch.).

3) *Disciplinary Committee.* This consists of the President and ten other members of the Council of whom at least four must be elected members and at least two must be neither elected members nor registered dentists. Excepting the President, no member of the Disciplinary Committee shall serve on the Preliminary Proceedings Committee.

The President of the Council acts as chairman. In his absence the Committee chooses one of their number to act in his stead.

The quorum is five of whom at least one must be an elected member. To assist the Committee on points of law an Assessor must attend.

The Assessor who must be a barrister, advocate or solicitor of at least ten years standing, is appointed by the General Dental Council (Dentists Act, 1957, 1st Sch. 12 and s. 28).

4) *Committee to carry out the experimental scheme for training ancillary dental workers.* The Committee required by section 43 of the Dentists Act, 1957 to conduct the experimental scheme for the training and testing the value to the community of ancillary dental workers is constituted thus:

> The President of the Council.
> Eight other members of the Council of whom at least three must be
>     members appointed by Dental Authorities
> and
>     at least two must be elected members
> Four persons, who need not be members of the Council, appointed
> by the Privy Council of whom
>     at least two shall be registered dentists employed in hospitals,
> health centres or the local authority service
> and
>     at least one shall be a person who is not a registered dentist.

The Committee appoints its own chairman who must be a registered dentist (Dentists Act, 1957, 1st Sch. 13).

5) *Ancillary Dental Workers Committee.* This Committee consists of:

> The President of the Council
> Eight members of the Council of whom not more than six shall be
>     registered dentists
> Three non-members of the Council appointed by the Government
>     of whom two must be registered dentists who are or have been
>     employed in hospitals, health centres, or the local authority service.
> Three persons elected by the ancillary dental workers.

The Chairman is chosen by the Committee from among its members but must be a registered dentist (Dentists Act, 1957, 1st Sch. 14).

## D. Powers and Duties of the Council

The first section of the Dentists Act, 1957 states that the general concern of the General Dental Council is to promote high standards of professional education and professional conduct among dentists. The Council has to concern itself with matters relating to:

1) Dental Education and examinations, 2) Registration of dentists, 3) Discipline and 4) Ancillary dental workers.

1) *Dental Education and examinations.* Sections 4 and 5 of the Dentists Act, 1957 entitle any of the following bodies to establish a board of examiners for the purpose of examining candidates desirous of obtaining a degree or licence in dentistry:

> any university in England, Wales, Scotland, or Ireland
> the Royal College of Surgeons of England
> the Royal College of Surgeons of Edinburgh
> the Royal Faculty of Physicians and Surgeons of Glasgow
> the Royal College of Surgeons in Ireland

From those who conduct such examinations, the 'Dental Authorities', the General Dental Council may from time to time call for information as to the courses of studies and the examinations. Following the arrangements made by the Medical Act, 1950 for the visitation of medical schools, the Dentists Act, 1957 empowers the General Dental Council to appoint persons (who need not be members of the Council) to visit places where instruction is given to dental students under the direction of a Dental Authority.

Visitors must furnish the General Dental Council with a report regarding the instruction provided in the dental school and after the Dental Authority concerned has been given the opportunity of commenting upon it, a copy is sent to the Privy Council together with observations from the General Dental Council. This procedure applies to all such reports whether laudatory or derogatory to a dental school.

Where it appears that a course of study is lacking (or the examinations are unsatisfactory) the General Dental Council has the power to inform the Privy Council and if the standard of training or examinations is not improved to the satisfaction of the General Dental Council, the Privy Council may order that certificates granted to candidates by the defaulting dental schools shall not entitle the holders to registration in the Dentists Register.

In all matters relating to dental education and examinations the Council shall be advised by its Education Committee (see page 25).

2) *Registration of dentists*

3) *Discipline*

The duties relating to registration and to discipline formerly assigned partly to the Dental Board and partly to the General Medical Council are now undertaken by the General Dental Council.

(See The Dentists Register—page 30) and
(See Discipline of the profession—page 41).

4) *Ancillary dental workers.* By the Dentists Act, 1957 the General Dental Council is empowered to make regulations establishing classes of ancillary dental workers. Certain restrictions are placed upon the general power. Thus by section 42 of the Act:

i] the Council must not permit any ancillary worker to extract a permanent tooth.

ii] an ancillary worker who is permitted to fill teeth or to extract deciduous teeth may do so only in the national and local authority health service, that is in the Hospital Service, in Health Centres, in Maternity and Child Welfare Clinics or in the School Dental Service.

iii] no ancillary worker may be authorized anywhere to fit, insert or fix dentures or artificial teeth.

iv] regulations made by the Council must ensure a certain amount of supervision of ancillary workers. For this purpose they are divided into two classes:

*a)* those who work in the National or Local Authority Health Services must *work under the direction of* a registered dentist.

The Council must also ensure for so long as they think it advisable that a registered dentist must first examine the ancillary worker's patients and prescribe for them the treatment necessary.

*b)* Those who work outside the National or Local Authority Health Services (for example a dental hygenist in a general practice) must work *under the direct personal supervision* of a registered dentist.

The Act also empowers the Privy Council to require the General Dental Council (after consulting that body) to carry out an experimental scheme for training ancillary workers to fill teeth and to extract deciduous teeth. The object of the scheme, states section 43 of the Act, is to enable 'the value to the community of the existence of such a class of ancillary dental workers to be judged'.

The General Dental Council must make to the Privy Council an interim report on the progress of the experiment and another report on its completion. Both reports must be laid before Parliament.

After the end of the experiment the Privy Council may require the General Dental Council to make regulations for the setting up of a permanent class of ancillary workers of this type. If a permanent class of such workers is not set up, those trained in the experimental scheme will be permitted to continue in their work.

The conduct of the experimental scheme is entrusted to a special Committee of the Council. Apart from the experimental scheme and whatever the result of it, the Council must set up an Ancillary Dental Workers Committee and refer to it all matters relating to ancillary dental workers services (see page 26).

# CHAPTER III

# The Dentists Register

## I. IN GENERAL

The Dentists Register was established by the Dentists Act, 1878, section 11 of which placed upon the General Medical Council certain duties concerning it. By the Dentists Act, 1921 most, though not all, of these duties were transferred to the Dental Board of the United Kingdom and by the Dentists Act, 1957 all these duties are now the concern of the General Dental Council. The Registrar of the General Dental Council is required to:

1) Keep the Register in the form of one alphabetical list for all persons in the United Kingdom registered under the Dentists Acts.

2) Keep in a separate alphabetical list all colonial dentists registered in pursuance of the Dentists Act, 1878.

3) Keep in a separate alphabetical list all foreign dentists who are similarly registered.

4) Keep a separate list 'in the prescribed manner' of companies carrying on the business of dentistry.

5) Keep the Register up to date by corrections or the erasure of names of deceased persons or of persons who, on retiral from practice, desire to be removed from the Register. (See page 33).

In addition, the General Dental Council must cause a correct copy of the Register to be made from time to time and, at least once a year, have it printed under its direction, published and offered for sale.

The Dentists Register is admissible in any legal proceedings as evidence of all matters it contains, when it is produced from the custody of the Registrar.

Regulations relating to the fees payable for registration and to the erasure of a name from the Dentists Register for non-payment of a fee require to be approved by the Privy Council (Dentists Act, 1957, s. 18(5)).

The General Dental Council is empowered to make Regulations

generally with regard to the form and keeping of the Register 1957 Act, 18 (1).

## 2. ADMISSION TO THE DENTISTS REGISTER

The following persons are entitled to have their names entered in the Dentists Register:

1) Any licentiate or graduate in dentistry of any of the Medical Authorities of the United Kingdom or the Republic of Ireland.

A person in this category may himself send to the Registrar the document proving that he is a licentiate or a graduate, or the Medical Authority granting the licence or degree may submit lists of persons to whom they have granted a licence or degree and the Registrar must accept any such list as evidence of entitlement to registration.

2) Any Commonwealth or foreign dentist who is of good character, holds a Commonwealth or foreign diploma and who satisfies the General Dental Council that he has the requisite knowledge and skill.

When an applicant for registration holds a diploma which in the opinion of the General Dental Council is not a guarantee of the requisite knowledge and skill, he may be required to submit himself for examination, conducted by a Dental Authority or group of Dental Authorities. On passing such examination the applicant may be registered and his name will appear as a person registered by virtue of the Statutory Examination.

3) Any person admitted to the Dentists Register by virtue of Dentists Act, 1921.

Bodies corporate carrying on the business of dentistry (often called dental companies) are not registered in the Dentists Register but in a separate list issued along with every copy of the Register. The list contains the name, registered address and date of registration of the body and the name of each director and of each member of the operating staff (who must be a registered dentist). The directors of such a body corporate need not all be registered dentists but a majority of them must be (Dentists Act, 1957, s. 39(a) (c)).

## 3. REGISTRATION OF ADDITIONAL QUALIFICATIONS

Any registered dentist who holds or obtains a qualification in addition to that which entitles him to be registered may apply to have the additional qualifications entered opposite his name in the Dentists Register.

It will be registered provided that it is one which is duly recognized by the General Dental Council and provided that the applicant pays the prescribed fee for the insertion.

## 4. REGISTRATION AND RETENTION FEES

Everyone whose name is entered in the Dentists Register is required to pay a registration fee. In addition an annual fee known as the retention fee is payable by every dentist registered after 28 July 1921. But a dispensation was given to those licentiates or graduates whose studies were interrupted because of service in the 1914–18 war and who therefore obtained their registerable qualification later than would otherwise have been the case. Persons in this category have an asterisk opposite their names in the Dentists Register. Section 18 of the 1957 Act provides that the amount of the fee payable for original registration or for retention in the Dentists Register shall not exceed £5 unless the Privy Council agrees that a larger sum is justified by changes in circumstances since the passing of the Dentists Act, 1956.

As from 1963 the fee for initial registration is £2 and the annual retention fee £5.

## 5. APPEAL AGAINST REFUSAL TO REGISTER

The Dentists Act, 1921 gave to a person, other than a colonial or foreign dentist, the right to appeal to the High Court against refusal by the Dental Board to enter his name in the Dentists Register. By the Dentists Act, 1878 a colonial or foreign dentist had a similar right to appeal to the Privy Council.

These rights no longer exist for the Dentists Act, 1957 repealed the 1921 Act and section 10 of the 1878 Act. The only right of appeal now existing for a dentist in either category is his right to appeal to the Privy Council if his name is erased from the Register on disciplinary grounds (Dentists Act, 1957, s. 29).

## 6. REMOVAL FROM THE DENTISTS REGISTER

The Registrar of the General Dental Council must remove from the Register the names of the following:

    *a) Persons who are liable and who fail to pay the Annual Retention Fee.*

    *b) Persons whose names have been incorrectly or fraudulently entered.*

The Council is required by section 22(1) of the Dentists Act, 1957 to erase from the Register an entry which has been incorrectly or fraudulently made. If it is alleged that an entry has been made fraudulently, the allegation must be inquired into and dealt with by the Disciplinary Committee of the General Dental Council.

*c) Deceased persons.* By section 21 of the 1957 Act, every registrar of deaths in the United Kingdom is required to notify by letter the Registrar of the Council of the death occurring within his district of any person registered under the Dentists Acts.

*d) Persons who have ceased to practise.* Erasure of the name of a person who has ceased to practise is not automatic unless he fails to answer the Council's inquiry regarding his position. If the Council receives no reply to its inquiry within six months from the date of posting it, the Registrar may erase the practitioner's name.[1] Otherwise, under the Council's Regulations, the name cannot be removed without the practitioner's consent and until the Council is satisfied that he is not liable to penal erasure from the Register. For this purpose the practitioner is required to sign a Statutory Declaration on these lines:

I . . . . . . . . . . . . . . . . residing at . . . . . . . . declare that I am unaware of any proceedings which might result in establishing a cause for the erasure of my name from the Register without my consent, or for depriving me without my consent of any degree or qualification entitling me to be registered.
In witness whereof I have subscribed these presents at . . . . . . . on the . . . . . . . . . day of . . . . . . . . . 19 . . . and before the Witnesses subscribing.

*e) Persons convicted of crime or guilty of disgraceful conduct.* See page 42.

[1] Dentists Act, 1957, s. 21 (3).

# CHAPTER IV

# Effects of Registration of Dental Practitioners

## I. PROHIBITION OF PRACTICE BY UNREGISTERED PERSONS

The Dentists Act, 1878 which introduced the registration of dental practitioners gave to those whose names were entered in the Dentists Register certain rights and privileges including the right to use the title 'dentist' or one similar to it, the right to sue for the recovery of fees and the right to practise dentistry. It placed a penalty on anyone who used the title unless he was registered: it expressly stipulated that the right to sue for the recovery of fees was confined to those who were registered in the Dentists Register and to registered medical practitioners. The Act did *not* prohibit the practice of dentistry by an unregistered person. This proved to be a serious fault for reasons explained on page 7 and the fault was remedied by the Dentists Act, 1921, which prohibited, with certain exceptions, anyone from practising dentistry whose name was not in the Dentists Register. This prohibition is now contained in section 34 (1) of the 1957 Act which reads as follows:

'A person who is not a registered dentist or a registered medical practitioner shall not practise or hold himself out, whether directly or by implication, as practising or being prepared to practise dentistry.'

The practice of dentistry is defined in section 33 (1) of the 1957 Act as follows:

'For the purposes of this Act, the practice of dentistry shall be deemed to include the performance of any such operation, advice or attendance as is usually performed or given by dentists, and any person who performs any operation or gives any treatment, advice or attendance on or to any person as preparatory to or for the purpose of or in connexion with the fitting, insertion or fixing of dentures, artificial teeth or other dental appliances shall be deemed to have practised dentistry within the meaning of this Act.'

There are three main exceptions to the foregoing prohibition:

*a*) A registered medical practitioner may practise dentistry without being registered in the Dentists Register. This is provided for in section 34 (1) of the 1957 Act quoted above.

*b*) The second exception is contained in sub-section (2) of the same section of the Act which provides:

'Nothing in this section shall operate to prevent the extraction of a tooth by a duly registered pharmaceutical chemist where the case is urgent and no registered medical practitioner or registered dentist is available and the operation is performed without the application of any general or local anaesthetic.'

*c*) The third exception is also to be found in section 34 of the 1957 Act for sub-section 2(*b*) provides:

Nothing in this section shall operate to prevent the performance in any public dental service of minor dental work by any person under the personal supervision of a registered dentist and in accordance with conditions approved by the Minister of Health after consultation with the General Dental Council or (in the case of conditions laid down before the setting up of the General Dental Council) with the Dental Board.'

Apart from these exceptions and others on pages 36-7, mentioned, no one is permitted to practise dentistry in any form unless he is registered in the Dentists Register and any one who contravenes the Act in this respect is liable on conviction on indictment to a fine not exceeding £500 and on summary conviction to a fine not exceeding £100.

Proceedings for an infringement of the 1957 Act in this respect may be instituted at any time within a year from the date of the alleged offence (Dentists Act, 1957, s. 34 (3)).

## 2. RIGHT TO PRACTISE DENTISTRY

**The following persons have UNLIMITED rights to practise dentistry in the United Kingdom:**

*A. Persons registered under the Dentists Acts*

1) Licentiates and graduates of any Dental Authority in the United Kingdom or any corresponding authority in the Republic of Ireland.

2) Commonwealth or foreign dentists who possess a recognized certificate and the requisite knowledge and skill.

3) Persons admitted to the Dentists Register by virtue of the Dentists Act, 1921 (1957 Act, s. 51 (3)).

Under the reciprocal arrangements made in the Medical and Dentists Amendment Act, 1927 persons registered in the Dentists Register are entitled, on payment of the prescribed fee, to be registered in the Dentists Register of the Republic of Ireland. By section 16 (9) of the Dentists Act, 1956 (which was not repealed by the 1957 Act) this privilege no longer extends to those whose names are in the Commonwealth and Foreign Sections of the Dentists Register.

The right to practise dentistry in any part of Her Majesty's dominions was extended by section 5 of the Dentists Act, 1878 to registered dentists but was made subject to any local law in force in that dominion by section 26 of the Medical Act, 1886.

### B. *Persons registered in the Medical Register*

A registered medical practitioner has the right to engage in dental practice but unless he is also a registered dentist he is not permitted to provide general dental services in the National Health Service (National Health Service Act, 1946, s. 40 and National Health Service (Scotland) Act, 1947, s. 39). From that point of view the medical practitioner's right to practise dentistry is not unlimited.

**The following persons have LIMITED rights to practise dentistry in the United Kingdom:**

1) Commonwealth and foreign dentists who are temporarily registered in the Dentists Register.

Section 13 of the Dentists Act, 1957 enables the General Dental Council to register on a temporary basis certain Commonwealth and foreign dentists on condition that they work for a specified time in a hospital or other institution. There they may carry out any dental operation but nowhere else.

2) Persons registered as pharmaceutical chemists.

They may extract a tooth for the relief of pain where there is no registered medical practitioner or registered dentist available and provided the operation is performed without the use of a general or local anaesthetic.

3) Persons engaged in the performance of minor dental work.

Permitted originally by the Dentists Act, 1921, such work may be undertaken only in the public dental service and under the personal supervision of a registered dentist and under conditions approved by the Minister of Health after consultation with the Dental Board or, subsequently, the General Dental Council.

4) Ancillary dental workers.

The Dentists Act, 1957 gives the General Dental Council power to establish classes of ancillary workers to undertake dental treatment, subject to the following limitations:

*a*) they may extract only deciduous teeth;

*b*) they may fill teeth or extract deciduous teeth only in the national and local authority health services, that is, only in hospitals, health centres and schools, and in the maternity and child welfare service;

*c*) they may not undertake the fitting, insertion or fixing of dentures or artificial teeth.

In 1957 the General Dental Council made regulations (S.I., 1957, No. 1423) establishing a class of dental hygienists who were permitted to scale and clean teeth and to give instruction in oral hygiene, both in the public service and in general practice.

5) Dental students.

Until the Dentists Act, 1956 was passed, the position of bona fide students undergoing instruction in a dental hospital was anomalous. Nowhere in previous Acts was any direct reference made to them and nowhere was it expressly stated that they were permitted to perform operations in the mouth.

This omission is rectified by section 33 of the Dentists Act, 1957 which, after defining what constitutes the practice of dentistry, states that dental work may be undertaken by a person recognized by a Dental Authority as a student of dentistry so long as he does so without monetary reward. A medical student and a person attending a course of instruction for membership of a class of ancillary workers are similarly entitled to perform dental work.

Before leaving the subject of the right to practise, it is necessary to refer to the right to carry on the business of dentistry by a layman who owns a dental practice but gives no treatment. This right is given by section 39 of the Dentists Act, 1957 to any body corporate (commonly

DDH

called a dental company) which is on the List of Bodies Corporate compiled and issued by the General Dental Council.

No dental company may be included in the list unless:

i] it was carrying on the business on or before 21 July 1955;

ii] it carries on no business other than the business of dentistry or some business ancillary to the business of dentistry;

iii] a majority of the directors are registered dental practitioners;

iv] all the operating staff are registered dental practitioners or ancillary dental workers;

v] it transmits to the General Dental Council each year on the prescribed form the names and addresses of all directors or managers and of all the operating staff.

While no company is permitted to carry on the business of dentistry unless registered before 21 July 1955, this prohibition does not apply to a society registered under the Industrial and Provident Societies Acts.

The Dentists Act, 1957 also empowers the General Dental Council to withdraw the right of a company to carry on the business of dentistry if, after 4 July 1956:

*a*) a director has been struck off the Dentists Register;

*b*) a lay director has been convicted of illegally practising or carrying on the business of dentistry;

*c*) a dentist employed by the company has been struck off the Dentists Register and a lay director was implicated in his offence.

The position of individuals carrying on the business of dentistry is also clarified by the Dentists Act, 1957. Section 37 prohibits any person other than a registered dentist or medical practitioner from carrying on the business of dentistry unless that person was carrying on the business prior to 21 July 1955.

If, however, a registered dentist (or medical practitioner) dies *after* 4 July 1956 his business may be carried on by his legal representatives, widow, children or trustees for three years from the date of his death. Should death have occurred *before* 4 July 1956 the business could be carried on by legal representatives, children or trustees until 4 July 1959 but his widow may carry on the business during her lifetime.

If a registered dentist (or medical practitioner) becomes bankrupt, his business may be carried on by his trustee in bankruptcy for three years from the date of commencement of the bankruptcy or (if he became bankrupt before 4 July 1956) until 4 July 1959.

### 3. RIGHT OF TITLE AND DESCRIPTION

By virtue of section 15 of the Dentists Act, 1957 a person whose name is in the Dentists Register is entitled to style himself 'dentist', 'dental surgeon' or 'dental practitioner'. This right applies to all registered persons irrespective of their entitlement to registration.

By the same section of the Act, the General Dental Council is empowered to make regulations to legalize the use of specialist titles if the Council considers that the use of such a title by a dentist specializing in some branch of dentistry would be to the convenience of the public or the profession. No such regulations have yet been made.

The title 'surgeon-dentist', now seldom used, was chosen by some older practitioners. According to the wording of section 15 of the 1957 Act, it would appear to be an inadmissible title. It is an inappropriate one for a dentist to use unless he combines the practice of general surgery with that of dentistry.

It is in order for a dentist who is registered by virtue of a registerable qualification to indicate the qualification by suitable letters after his name on a door-plate or on notepaper. It is equally in order for a licentiate or graduate to designate by suitable letters the origin of his licence or degree thus: A . . . . . . . . B . . . . . . . . ., L.D.S.R.C.S.Eng. When this plan is adopted there should be no comma between the L.D.S. and R.C.S. or letters indicating any other licensing body, for the insertion of a comma might lead to the misunderstanding that the dentist possessed two qualifications.

It is equally proper for a dentist to add after his name an abbreviation indicating any additional qualification which he may possess *and which is registered in the Dentists Register*. Care should be taken to use nothing but the abbreviation which appears in the Dentists Register opposite his name for it is an infringement of the Act for a dentist to use any title or description 'reasonably calculated to suggest that he possesses any professional status or qualification other than a professional status which he in fact possesses and which is indicated by particulars entered in the register in respect of him'. Infringement of the Act in this respect renders a dentist liable, on summary conviction, to a fine not exceeding £50.

Section 35 of the Dentists Act, 1957 prohibits the use of the title dentist, dental surgeon or dental practitioner by any except registered dentists and medical practitioners and forbids the use of any other title or description implying that the person is a registered dentist if he is not.

Sub-section (4) of section 41 of the Act indicates that ancillary dental workers may be permitted to use a title specifying the class to which they belong but no one else may use that title. Sub-section (5) prohibits an ancillary dental worker from using any title other than the prescribed one. The penalty for infringement of either sub-section is a fine not exceeding £50.

## 4. RIGHT OF EXEMPTION FROM CERTAIN DUTIES AS A CITIZEN

Section 2 of the Dentists Act, 1957 exempts registered dentists *if they so desire* from serving on juries.

Regarding his liability to serve as a juryman, the registered dentist is not quite in the same position as a registered medical practitioner, for the latter is automatically exempted by the Juries Acts.

It would seem, therefore, that a Registration Officer would be acting correctly if he included in a jury list the name of a registered dentist from whom he had received no claim to be excluded from any such list. If a registered dental practitioner's name is on the list, he may be compelled to serve notwithstanding the right conferred upon him by the Dentists Act.

At the beginning of this chapter there was mentioned amongst the rights given to registered dentists by the 1878 Act the right to sue for the recovery of professional fees. That part of section 5 of the Act which decreed that a person shall not be entitled to sue for recovery of fees unless he was a registered dentist or a duly qualified medical practitioner was repealed by the Dentists Act, 1921.

# CHAPTER V

# Discipline of the Profession

## I. INTRODUCTION

In contrast to a *trade* which is concerned chiefly with financial reward, a *profession* is, or should be, concerned principally with service to the community. While men and women enter a profession in order to make a livelihood, the measure of the success which they achieve in it is the service which they perform and not the amount of money they may amass. The science of morals, which we call ethics, is particularly applicable to a profession and it has been said with truth that the status of a profession can be gauged by the standard of its ethical code.

Dentistry is a profession, albeit a comparatively young one, and the primary purpose of its members is the promotion and maintenance of the dental health of the community. Like other professions, it has its own professional organization, the British Dental Association, which formulates rules of professional conduct framed with the object of maintaining professional integrity among dental practitioners. The Association achieves this object in a variety of ways. Its members are elected only after being vouched for by sponsors and after scrutiny by its Council: its governing body has definite powers enabling it to expel a member whose conduct is considered to be unprofessional: its Representative Board has a standing committee which issues from time to time guidance on professional conduct and which keeps a vigilant eye upon defaulters. Matters relating to the ethical code within the dental profession are dealt with in Chapter X (see page 122). But there is also statutory control of the profession, for the Dentists Act, 1878 placed upon the General Medical Council definite duties of this nature, some, though not all, of which were transferred to the Dental Board of the United Kingdom when that body was set up by the Dentists Act, 1921. With the passing of the Dentists Act, 1957 the General Dental Council became solely responsible for the statutory control of the dental profession. This statutory control is considered in some detail in this chapter.

## 2. PENAL ERASURE FROM THE DENTISTS REGISTER

Section 25 of the Dentists Act, 1957, dealing with erasure from the Dentists Register, contains the following:

'A registered dentist who either before or after registration *a*) has been convicted either in Her Majesty's dominions or elsewhere of an offence which, if committed in England, would be a felony or a misdemeanour, or *b*) has been guilty of infamous or disgraceful conduct in a professional respect, shall be liable to have his name erased from the register.'

Each class of case in which disciplinary action may be taken against a dentist requires to be considered.

### A. Persons Convicted of an Offence which in England would constitute a Felony or a Misdemeanour

In English law, crimes are divided into treason, felonies and misdemeanours. Felonies include murder, forgery, coining, burglary, etc., and misdemeanours include offences which are neither treason nor felonies. Misdemeanours therefore include such serious offences as sedition and perjury and a host of less serious offences like dredging for oysters and cheating at games played for money.

If a dentist is convicted in any court having criminal jurisdiction (see page 145) the fact of his conviction is notified to the General Dental Council who may or must take action depending on certain circumstances. When the conviction took place is immaterial: it may have been before or after the passing of the Act or before or after the dentist was registered in the Dentists Register. But section 25 of the 1957 Act goes on to explain that a person's name shall not be erased from the Register on account of a conviction for an offence which from its trivial nature or from the circumstances under which the offence was committed does not 'disqualify a person for practising dentistry'. Nor will the conviction for a 'political offence' committed outside Her Majesty's dominions jeopardize a dentist so far as his registration in the Dentists Register is concerned. The section of the Act also makes it clear that a dentist cannot be struck off the Register on account of his 'adopting or refraining from adopting the practice of any particular theory of dentistry.'

### B. Persons Guilty of Infamous or Disgraceful Conduct in a Professional Respect

The term 'infamous conduct in a professional respect' appeared in

section 29 of the Medical Act, 1858, and it was upon that Act that the
first Dentists Act in 1878 was framed. In section 13 of the Dentists Act,
1878 the phrase appeared and the whole phrase is repeated in section 25
of the Dentists Act, 1957 with the addition of the words 'or disgraceful'. Both are strong words. They are defined in the *Oxford English
Dictionary* as follows:

'Infamous'—deserving of infamy; of shameful badness, vileness or
abominableness; of a character or quality deserving utter reproba-
tion.

'Disgraceful'—full of or fraught with disgrace; shameful, dishonourable, disreputable.

The last words of the phrase 'in a professional respect' are important
for they envisage that the dentist may be guilty of infamous or disgraceful conduct outside his profession without jeopardizing his right
to be registered. If, for example, a dentist were a co-respondent in a
divorce suit, his conduct might be infamous or disgraceful but it would
probably not be so in a professional respect unless the woman in the
case was one of his patients. In more than one case the Court has given
an interpretation of the meaning of the phrase used in the Medical Act
and what holds good for that phrase is equally applicable to the phrase
in the Dentists Act. In *Allinson* v. *General Medical Council*[1] Lord Esher,
M.R., said: 'If a medical man in the pursuit of his profession has done
something with regard to it which will be reasonably regarded as disgraceful or dishonourable by his professional brethren of good repute
and competency, then it is open to the General Medical Council, if
that be shown, to say that he has been guilty of infamous conduct in
a professional respect.'

In *Felix* v. *General Dental Council*[2] Lord Esher's definition was
qualified in an important respect. The case was one where a dentist had
wrongly claimed fees in the National Health Service. After due inquiry, the Disciplinary Committee of the General Dental Council
determined that the allegation had been proved and found the dentist
guilty of infamous or disgraceful conduct in a professional respect.
The Disciplinary Committee decided that his name should be erased
from the Dentists Register and from that decision the dentist appealed
to the Judicial Committee of the Privy Council.

In a reserved judgement and referring to standard dictionaries, Lord
Jenkins said 'to make good a charge of "infamous or disgraceful conduct in a professional respect" in relation to such a matter as the keeping

[1] (1894), 63 L. J. (Q. B.) 534.       [2] (1960) 2 All. E. R. 391.

of the prescribed dental records it is not, in their Lordships view, enough to show that some mistake has been made through carelessness or inadvertence. . . . To make such a charge good there must (generally speaking) be some element of moral turpitude or fraud or dishonesty in the conduct complained of, or such persistent and reckless disregard of the dentist's duty in regard to records as can be said to amount to dishonesty for this purpose. The question is to some extent one of degree, but in their Lordships view, the cases of overcharging with which this appeal is concerned clearly fall short of the degree of culpability required.'

The appeal was allowed and the finding of the Disciplinary Committee set aside.

To every registered dentist there are sent from time to time Notices (formerly called Warning Notices). These deal with conduct which in the opinion of the General Dental Council might come within the meaning of the words in section 25 of the 1957 Act and give advice on matters of professional behaviour. In their Notice circulated in 1957, the General Dental Council made it clear that the examples of professional misconduct set out do not constitute and are not intended to constitute a complete list of the offences which may result in the erasure of a name from the Dentists Register and that nothing in the Notice is 'to be held to limit the discretion of the Disciplinary Committee in reaching a determination in any case in accordance with the facts brought before them'.

In spite of the fact that the lists of offences included in such publications are not complete and are not meant to be, every registered dental practitioner should be familiar with the contents. The General Dental Council's current Warning Notice is reproduced in Appendix III.

Penal erasure from the Dentists Register is not automatic. Every case must first be investigated and section 26 of the 1957 Act places upon the Disciplinary Committee of the General Dental Council the duty of investigating any case referred to them by the Preliminary Proceedings Committee of the Council. If after due inquiry, the Disciplinary Committee decide that the name should be erased, the offending dentist is notified accordingly and his name is removed from the Register. He has, however, the right of appeal to the Judicial Committee of the Privy Council. As an investigation by the Disciplinary Committee may have the extremely serious consequence of erasure from the Register, it is only right and proper that any such investigation be conducted with care. The Rules of the Disciplinary Committee accordingly prescribe in detail the procedure which must be followed.

### 3. PROCEDURE IN DISCIPLINARY CASES

Each case reported to the General Dental Council must first be considered by their Preliminary Proceedings Committee (see page 25) subject to this proviso—that when information is received that a dentist has been convicted in a Court of Law, the President shall be notified and he may determine that the offence was so trivial that it need not concern the Council.

Otherwise, the Preliminary Proceedings Committee must consider the case and decide (from the documentary evidence only) whether it is one which should properly be inquired into. They have no other duty but when they notify a dentist that an inquiry shall not be held, they may issue a warning that any further complaint regarding his conduct may have more serious consequences.

When the Committee decide that there should be an inquiry, that inquiry must be conducted by the Disciplinary Committee of the Council strictly in accordance with the rules,[1] which by section 27 of the Dentists Act, 1957 may be framed to ensure that:

1) proper notice shall be given to the dentist concerned;

2) any party to the proceedings who so desires shall be heard;

3) any party to the proceedings may be represented by counsel or solicitor;

4) the proceedings shall be heard in public but in the interests of justice or for any special reason, the Committee may deliberate *in camera* (though decisions must be made known in public);

5) where the case is one where the dentist is alleged to be guilty of infamous conduct and the charge is not proved, the Committee must record the dentist as being not guilty of that conduct.

Before making these rules for the guidance of their Disciplinary Committee, the General Dental Council was required to consult the dental profession and the rules had to be approved by the Privy Council before they could be brought into effect.

To assist the Disciplinary Committee on points of law which may arise during an inquiry, the Council appoints a Legal Assessor (see page 26). His advice must be given in the presence of the parties or

[1] The General Dental Council Disciplinary Committee (Procedure) Rules Approval Order of Council, 1957 (No. 1265).

communicated to them and they must also be informed if the Committee rejects his advice.

The dentist whose conduct is the subject of the inquiry (the 'Respondent') may be present but the inquiry may proceed in his absence. Witnesses may be compelled to attend and their evidence is given on oath. The procedure during the hearing is, broadly speaking, similar to that in a Court of Law, the sequence of events being briefly as follows:

1) the charge is read to the parties;

2) the person bringing the charge (the 'Complainant') if any, or the Solicitor of the General Dental Council produces evidence to support the charge;

3) the Respondent or his legal representative may deny the charge or argue that his misconduct was not sufficiently serious to warrant erasure of his name from the Register. He may produce witnesses to support his contention;

4) the Complainant or the Solicitor may adduce evidence to rebut these statements and may address the Committee.

5) the Respondent has the right to reply;

6) at the conclusion of the hearing the Committee arrives at a decision by a show of hands. The proceedings are not invalidated by the absence of any member at any stage of the hearing.

### 4. FINDINGS OF THE DISCIPLINARY COMMITTEE

At the conclusion of an inquiry the Disciplinary Committee may arrive at any one of the following decisions:

1) that the name of the person whose conduct was inquired into should not be erased from the Register;

2) that the case should be held over for a period (usually twelve months) and reconsidered in the light of the dentists conduct in the interval;

3) that the dentist's name should be erased from the Register.

Subject to what is stated below regarding the dentist's right to apply for restoration to the Register, it should be noted that when the Disciplinary Committee decide that the name should be erased, the erasure is for an indefinite period or for all time. Erasure cannot be ordered for a specified period. Furthermore, there is no power vested either in the Disciplinary Committee or the General Dental Council to inflict any other form of penalty such as a fine.

## 5. APPEAL AGAINST REMOVAL FROM THE DENTISTS REGISTER

A person whose name has been removed from the Dentists Register on penal grounds had, by the Dentists Act, 1921, the right of appeal to the High Court. When by the establishment of the General Dental Council, the profession was given the privilege of self-government and the sole control of its own discipline, the right to appeal to the High Court was withdrawn.

Section 29 of the Dentists Act, 1957 gives the dentist, like the doctor in similar circumstances, the right to appeal to the Judicial Committee of the Privy Council, provided the appeal is lodged within twenty-eight days from the date on which the dentist is notified of the decision to erase his name.

## 6. RESTORATION TO THE DENTISTS REGISTER AFTER PENAL ERASURE

When a person has been struck off the Register in pursuance of section 25 of the Dentists Act, 1957 his name cannot be restored to the Register unless by direction of the General Dental Council or by order of the Judicial Committee of the Privy Council in the event of a successful appeal to that body.

The General Dental Council may direct that a name be restored to the Register provided that:

1) the question is referred to the Disciplinary Committee and the latter recommend reinstatement;
2) an application for restoration of a name shall not be made within ten months from the date of erasure or ten months from the date of a previous application.

Against a decision not to restore a name to the Register there is no right of appeal.

# CHAPTER VI

# Development of Organized Dental Services

## I. HISTORICAL

As is so often the case in the development of our social services, organized dental services had their origin in humble beginnings. Dental dispensaries, clinics, and hospitals were opened in various places by the enterprise of enthusiastic members of the profession who were alive to the needs of that section of the public unable to afford to pay fees for dental treatment. It was in those institutions that the dental needs of the necessitous poor were catered for and several of them became teaching centres after the passing of the Dentists Act of 1878. In the larger general hospitals where facilities existed for providing dental treatment those facilities were meagre and unsatisfactory and remained so for a long period. Even now, fourteen years after the introduction of the National Health Service, the need for proper dental care of certain patients in general hospitals is only being gradually recognized and, in some instances, met.

Though it was about the middle of the Victorian era that dental treatment was made available by individual enterprise, it was not till the beginning of the twentieth century that the State began to lend its legislative hand to the problem of providing dental services to those requiring them and unable to pay for them.

The Report of the Interdepartmental Committee on Physical Deterioration, published in 1904, painted a pitiful picture of the physical condition of the masses and focused attention on the very high proportion of recruits rejected for the Army because of poor health. The importance of dental health was adequately dealt with and reported on by the Committee. The Report may have had some influence in official circles for the Government, realizing that workhouse children formed the great reservoir for the Army and Navy, attempted to improve the general health of the potential recruits by agreeing, among other things, to share with Boards of Guardians of workhouses the cost of dental treatment, though no obligation was placed on Guardians to provide that treatment.

During the Boer War one dental surgeon served the British troops in South Africa. Though he was assisted later by three others, the service rendered was inadequate to deal with the needs of the troops, many of whom were invalided home because of dental defects. In spite of this experience, no arrangements existed for the dental inspection and treatment of Army and Navy personnel when war broke out in 1914, though dental officers were appointed as the war progressed, and a permanent establishment of dental officers remained after its conclusion. So important did the Army Dental Corps become that, according to authoritative statements, more dental officers accompanied the troops on 'D' day, 1944, when the Allies landed on French soil in the Second World War, than served the whole Army in 1918. The Dental Services in the Navy and the Royal Air Force were equally efficient but the story of the development of these services illustrates the time-lag which so often exists between the recognition of a need and the provision of adequate facilities to meet that need.

A similar story surrounds the development of the School Dental Service. Following a conference of independent public schools in 1870, several of these schools appointed dentists on a part-time basis to undertake the systematic inspection of the scholars under their care. This may be said to be the origin of the School Dental Service though its development into the Service as we know it today has been lengthy and gradual. In 1885, W. M. Fisher of Dundee, at the Annual Meeting of the British Dental Association, read his paper on 'Compulsory Attention to the Teeth of School Children' and from 1890 to 1897 the Association considered periodically reports of the committee which it had set up to investigate the problem propounded by Fisher. Meanwhile, a few dentists were appointed to Poor Law schools and institutions, following the passing of the Education Act in 1907, to State-aided 'board schools' for that Act enabled education authorities in England and Wales for the first time to provide medical inspection for school children. About 1907 the first dental clinic for school children was opened in Cambridge as a result of a charitable endowment.

In 1918 a further development became possible when the Maternity and Child Welfare Act enjoined town councils and county councils to provide medical care for expectant and nursing mothers and for children below school age. As Webster[1] has shown, dental care was not made obligatory by the Act; it was only permissive, and it is regrettable that full advantage was not taken of the powers conferred on local authorities in this direction. Even where schemes were introduced for the dental care of expectant and nursing mothers they were, in the main, far from ideal in that dental care consisted of tooth extraction and the provision of dentures while preventive dentistry was non-existent.

According to Weaver[2] there was in England and Wales in 1928 the equivalent of one full-time dental officer for every 11,300 children while in 1939 the corresponding figure was one dental officer to every 5,780 children. This gradual improvement was interrupted when the National Health Service Act, 1946 and the National Health Service (Scotland) Act, 1947 became operative because the arrangements for a General Dental Service made under those Acts attracted many who were formerly School Dental Officers and distracted others from entering the School Dental Service. In 1951 there was the equivalent of one full-time dental officer for every 8,058 school children and in 1959 one for every 6,889 children. The position is therefore again improving and it is hoped that it will continue to do so until the ratio more nearly approximates to one dentist for every 3,000 children which is generally regarded as the ideal. A full complement of school dental officers is essential for it is surely illogical and unwise to spend public funds in repairing the ravages of dental disease in the adult without taking adequate steps to prevent or minimize dental disease in the child.

Returning now to the general population, we find that anything in the way of organized service was inclined to be piecemeal and slow of development.

Though the Boards of Guardians had for many years employed dentists to treat the sick and infirm in their institutions, it was not until 1929 that the Local Government Act enabled local authorities through their Public Assistance Committees to provide dental treatment (usually confined to the provision of artificial dentures) to persons coming within their responsibility.

Arrangements for the relief of pain of dental origin were made in H.M. prisons and in asylums while free dental treatment for members of the police force became possible by a Home Office Order made in 1930.

Industrial dental schemes originated in 1905 when Messrs. Cadbury

[1] WEBSTER, K. C. B., 'The Story of School Dentistry', *Public Health*, 60 (4), p. 82.
[2] WEAVER, R., *Brit. dent. J.*, 73, p. 278.

arranged for their workers to be made dentally sound and thereafter made dental fitness a condition of employment. Many industrial firms have learned the benefit of organized dental service for their employees and the State during the last war instituted schemes in munition factories.

What of the great mass of the people—the general public?

## 2. NATIONAL HEALTH INSURANCE ACTS

By the National Health Insurance Act of 1911, millions of employed persons were compulsorily insured against sickness and a proportion of these insured persons were entitled to dental benefit under the scheme.

The scheme was administered by Approved Societies and all insured persons were required to join an Approved Society. Dental benefit was an additional and not a statutory benefit, and only those Societies whose surplus funds were considered by the Minister of Health to be adequate were permitted to include dental treatment as one of the additional benefits which they might give to their members. Some Societies paid the full cost and others half the cost of treatment estimated on a dental letter by a dental practitioner who was willing to participate in the scheme.

Dental practitioners who undertook the treatment of insured persons were in legal relationship with the State through the statutory Dental Benefit Council; they entered into a contract with that Council for each patient whom they treated and were required to conform to regulations issued from time to time by the Council.

The dentist participating in the scheme was required to:

*a*) Furnish to the patient's Approved Society an estimate of the treatment to be undertaken which had to include the whole of the treatment which the dentist considered was necessary to secure dental fitness.

*b*) Await approval of the estimate before undertaking any treatment (except for the relief of pain or where the total cost was estimated not to exceed 15s.).

*c*) Employ a proper degree of skill and attention which was not less than he would have given to a private patient.

*d*) Keep accurate records in a prescribed manner.

*e*) Refrain from making or suggesting any charges in excess of the prescribed fee.

*f*) Certify on completion of treatment that he had performed the work in accordance with his estimate.

About 1926 a Regional Dental Officer service was instituted for the purpose of making available to the dental practitioner, the Approved Society and the Ministry and Department of Health advice on problems arising in the working of the scheme.

Complaints and disputes were dealt with in England and Wales by Referees, and in Scotland by Reference Committees, and the Dental Benefit Council had disciplinary powers over practitioners referred to them for alleged contravention of the Regulations made under the National Health Insurance Acts.

The advantage of the scheme was that many were assisted in getting dental attention who could not otherwise have afforded to pay fees for it. Nevertheless, the demand rate among those entitled to dental benefit was small, being less than 10 per cent. each year.

The Scheme had definite shortcomings which may be briefly enumerated here:

*a*) All the insured persons were not eligible for dental benefit. Some belonged to Approved Societies which could not afford to give dental treatment as an additional benefit. If a Society did disburse funds in this way, a person had to be a member for at least two years before becoming eligible for dental benefit. (There was therefore a gap of two years at least at the very time when dental treatment was most needed, immediately after leaving school.)

*b*) The standard of treatment given to patients treated under the scheme tended to be less satisfactory than that given outwith the scheme.

*c*) Dental treatment under the scheme became more and more a breakdown service. For a variety of reasons conservation of teeth was less frequently undertaken than their extraction and replacement by artificial dentures.

*d*) There was a considerable limitation on the clinical freedom of the dentist whose estimates required to be approved (or rejected) by officials of Approved Societies. This interference by laymen caused resentment in the dental profession.

When, in July 1948, the National Health Service Act, 1947 and the National Health Service (Scotland) Act, 1948 came into force, the National Health Insurance scheme was replaced by what might well be described as the most ambitious organized health service ever introduced in any country.

### 3. NATIONAL HEALTH SERVICE ACTS

Details of the National Health Service Acts as they affect the dental practitioner will be found on pages 68–74. Suffice it here to consider briefly some general aspects of the scheme from a dental point of view.

The Service is a comprehensive one and under the General Dental Services arrangements anyone in the British Isles had at first the right to obtain dental treatment without the payment of a fee. The demand for treatment proved to be great and the cost to the State considerable. Subsequent amending Acts have introduced limited charges which have had the effect of lessening the demand to some extent.

While it is perhaps too early to pronounce upon the success or otherwise of the scheme, it may be permissible to review the trend in certain directions. This can best be done by enumerating some of the principles which might reasonably be expected to govern a national health scheme and observing the extent to which these principles are being followed.

### 4. PRINCIPLES OF A NATIONAL HEALTH SCHEME

#### A. Safeguard the Birthright of a Sound Dentition by Proper Nutrition in Motherhood and Infancy[1]

Through the medium of ante-natal clinics and maternity and child-welfare clinics (introduced before the advent of the National Health Service Acts) much good work is being done in emphasizing the fundamental principle that good teeth cannot be produced without the essential substances in the diet of the mother and of the child.

#### B. Secure Better Nutrition for the People[1]

The general standard of living in this country today is probably as high as ever it was. Food rationing made necessary by war and post-war conditions tended to reduce the variety of food-stuffs though in some respects it may have had beneficial effects, i.e. in lowering the incidence of dental caries. Nevertheless, there remains a great need to educate the public regarding those foods which from a dental view-point are beneficial and those which are harmful. No serious attempt appears to have been made in the new health service to act upon this principle.

[1] Adapted from NEWMAN, Sir G., *Brit. dent. J.*, 61, p. 321.

## C. Educate the Public to the Desirability of Preserving their own Teeth[1]

In ante-natal and school clinics, in dental hospitals and in the surgeries of some private practitioners the advantages of retaining healthy natural teeth are propounded. Such propaganda, however laudable, is inadequate, for the majority of people of adult age in this country are still content to lose teeth through neglect and regard the wearing of artificial dentures as almost a natural event. Dental education of the public deserves to be undertaken on a national basis with the object of rectifying this unfortunate attitude. There appears to be no provision in the Health Acts for work of this kind to be undertaken on the scale which it deserves. A step in the right direction was, however, taken in 1959 when the Government set up a Standing Committee on Dental Health Education in both England and Wales and in Scotland.

## D. Encourage Early and Perodic Dental Inspection and Treatment[1]

Local authorities are awaking to their obligations to provide for the dental care of expectant and nursing mothers and children under school age. Further improvements in this direction can be anticipated.

The School Dental Service has done and is doing excellent work among school children but its efficiency is necessarily dependent upon its strength. Through the depletion of its ranks, the Service became less efficient after the introduction of the Health Service. This is a deplorable state of affairs which calls for immediate remedy.

By the National Health Service Amendment Act, 1952 the person seeking dental attention under the General Dental Service arrangements is required to pay up to 20s. towards the cost of most kinds of treatment. Fortunately, this does not apply to anyone under twenty-one years of age which is an encouragement for the adolescent (whose needs are great) to visit his dentist periodically, nor does it apply to expectant or nursing mothers. But the charge does discourage the adult from undergoing that periodic inspection which is so desirable and often essential for the conservation of the natural teeth.

## E. Encourage Research into the Causation of Dental Disease

The ravages of dental disease cost the State each year a very considerable sum but as yet no arrangements appear to have been made for the

[1] Adapted from Newman, Sir G., *Brit. dent. J.*, **61**, p. 321.

State to finance research into the causation of dental disease. Attention is concentrated on treatment and prevention is apt to be forgotten in the existing scheme. The first step in preventing disease is thoroughly to understand its causes and, though much has been done in research into the causation of dental disease, much remains to be done. The Minister of Health is empowered by the Health Acts to spend public funds for this purpose but does not appear to have made any noticeable use of his power in this direction.

## 5. ORGANIZED DENTAL SERVICE FOR THE PRIORITY CLASSES

From a dental point of view the Priority Classes are those whose need for dental care is greater than that of other members of the community. Included in the Priority Classes are the expectant and nursing mother, the pre-school and the school child and the adolescent. Organized dental service for these groups is considered here under *a*) Maternity and Child Welfare; *b*) School Dental Service; and *c*) Service for the adolescent.

### A. Maternity and Child Welfare Service
The advisability of attending to the general health and dental care of expectant and nursing mothers and infants has long been recognized. It is essential for safeguarding the birthright of a sound dentition. Nevertheless, it was not until the Notification of Births (Extension) Act was passed in Scotland in 1915, and the Maternity and Child Welfare Act in England and Wales in 1918, that serious attention was paid to the matter. Even then, the Acts merely *permitted* local authorities to institute schemes for the medical supervision of such persons; it was not obligatory upon local authorities to provide dental treatment for them. As a consequence, development of dental schemes was, on the whole, unsatisfactory. Some local authorities were notably successful in organizing dental services: some entirely ignored the powers granted to them by the Acts.

This state of affairs was altered by the National Health Service Act, 1946, for section 22 (1) reads: 'It shall be the duty of every local health authority to make arrangements for the care, including in particular dental care, of expectant and nursing mothers and of children who have not attained the age of five years and are not attending primary schools maintained by a local education authority'. The wording of section 22 of the National Health Service (Scotland) Act, 1947 is materially the same. The importance of each lies in the fact that, for the first time, dental care is specifically mentioned as an obligation placed upon a local authority by an Act of Parliament.

No person in this class is compelled to utilize whatever service is provided by the local authority: she may elect to have her dental treatment, and that of her child, undertaken by a practitioner in the General Dental Service or by a dentist privately.

## B. The School Dental Service

The School Dental Service has often been called the Cinderella of dental services in this country and not without cause for it has suffered vicissitudes. Slow of development, it may be said to have received an occasional stimulus from such statutes as the Local Authorities (Medical Treatment) Act in 1909 and the Education Act in 1921 and its main one by the Education Act of 1944.

It is true that these Acts and the Regulations made subsequent to them have been beneficial, for they require a local education authority to appoint a Chief Dental Officer and such other dental officers and nurses as may be necessary for securing the efficiency of the School Health Service. In addition, dental records, in an approved form, are required to be kept for every pupil inspected or treated and the Chief Dental Officer must furnish a report to be included in the report of the School Medical Officer in each calendar year. By regulation the responsibility for the dental care of pupils is placed upon the School Medical Officer. Two disadvantages have tended to result. The Chief Dental Officer, having no direct approach to his local education authority, is less able to bring about a development of the service which the circumstances in his area may demand and the status of the School Dental Officer is necessarily lowered, which has a very material effect upon recruitment into the Service.

Under the School Dental Service arrangements the pupil's parent may refuse treatment of his child altogether or may have the treatment at the hands of a private practitioner (within or without the National Health Service).

The results achieved in the School Dental Service have been, in many instances, remarkably good. They can be gauged by the 'acceptance rate' which means the proportion of pupils needing treatment who elect to be treated by a school dental officer and by the dental condition of the children on the point of leaving school. Cambridge, where the first school dental clinic was established in 1907, is rightly regarded as having one of the most efficient School Dental Services in the United Kingdom, and figures published[1] in 1943 reveal that in Cambridge the acceptance rate was 96 per cent. and that, out of 382 children leaving school annually, no less than 354 showed a complete absence of signs of active dental decay. To compare these figures with those of other local education authorities is not easy for a variety of reasons, but it can safely be stated that efficiency varies very much throughout the country.

One important factor upon which efficiency depends is staffing and here again great variation is found in the proportion of dental officers employed by local education authorities compared with the number of children under their care. Until recently the main reason for such variation was the economic factor. Many local education authorities found it impossible to augment their staff of dental officers without placing on the ratepayers a heavy burden for only part of the cost of medical and dental services given by the local authorities is met by grants from Exchequer funds. Since the introduction of the National Health Service, the position has become worse because of an economic factor of another kind. Dental practitioners participating in the General Dental Service have earned, on an average, fees considerably in excess of the salaries paid to school dental officers. Though the disparity has recently become less, disparity remains and, so long as it does so, it will have the effect of distracting dentists from the School Dental Service.

It has been argued that, because of the comprehensive nature of the National Health Service, the School Dental Service is no longer required. On this important question the British Dental Association expressed the view that the Public Dental Officer Service should remain in being and should continue to provide complete treatment and education in oral hygiene for school children. There can be little doubt that periodic inspection followed by adequate and early treatment must be beneficial to the youthful population. Compulsory inspection generally could not be undertaken by any other service than the School Dental Service and, though dentists in the General Dental Service can and already do a great deal to assist in the treatment of children, there is a limit to what they can do in this direction. The value of educating the child in oral hygiene can scarcely be over-emphasized and nowhere better than in the School Dental Service can this education be given. If the School Dental Service should be maintained or augmented, as seems desirable, steps will have to be taken to encourage more dentists

[1] British Dental Association, *Memorandum to the Inter-departmental Committee on Dentistry* (1943), p. 18.

to enter it. What those steps should be is a problem requiring careful consideration and an early solution.

No attempt to solve the problem need be made here though the reader will have gathered from what has gone before that steps to improve the status and remuneration of the School Dental Officer would at least be logical. There is one aspect of the problem, however, which deserves some attention. In the minds of some, the utilization of dental ancillary workers is considered highly desirable in the Public Dental Service (which term includes organized service for the Priority Classes and for the public in Health Centres). To a limited extent the Dentists Act, 1921 enabled this to be done and the power to employ persons who are not registered dentists was extended by the Dentists Act, 1957 which makes provision for the setting up of classes of ancillary dental workers (see page 37).

## C. Service for the Adolescent

There is as yet in this country no national scheme for the provision of organized dental service for adolescents. The British Dental Association has pleaded long and earnestly that special arrangements should be instituted for the dental care of persons between the ages of fifteen and twenty. And with good reason, for the incidence of dental caries between those ages is as high if not higher than it is in the school child. It seems illogical to spend public money in rendering the school child dentally fit without at least encouraging the child, after leaving school, to maintain dental fitness. It has been estimated that the average requirement in the adolescent to maintain dental fitness is between two and three fillings in the teeth each year and that implies at least two inspections each year.[1]

To some extent the adolescent is encouraged, for up to his twenty-first birthday he is exempt from paying up to 20s. towards the cost of treatment obtained in the General Dental Service. But some additional encouragement seems desirable, perhaps by introducing some form of organized service or by arranging a greater degree of priority in the General Dental Service than the adolescent at present enjoys.

If and when the provisions of the Education Act, 1944 regarding compulsory part-time education of adolescents are implemented, arrangements could well be made for the dental care of those persons. Until they are fully implemented, other alternatives deserve to be considered.

[1] British Dental Association, *Memorandum to the Inter-departmental Committee on Dentistry* (1943), p. 18.

# CHAPTER VII

# The National Health Service

## I. INTRODUCTION

Introduced in the British Isles on 5 July 1948, the National Health Service was made possible by the National Health Service Act, 1946 and the National Health Service (Scotland) Act, 1947. The provisions of these Acts are similar though the Act for Scotland differs from that for England and Wales in a few details, some of which are important and are noted in this chapter.

The Service is a comprehensive one entitling the people to receive advice and treatment in hospitals, from consultants and specialists, from general practitioners and from persons employed by the local health authorities. The cost of running the Service is met from Exchequer funds, to a lesser extent from contributions from local rates, and to a very small extent by contributions made weekly by those individuals who are compulsorily insured under the National Insurance Acts.

The general plan of the Service can best be described under Central Administration, Hospital and Consultant and Specialist Services, General Practitioner Service, Health Centre arrangements and Local Health Authority services.

## 2. CENTRAL ADMINISTRATION

### A. Duty of the Minister

Responsibility for the National Health Service in England and Wales rests upon the Minister of Health and in Scotland upon the Secretary of State for Scotland. Each Minister must lay before Parliament each year a report of the proceedings of his Health Services Council (along with such comments as he may think fit) unless, after consulting the Council, he considers it contrary to the public interest to do so.

The Minister has the duty of constituting Regional Hospital Boards and of appointing the Chairman of each. He is also empowered to make arrangements to provide for Research and for Bacteriological and Blood Transfusion Services.

In Scotland, the Minister is also responsible for the establishment and maintenance of Health Centres and the Ambulance Services (both of which in England and Wales are the direct responsibility of the local authorities). By section 3 (2) of the Scottish Act, the Minister has the additional duty of providing 'such facilities for undergraduate and post-graduate clinical teaching and research as he considers necessary to meet all reasonable requirements'.

## B. Health Services Council

The Health Services Council is a statutory advisory body having the duty of advising the Minister on matters relating to the services provided under the National Health Service Acts. The composition of the Council is as follows:

|  | In England and Wales | In Scotland |
|---|---|---|
| President, Royal College of Physicians of London | 1 | — |
| President, Royal College of Surgeons of England | 1 | — |
| President, Royal College of Obstetricians and Gynaecologists | 1 | — |
| Chairman of Council of the British Medical Association | 1 | — |
| President of the General Medical Council | 1 | — |
| Chairman of Council of the Society of Medical Officers of Health | 1 | — |
| Medical Practitioners | 15 | 18 |
| Lay persons with experience in hospital management | 5 | 4 |
| Lay persons with experience of local government | 5 | 5 |
| Registered dentists | 3 | 3 |
| Registered pharmacists | 2 | 2 |
| Registered nurses | 2 | 2 |
| Lay persons with experience in mental health services | 2 | — |
| Certified midwife | 1 | 1 |
|  | 41 | 35 |

The Chairman of the Health Services Council is elected by the Council from among its members. Each member is appointed for three years (except the *ex officio* members in England and Wales) and each may be reappointed.

It should be noted that, while the Minister may consider nominations made by interested bodies such as the British Dental Association, he is not bound to appoint any such nominee and the members appointed by the Minister do not hold office as the representatives of any organization which may have nominated them.

## C. Standing Dental Advisory Committee

After consultation with the Health Services Council, the Minister may set up Standing Advisory Committees to advise him and the Council on particular branches of the Service. A Dental Advisory Committee is one of the Committees which has been constituted in England and Wales and in Scotland.

Like other similar Committees, the Standing Dental Advisory Committee is composed partly of members of the Health Services Council and partly of persons, not necessarily members of the Health Services Council, appointed by the Minister after consultation with those organizations which the Minister considers to be representative of the dental profession.

The Chairman is chosen by the Committee from among its members. The duty of the Standing Dental Advisory Committee is to advise the Minister and the Health Services Council on matters relating to dental services. It may advise the Minister direct though if it does so it must also inform the Council of the advice given.

### 3. HOSPITAL AND CONSULTANT AND SPECIALIST SERVICES

As the arrangements for dental treatment in hospitals do not differ from those made for medical, surgical or other specialist treatment, the reader should become familiar with the general plan of the hospital and consultant and specialist services.

The administrative bodies concerned in this part of the Health Service are Regional Hospital Boards, Hospital Management Committees (or, in Scotland, Boards of Management) and Boards of Governors of Teaching Hospitals (in England and Wales only).

## A. Regional Hospital Boards in England and Wales

i] *Constitution.* For the purpose of hospital administration England and Wales have been divided by the Minister into fourteen regions in each of which the Minister has set up a Regional Hospital Board. It is his duty to appoint the Chairman of each Board and, as members, such persons as he thinks fit, including:

*a*) persons after consultation with the university within the area;
*b*) persons after consultation with such organizations as the Minister considers to be representative of the medical profession;

STRUCTURE OF THE HEALTH SERVICE IN ENGLAND AND WALES

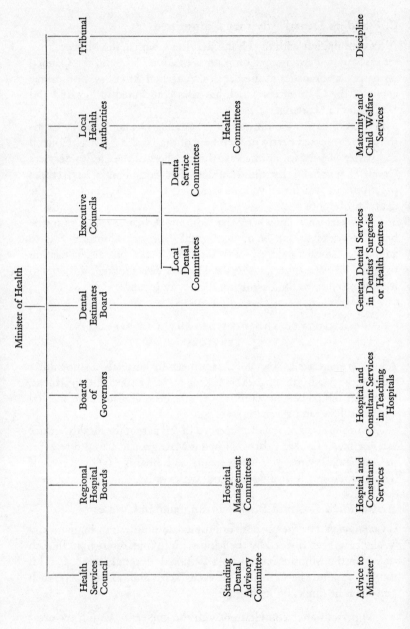

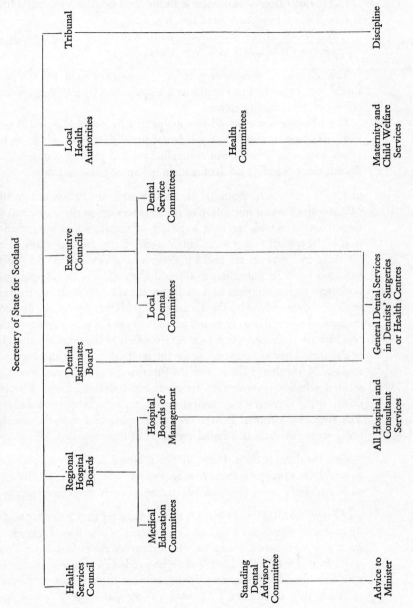

STRUCTURE OF THE HEALTH SERVICES IN SCOTLAND

Secretary of State for Scotland

Health Services Council — Standing Dental Advisory Committee — Advice to Minister

Regional Hospital Boards — Medical Education Committees — Hospital Boards of Management — All Hospital and Consultant Services

Dental Estimates Board

Executive Councils — Local Dental Committees — Dental Service Committees — General Dental Services in Dentists' Surgeries or Health Centres

Local Health Authorities — Health Committees — Maternity and Child Welfare Services

Tribunal — Discipline

*c*) persons after consultation with the local health authorities in the area (defined in section 19 of the 1946 Act);

*d*) persons after consultation with such other organizations as appear to the Minister to be concerned.

The number of persons required to constitute a Regional Hospital Board is not specified and members are appointed by the Minister and are not democratically elected.

The Minister is not bound to appoint to a Regional Hospital Board any person representative of the dental profession. He may do so by virtue of *d*) above but is not compelled to, and in quite a number of Boards there is in fact no dentist included among the members.

ii] *Duties and powers.* Regional Hospital Boards are answerable to the Minister for the administration of hospital services in their area except those connected with teaching hospitals, which are under the jurisdiction of Boards of Governors. The Boards' duties are laid upon them by Act, by Regulations and by directions given by the Minister. Included in these duties is the Boards' duty of maintaining hospital buildings and equipment and of financing the service in their areas with money provided by the Treasury. Boards are also required to co-ordinate the hospital services and to make plans for presentation to the Minister for their expansion to meet the needs of the population within the area. They are responsible for the medical, nursing and ancillary staffing of the hospitals as well as for the consultant and specialist services whether these services are given in a hospital, a clinic, a health centre or, if necessary on medical grounds, in the home of a patient. The Regional Hospital Boards engage, employ and may dismiss the more senior medical and dental members of their staffs.

To assist them in these duties, Regional Hospital Boards are required to establish as many Hospital Management Committees as are deemed to be necessary and to appoint persons to serve on these (see page 65).

iii] *Committees.* Regional Hospital Boards may set up Committees, the members of which need not all be members of the Board, except in the case of a Finance Committee which must consist of Board members only. In order that the Boards may be guided in matters relating to specialist dental services and dental services in hospitals, it is very desirable that among the Committees there should be a Dental Advisory Committee. Many Regional Hospital Boards have appointed such a Committee.

When there is a vacancy on the senior medical or dental staff, the

Regional Hospital Board fills the vacancy, but it must be advertised in appropriate journals or newspapers and the Board must seek the advice of its Advisory Appointments Committee.

The constitution of the Advisory Appointments Committee is laid down in Regulations,[1] and a majority of the members are required to be dentists where the appointment of a dentist is in question.

## B. Regional Hospital Boards in Scotland

In Scotland there are five Regional Hospital Boards. Their composition and duties are similar to those in England and Wales but they differ in one important respect, namely, they are responsible for *all* the hospital services in their area. There are no bodies in Scotland similar to Boards of Governors in England and Wales, and the Regional Hospital Boards in Scotland administer teaching as well as non-teaching hospitals.

To assist the Regional Hospital Boards in matters relating to the provision of facilities for undergraduate or post-graduate clinical teaching, or for research, there is in the area of each Board a Medical Education Committee. While this Committee may consist of as many members as the Secretary of State thinks fit, not less than one-third of the members must be appointed by the university in the area and an equal number must be appointed by the Regional Hospital Board. The Committee appoints one of its members to be Chairman.

As in England and Wales, the Regional Hospital Board must consult its advisory Appointments Committee before appointing senior medical and dental staff.[2]

## C. Hospital Management Committees in England and Wales

Each Regional Hospital Board is required to set up as many Hospital Management Committees as are considered necessary to control and manage individual hospitals or groups of hospitals in the area. The number and disposition of these Committees requires to be approved by the Minister.

i] *Composition*. The Regional Hospital Board appoints the Chairman of each Hospital Management Committee and, as members:

*a*) persons appointed after consultation with any local health authority in the area;

---

[1] Appointment of Specialists Regulations, 1950, S. I, 1950, No. 1259 and 1959, No. 909.
[2] Appointment of Medical and Dental Officers (Scotland) Regulations, 1948, S. I., 1948, No. 1390.

*b*) persons appointed after consultation with the Executive Councils in the area;

*c*) persons appointed after consultation with the senior medical and dental staff in the hospital(s);

*d*) persons appointed after consultation with such other organizations as appear to the Board to be concerned.

Members retire in rotation, normally after a period of three years, but in certain circumstances a member may be dismissed from membership by the Minister.

ii] *Duties and powers.* Hospital Management Committees are answerable to the Regional Hospital Board: they have no direct responsibility to the Minister. Their duty is to manage the hospital(s) on behalf of the Board which, however, exercises control over expenditure, general policy, planning and so forth. Hospital Management Committees engage and pay junior medical and dental staff. They may appoint Sub-Committees and must do so if so requested by the Regional Hospital Board or by the Minister.

## D. Boards of Management in Scotland

Boards of Management in Scotland correspond to Hospital Management Committees in England. They have similar duties and powers but they are constituted in a slightly different manner.

The Regional Hospital Board appoints the Chairman and, as members:

i] persons appointed after consultation with any local health authority in the area;

ii] persons appointed after consultation with any local Executive Council in the area;

iii] persons appointed after consultation with the senior medical and dental staff of the hospital(s);

*or*

persons nominated by the senior medical and dental staff of the hospital if it is a teaching hospital. Persons so nominated must not exceed one-fifth of the total number of members of the Board of Management;

iv] persons appointed after consultation with such other organizations as appear to the Regional Hospital Board to be concerned;

v] such other persons as the Regional Hospital Board thinks fit.

### E. Boards of Governors

In England and Wales those hospitals in which there are facilities for undergraduate and post-graduate clinical teaching and which are recognized by the Minister (after consultation with the university authorities) to be teaching hospitals are outwith the jurisdiction of Regional Hospital Boards or Hospital Management Committees. Each teaching hospital or group of teaching hospitals is managed by a Board of Governors.

i] *Composition*. The Minister appoints the Chairman of each Board of Governors and whatever number of members he determines so long as they are in the following proportions:

*a*) not more than one-fifth nominated by the university with which the hospital is associated;

*b*) not more than one-fifth nominated by the Regional Hospital Board for the area in which the teaching hospital is situated;

*c*) not more than one-fifth nominated by the medical and dental teaching staff of the hospital; and

*d*) other persons appointed after consultation with such local health authorities and other organizations as appear to the Minister to be concerned.

ii] *Duties and powers*. Boards of Governors manage and administer teaching hospitals in the same way that Regional Hospital Boards and Hospital Management Committees manage and administer non-teaching hospitals. They have the additional duty of providing for the associated university such facilities for clinical teaching and research as appear to the Minister to be required.

They have the duty of appointing all grades of officers to their staff or staffs. When a vacancy occurs on the medical or dental staff that vacancy must be advertised and the Board of Governors must seek the advice of its Advisory Appointments Committee. Here again the majority of the members of the Committee must be dentists where a dental officer is to be appointed.[1]

#### 4. GENERAL DENTAL SERVICES

Arrangements for providing for the people a general dental service are made in accordance with section 40 of the National Health Service Act, 1946 and section 39 of the National Health Service (Scotland)

[1]Appointment of Specialists Regulations, 1950, S. I., 1950, No. 1259 and 1959, No. 909.

Act, 1947 and with Regulations made under these Acts. These sections of the Acts are worded differently from the corresponding sections relating to the General Medical Service. Whereas a general medical service is guaranteed, no such guarantee is made in respect of a general dental service, which will be provided only if there is a sufficient number of dental practitioners available and willing to give the service.

## A. Administrative Bodies

The body responsible to the Minister for making and carrying out the arrangements locally is the Executive Council which may be assisted by the Local Dental Committee. The Acts also provide for the establishment of a central Dental Estimates Board in England and Wales and another in Scotland. A dentist alleged to have infringed the Regulations may have to appear before the Dental Service Committee of the Executive Council, and, in the more serious cases, before the Tribunal. He should therefore be familiar with the composition and functions of all these bodies.

i] *Executive Council.* There is an Executive Council for every county or county borough area, though in some instances it may have jurisdiction over more than one of these areas.

In addition to a Chairman, there are a number of lay members and an equal number of persons representing the professions.

|  |  |  |
|---|---|---|
| Lay members | Chairman | appointed by the Minister |
|  | eight persons | appointed by local health authority for the area of the Council |
|  | four persons | appointed by the Minister |
| Professional members | seven persons | appointed by the Local Medical Committee |
|  | three persons | appointed by the Local Dental Committee |
|  | two persons | appointed by the Local Pharmaceutical Committee |

Being responsible to the Minister for the arrangements for the medical, pharmaceutical and supplementary ophthalmic services as well as the dental services, the Executive Council has to undertake a wide variety of duties. Those relating to the General Dental Services include the preparation and keeping of a Dental List on which must appear the names and addresses of all the dental practitioners who are willing to provide treatment under the scheme.

The Executive Council has also the duty of paying, on the authority of the Dental Estimates Board, the dentist for services he renders to patients under the scheme. A third duty placed upon the Executive Council is that of dealing with complaints made against a dentist by a patient or by the Dental Estimates Board and the Executive Council is required to set up a Dental Service Committee to which it is bound to refer to such matters in the first instance.

The constitution, duties and powers of the Dental Service Committee are set forth on pages 77–79.

ii] *Local Dental Committee.* In the area of an Executive Council, the Minister may recognize a Committee formed for that area as the Local Dental Committee if he is satisfied that such a Committee is representative of the dental practitioners in that area. A Local Dental Committee, like its medical and pharmaceutical counterparts, may be said to have statutory recognition without being a statutory body in the true sense. The Local Dental Committee is usually elected by the dental practitioners in the area. There is no limit to the size of the Committee.

The Local Dental Committee appoints three persons to serve on the Executive Council, and three persons to serve on the Dental Service Committee.

The Committee is given the power to investigate any complaint made against a dentist practising in the area of its Executive Council by another dentist, provided the complaint involves any question of the efficiency of the general dental service. The Committee also has the duty of investigating any complaint made by the Minister against a practitioner regarding the keeping of records of treatment. Apart from these powers and duties the Regulations require the Executive Council to consult with the Local Dental Committee on certain occasions, for example before making any alteration in the dentist's terms of service. In addition, many Executive Councils choose to consult the Committees on problems arising out of the administration of the dental services in their areas.

iii] *Dental Estimates Board.* The National Health Service Acts provide for the establishment of a Dental Estimates Board in England and Wales and another in Scotland. After consultation with the dental profession, the Minister appoints to the former and the Secretary of State for Scotland to the latter the Chairman and other members.

In England and Wales the Board consists of a Chairman and Vice-Chairman, who must be dental practitioners, five dental practitioners, and two persons who are not dental practitioners. The Chairman and members hold office during the Minister's pleasure.

In Scotland the Board consists of a Chairman, who must be a dental practitioner, five dental practitioners, and two persons who are not dental practitioners. The Chairman holds office during the Minister's pleasure but the members are appointed for a period of three years though each member is eligible for reappointment.

The main functions of the Dental Estimates Board are to approve estimates for dental treatment and to authorize the appropriate Executive Council to pay dentists on the completion of their work.

iv] *The Tribunal.* The Tribunal is a purely disciplinary body established for the purpose of investigating the more serious complaints against dental and other practitioners. There is one Tribunal for England and Wales and one for Scotland. The composition of the Tribunal and its functions are dealt with on page 81.

v] *Dental Officer Service.* In addition to the Chief Dental Officer, the Ministry of Health and the Department of Health for Scotland each employ a number of Dental Officers who are selected by open competition under arrangements made by the Civil Service Commissioners. A candidate must have at least ten years experience as a practising dentist.

Their duties are to advise the Minister, Dental Estimates Boards, Executive Councils, Local Dental Committees and practitioners on matters arising in connexion with the general dental services. They also advise local authorities in matters relating to the dental services which they must provide.

The duties of the Dental Officer are chiefly clinical and may be summarized thus:

*a*) to advise the Dental Estimates Board on what appears to him to be the necessary treatment for a patient;

*b*) to advise the Board or an Executive Council upon the satisfactory nature of the treatment on its completion;

*c*) to advise an Executive Council when a complaint is made to it regarding the treatment given to a person;

*d*) to advise a practitioner who has difficulty in determining the proper line of treatment or in satisfying a patient over the wearing of a new artificial denture;

*e*) to inspect a dentist's premises and advise whether they conform to the requirements laid down by regulation;

*f*) to approve expensive treatment proposed to be carried out by a dentist in a Health Centre.

It should be noted that, except in *f*), the Dental Officer merely gives his opinion or advice when either is sought, nor does he lay down a line of treatment which is binding on anyone. It is no part of his duty to advise upon fees payable to dental practitioners.

The function of the Dental Officer in relation to Local Authority Dental Services is to encourage the development of the School Dental Service and the Maternity and Child Welfare Dental Service. On such matters he reports to the Ministry or Department of Health.

## B. Privileges and Obligations of Patient and Dentist

Having enumerated the bodies concerned in the administration of the General Dental Service, the privileges and obligations of the patient who utilizes the Service, and of the practitioner who participates in giving it, will be briefly considered.

i] *The patient's privileges.* Every person has the right to benefit by the Service provided he finds a dentist who is willing to accept him as a patient under the scheme. The patient is not restricted in any way as to his choice of dentist and he is free to change his dentist as often as he likes. If the person seeking treatment is entitled, as a person in the Priority Classes (i.e. an expectant or nursing mother, a pre-school or a school child) to treatment provided by a local authority, that person is still entitled to free choice of dentist under the General Dental Service arrangements.

At the start of the General Dental Service all treatment was free of charge to the patient with two exceptions. If the patient required specially expensive treatment, such as gold filling or a metal denture, he was (and still is) required to pay part of the cost: and if he needed the replacement of a dental appliance because of his own carelessness he might be (and still may be) required to bear part or whole of the expense.

The National Health Service Act, 1951 introduced as an economy measure a requirement that all patients receiving dentures in the General Dental Services must pay approximately half the cost. The need for further economy resulted in the National Health Service Acts, 1952 and 1961 (see page 15). Under the 1952 Act all patients, except those under twenty-one, and expectant and nursing mothers, were required to pay the whole or part of the cost of treatment (with a few exceptions) up to a maximum payment of 20s.

ii] *The patient's obligations.* The Act and Regulations are remarkably silent as to the obligations of the patient in the General Dental Services. Under the Regulations it is made a condition of his right to receive treatment that, if required by the Dental Estimates Board he shall submit himself for examination by a Dental Officer. This is the sole restriction on the patient. In contrast to the arrangements which formerly existed under the National Health Insurance Scheme of dental benefit, he is not required by the Regulations to accept all the treatment he needs to make him dentally fit. So far as the Regulations are concerned he is even at liberty to change his mind, and his dentist, in the middle of a course of treatment.

The arrangement made between the dentist and the patient for treatment to be given is, however, a contract binding upon both parties. Thus, if a patient agrees to undergo certain treatment but subsequently seeks that treatment elsewhere, the dentist would appear to be able to recover damages for any loss he suffers as the result of the patient's action.

iii] *The dentist's privileges.* The dentist is free to enter the National Health Service or not as he pleases. If he agrees to undertake to give treatment under the General Dental Service arrangements and accordingly enters his name on the Dental List of the Executive Council, he is not thereby compelled to accept as a patient every person who presents himself but is free to accept or refuse as he desires. But, having accepted a person as a patient, he is bound, except in certain emergency cases, to complete the treatment necessary for dental fitness which the patient is willing to undergo. He may retire from attendance upon the patient before completion of such treatment only with the consent of the Executive Council.

The question as to when the dentist accepts a person as his patient therefore becomes important. For this and other aspects of the dentist's contract under the National Health Service, the reader is referred to page III.

Within certain limits, the dentist is free to use his own clinical judgement in his examination and treatment of the patient.

In the case of certain treatment, specified in the Regulations, the dentist may proceed immediately to treat the patient: in other cases, also specified, the dentist must submit to the Dental Estimates Board a statement of what is proposed and must await its approval before he proceeds with treatment. The dentist is paid for his work in accordance with a Scale of Fees laid down in the Regulations. The Scale can be varied at any time by Regulation. The Scale specifies the exact fee payable in respect of certain items of treatment. In respect of other items the dentist must submit an estimate of the fee to be charged for the approval of the Board. The dentist and the patient have the right to appeal against any decision of the Dental Estimates Board. Appeal lies to the Minister and is decided by two assessors, both dentists, appointed by him.

The dentist may employ another dentist as his deputy or assistant, and it is not essential for the deptuy or assistant to have his name on the list of the Executive Council. The name of any assistant employed for three months or more must, however, be notified to the Council. The Regulations make the principal dentist responsible for all the acts or omissions of his deputy or assistant.

Where the dentist feels that the condition of the patient requires treatment which he is unable to give, if he knows that the treatment can be provided by another practitioner in the General Dental Services or under the hospital service, he must inform the patient accordingly and, if the patient wishes it, refer him to the other practitioner or to the hospital.

Finally, the dentist may withdraw from the Service when he wishes provided *a*) he gives three months notice to the Executive Council, or such shorter period as the Council agree to accept, *b*) he makes satisfactory arrangements for the completion of treatment of patients under his care and *c*) no representations to the Tribunal are pending against him.

iv] *The dentist's obligations.* To participate in the General Dental Service, a dentist must apply to have his name placed on the Dental List of the Executive Council of the area in which his practice is situated. Provided he gives the information necessary when applying, his name must be added to the List by the Executive Council unless he is disqualified for inclusion by decision of the Tribunal.

Having agreed to accept a person for treatment in his own surgery, the dentist is required to deal with that person in accordance with the Terms of Service laid down in the Regulations. He must therefore familiarize himself with the regulations in force. The main requirements with which he has at present to comply are:

*a*) In accepting the patient, he must complete the dental estimate form[1] giving the necessary particulars of the patient, details of his dental state and details of the treatment which he considers necessary to secure dental fitness.

*b*) He must employ a proper degree of skill and attention and

[1] See Appendix V, page 304.

provide the treatment necessary to secure dental fitness that the person concerned is willing to undergo.

*c*) He must complete that treatment satisfactorily and must generally do so within twelve months in cases including extractions and dentures, and within six months in all other cases.

(In a limited class of emergency cases, parts of the three foregoing requirements are relaxed.)

*d*) He must provide proper waiting-room and surgery accommodation suitably equipped with furnishings and instruments, and, on being given adequate notice, must admit a Dental Officer at all reasonable times for the purpose of inspecting his premises.

*e*) He must provide, when necessary, the services of a medical or dental practitioner to administer an anesthetic to his patient.

*f*) He must visit in the patient's house or in a nursing home any person whom he has accepted as a patient when that patient's condition so requires. He is exonerated from this obligation if the house or nursing home is situated more than five miles from his surgery.

*g*) He must keep clinical records relating to his patients and these records must conform substantially to the pattern prescribed and must be produced on the request of a Dental Officer or of the Executive Council or Dental Estimates Board.

*h*) He must carry out the treatment required by the Regulations at the prescribed fees and must not suggest, demand, or accept any additional payment from the patient except in those instances where the patient is required by Statute or Regulation to pay a fee or the proportion of a fee.

*i*) If he employs a dental technician, the dentist must observe hours and conditions of work and pay wages not less favourable than those approved for the time being by the National Joint Council for the Craft of Dental Technicians.

### 5. HEALTH CENTRE ARRANGEMENTS

A novel feature of the Health Service introduced in section 21 of the National Health Service Act, 1946 and in section 15 of the National Health Service (Scotland) Act, 1947 is the establishment of Health Centres. Apart from several centres at which dental treatment was previously provided by local authorities, few Health Centres have so far been set up and it will take a long time before they can be created on the extensive scale envisaged in the Acts. The final form which Health Centres will take and the arrangements to suit them will be evolved in the light of experiment and experience but the reader should be familiar with the general plan and arrangements already determined by the Acts.

## A. Responsibility for Establishment of Health Centres

In England and Wales the responsibility for setting up Health Centre, rests upon the local health authorities who are required to provides equip and maintain them to the satisfaction of the Minister of Health.

In Scotland, it is the duty of the Secretary of State to provide, equip and maintain Health Centres though he may delegate the duty wholly or partly to local health authorities.

In addition to providing suitable premises for Health Centres and equipping and maintaining them, the local health authority in England and Wales is required to provide all the staff necessary except the medical and dental staff for the general practitioner services. In Scotland the Minister has the power to provide staff for the Health Centres except for the maternity and child welfare services, where the responsibility rests upon the local authority.

## B. Purposes of Health Centres

The National Health Service Acts provided that the following services may be made available in Health Centres:

General medical services;
General dental services;
Pharmaceutical services;
Specialists and other services such as are provided for outpatients in hospitals;
In England and Wales, any of the services which the local health authority is empowered or required to provide—that is the maternity and child welfare services. In Scotland, the school dental service also may be provided in the Health Centre;
Health education.

## C. Arrangements for Dentists Working in a Health Centre

Arrangements may be made by the Executive Council for general dental practitioners to work in a Health Centre in any one of three ways: i] The Dentist may work as a full-time or part-time salaried officer employed by the Local Executive Council; ii] The dentist may work on a sessional basis as an employee of the Local Executive Council and may do so for any number of sessions not exceeding six per week;

iii] Under the 1946 Act and the Scottish Act, it is also envisaged that accommodation at a Health Centre may be made available by the Executive Council in which dentists may treat patients under the General Dental Services, paying a rent to the Executive Council for the use of the premises. No arrangements of this kind have in fact yet been made and dentists so far engaged to work at Health Centres have been given appointments of the kind described in i] and ii] above.

### D. Conditions of Service

The dentist employed in a Health Centre on a salaried or sessional basis is governed by much the same terms of service as apply to the dentist providing general dental service in his own establishment (see page 73). The essential differences are:

i] The dentist is remunerated in accordance with a salary scale set forth in the Regulations. For this purpose the dentist is placed in one of three grades depending on his experience and capability.

ii] Since he is not paid for each operation he performs, the dentist is not required to submit estimates to the Dental Estimates Board, though he must obtain prior approval of the Dental Officer employed by the Ministry of Health (or the Department of Health for Scotland) before proceeding to provide especially expensive treatment.

iii] Where charges are payable by a patient in respect of more expensive types of treatment or the replacement of dentures lost or damaged through carelessness, the dentist must collect these and account for them to the Executive Council.

iv] The dentist must attend at the Centre at the agreed hours.

### 6. LOCAL HEALTH AUTHORITY SERVICES

The dental services provided by Local Health Authorities are limited to those given under the maternity and child welfare scheme. This is dealt with on page 55.

### 7. DISCIPLINARY PROCEDURE IN THE GENERAL DENTAL SERVICES

This part of the chapter summarizes the disciplinary procedure in the General Dental Services in England and Wales in accordance with the provisions of the National Health Service Act, 1946 and the Regulations made under that Act. The National Health Service (Scotland)

Act, 1947 and its Regulations prescribe a very similar procedure for Scotland.

## A. The Procedure in Outline

The Regulations governing the General Dental Services lay down certain terms of service for practitioners. If a complaint is made to an Executive Council that a practitioner has failed to comply with any of these terms of service, it must be referred by the Council to their Dental Service Committee. This Committee may hold an inquiry and make the following recommendations to the Executive Council.

    i] That no action should be taken against the practitioner, or

    ii] That a penalty should be imposed, and/or

    iii] That representations be made to the Tribunal that the practitioner's name should be removed from the Executive Council's List (which would have the effect of disqualifying the dentist from providing General Dental Services in the Council's area).

An appeal lies to the Minister of Health against any decision by an Executive Council on a report of its Dental Service Committee, except where the Executive Council decides to make representations to the Tribunal as described below. There is no right of appeal beyond the Minister.

The Tribunal has power to direct the removal of a practitioner's name from the list of an Executive Council and, if they think fit, may also direct that his name be removed from and not included in any corresponding list kept by any other Executive Council. When a practitioner is thus prohibited from participating in the General Dental Service in England and Wales, he is similarly debarred in Scotland and vice versa by reciprocal arrangements which exist between the Ministry of Health and the Department of Health for Scotland. An appeal lies to the Minister against any decision of the Tribunal to direct the removal of a practitioner's name. The Regulations do not provide for any appeal beyond the Minister.

## B. The Dental Service Committees

The Dental Service Committee of the Executive Council consists of a Chairman and six other persons. The Chairman is usually a member of the Council but not a practitioner. Of the six other persons, three must be appointed by and from the lay members of the Executive Council, and three by the Local Dental Committee. The period of office of the Committee is determined by Standing Orders made by the Executive Council. The quorum for the Committee is the Chairman, together with one lay member and one dental member.

i] *The Complaint.* Any complaint made by any person against a dental practitioner in respect of an alleged failure to comply with the terms of service must be referred to the Dental Service Committee. The complaint must be made in writing within either six months after the completion of treatment[1] or six weeks after the cause of the complaint came to the complainant's notice, whichever is the sooner. The second period may be extended to two months if the Service Committee is satisfied that there is reasonable cause for delay. If this time limit has expired the Committee may still consider the complaint, if it is satisfied that there is reasonable cause for delay, and provided the dentist consents, or the Minister consents. If application is made to the Minister for his consent to the complaint being heard out of time, the Executive Council must tell the dentist that the application is being made and the dentist has the right to make his objections in writing to the Minister within seven days of receiving notice of the Council's application.

The Service Committee must hold a hearing into any complaint referred to it unless it is satisfied that it is groundless, frivolous or vexatious, in any of which cases it may dismiss the complaint without a hearing, reporting to the Executive Council that it has done so.

The dentist must be supplied with a copy of the complainant's statement and copies of any ensuing correspondence on the matter. If the complaint is not dismissed as groundless, frivolous or vexatious, the dentist must be given at least fourteen days' notice of his right to attend a hearing before the Committee.

ii] *Assistants.* If the complaint against a dentist concerns the conduct of a practitioner whom he employed as his deputy or assistant, the deptuy or assistant also must be supplied with a copy of the complaint and then he has the right to be treated as if he were a party to the proceedings before the Committee. In such a case, however, the Executive Council would have no power to award any penalty of any kind against the deputy or assistant and the Regulations give no right of appeal to the deputy or assistant against any decision of the Executive Council on the report of the Committee.

iii] *The hearing.* The proceedings at the hearing before the Committee are private and only the following persons are entitled to attend:

---

[1] '. . . treatment so far as it relates to the provision of dentures shall not be regarded as completed until the dentures have been delivered to and remain in the possession of the patient (S. I., 1951, No. 2001, Reg. 3 (5)).'

*a*) The complainant and any person permitted to assist him.

*b*) The dentist answering the complaint and any person permitted to assist him.

*c*) The Secretary or other representative of the Local Dental Committee.

*d*) Witnesses. They must, however, withdraw before and after giving their evidence unless the Committee direct otherwise.

*e*) Officers of the Executive Council.

The dentist has the right to be assisted in the presentation of his case by some other person and the complainant has the same right. The relevant Regulation provides that no person 'shall be entitled in the capacity of counsel, solicitor, or other paid advocate to conduct the case for any party by addressing the Committee or examining or cross-examining witnesses'. This is commonly interpreted by Dental Service Committees as meaning that if counsel, solicitor or a paid official of the dentist's professional association or of the complainant's union attends the hearing, his functions are limited to giving advice to the party as to the conduct of his case. If, however, some other person, such as a fellow practitioner, attends to help the dentist, he has the right to do all those things which a counsel, solicitor or paid advocate may not do.

The dentist has the right to give evidence himself before the Committee and to call witnesses whose evidence the Committee considers will be relevant. He may question the complainant or any witness called by him, although the Committee may direct that questions must be put through the Chairman. The complainant has a similar right to question the dentist and his witnesses. The Committee has no power to compel the attendance of any witness.

iv] *The Committee's report.* After the hearing the Dental Service Committee reports to the Executive Council and recommends what action the Council should take. The Executive Council has no power to alter the Committee's findings of fact but may vary the Committee's suggested inferences from those facts and its recommendations as to a penalty.

v] *Penalties.* The Council may then take the following action:

i] If the dentist has failed to comply with the terms of service and has thereby caused any person to incur any expenditure, the Council may recover the amount of that expenditure and pay it over to the person who incurred it. But the total amount which may be recovered in respect of treatment provided by another dentist to the person concerned must not exceed the cost of that treatment according to the current scale of fees.

ii] The Council may require the dentist until further notice to submit estimates for all treatment except examination and emergency treatment to the Dental Estimates Board for prior approval.

iii] The Council may recommend to the Minister that because of failure to comply with the terms of service the dentist should be fined. No maximum is laid down.

iv] The Council may make representations to the Tribunal that the dentist should be excluded from the Council's list of practitioners if the Council is of the opinion that it would be prejudicial to the efficiency of the Dental Services to retain him on the list.

## C. Appeal Against Decisions of the Executive Council

The dentist and the complainant have the right to appeal to the Minister against any decision of the Council, except a decision to make representations to the Tribunal. The complainant may appeal against a decision of the Dental Service Committee, endorsed by the Executive Council, that his complaint should be dismissed as groundless, frivolous or vexatious.

Notice of appeal must be given to the Minister within one month of the date on which notification of the Council's decision is received by the appellant. The Minister has power to extend this time limit if he thinks fit.

With a few exceptions the Minister must hold an oral hearing of any appeal. The appeal is heard by one, two or three persons appointed by the Minister who may or may not be officers of the Ministry. If the decision of the Executive Council involves the finding that the dental practitioner has failed to complete satisfactorily dental treatment, or has failed to exercise reasonable care and skill, the persons appointed to hear the appeal must include one practitioner selected by the Minister from a Panel nominated by the British Dental Association. A party to an appeal is entitled to representation by counsel, or solicitor, or any other person. The persons hearing the appeal draw up a report to the Minister, who considers it and gives his decision, which is final and conclusive. No further appeal lies.

## D. Imposition of Fines

The Minister has power to impose a fine upon a practitioner after considering the report of an Executive Council, if he considers that the dentist has failed to comply with his terms of service. This power may be exercised where the Council itself has not recommended the imposition of any fine and even in cases where the Council has reached the conclusion that the dentist is not at fault in any way. Similarly the power may be used by the Minister to increase or reduce a fine recommended by the Council. The Regulations set no limit to the amount of the fine which may be imposed.

If the dentist has not already appealed against the decision of the Executive Council the Minister must give him the opportunity to make representations against the imposition of a fine. These representations are heard by a person, or persons, appointed by the Minister. The Minister has a free hand in his appointments except that he must include one practitioner from the Panel nominated by the British Dental Association. The persons hearing the representations report to the Minister, who makes his own decision whether to fine or not.

If the fine proposed is in respect of a breach of the terms of service consisting of failure to complete treatment satisfactorily or failure to exercise reasonable care or skill, the Minister must refer the case to a Dental Advisory Committee and consider any report that Committee may make to him. This Committee consists of the Principal Dental Officer of the Ministry of Health or his deputy (who acts as Chairman), two other dentists in the employment of the Ministry of Health, and three practitioners selected by the Minister from the Panel nominated by the British Dental Association. While the Minister *must* refer to the Dental Advisory Committee cases of the kind described above, he may refer any other case to them if he wishes.

## E. The Tribunal

The Tribunal consists of a Chairman and two other members. The Chairman must be a practising barrister or solicitor of not less than ten years' standing and is appointed by the Lord Chancellor. Of the other members one must be a person appointed by the Minister after consultation with the Association representing Executive Councils. The third member, when the defendant practitioner is a dentist, is appointed by the Minister from a Panel of practitioners nominated by the British Dental Association.

Any person may complain to the Tribunal against a dentist. If the complainant is an Executive Council the Tribunal must in most cases hold an inquiry into the complaint. If, however, another body or person complains, the Tribunal may refuse to hold an inquiry if it is satisfied that no good cause for an inquiry has been shown. Proceedings of the Tribunal at an inquiry are *in camera* unless the dentist has applied for a public hearing. Full legal representation is permitted to both the complainant and the dentist.

The Tribunal has the power to direct the removal of the dentist's name from the list of one or more Executive Councils (see page 77).

Appeal against the decision of the Tribunal is open to the dentist alone and not to the complainant. Appeal lies to the Minister of Health and notice of appeal must be lodged within fourteen days after the decision of the Tribunal has been forwarded to the respondent. The appeal is heard by a person appointed by the Minister, who is not restricted as to the nature of his appointee. In addition the Minister, where the defendant is a dentist, must appoint a practitioner from the Panel nominated by the British Dental Association 'for the purpose of assisting the person hearing the appeal'. The dentist is entitled to full legal representation at the hearing of the appeal. The person hearing the appeal makes a report to the Minister, who, after considering the report, makes his decision. There is no further appeal against the decision of the Minister.

### E. The Powers of the Courts

It will be seen that the Regulations outlined above make no provision for the dentist to appeal to the ordinary Courts at any stage. In the great majority of cases decided by Executive Councils, by the Tribunal, or by the Minister, no recourse to the Courts is therefore possible.

In certain circumstances, however, it may be possible for the High Court to intervene in disciplinary proceedings against the practitioner. The High Court has a general power to review the proceedings of any inferior judicial or quasi-judicial body where it is alleged that there has been a disregard of certain fundamental principles of justice; or that the tribunal has not complied with rules of procedure laid down for it by Act or Regulations; or that the report of the tribunal makes it clear that a mistake has been made in the interpretation of the law.

The High Court acts in this way by the grant of one of the prerogative orders which are known as mandamus, prohibition or certiorari. If, for example, it were clear that a Dental Service Committee was about to act in excess of its jurisdiction, an order of prohibition might be granted, which would prevent the Committee from acting in this way. Failure by a Service Committee or by the Tribunal to conform with the procedure laid down in the Regulations for dealing with complaints might lead to the issue of certiorari, which would have the effect of quashing the finding complained of. Thus in one case[1] the

---

[1] *Rex* v. *Wolverhampton Executive Council* (*ex parte D.*), 1949 (not reported).

Court granted an order of certiorari to quash the decision of the Executive Council on a complaint made against the dentist where the Dental Service Committee had failed to give the dentist the opportunity required by the Regulations to appear before it and present his case.

The High Court would not, however, intervene where the defendant was trying to upset a finding of *fact* on the part of the Service Committee or Executive Council; where for example the dentist considered that the finding against him was not justified on the weight of the evidence his only remedy would be an appeal to the Minister and the prerogative orders would not be available to him.

# C. The Dentist and the Public

# CHAPTER VIII

# Negligence

## 1. INTRODUCTION

In common with members of other professions, the dentist is under an obligation to use reasonable skill and care in treating his patients, whether he does so under private contract or under National Health Service regulations. The dentist who fails in this respect renders himself liable to be sued for damages either on the ground that he was guilty of negligence or that he was in breach of his contract with his patient, for the law ordinarily assumes that in such a contract, whatever its exact nature, there is an undertaking by the dentist to use reasonable care and skill.

This chapter deals with those questions which arise when damages are claimed for the tort of negligence, though the rules explained under this heading are, in the main, equally applicable when the action raised against the practitioner is one for breach of contract. There are other matters of importance relating to contracts made between the dentist and his patient and these are referred to under 'Professional fees' in Chapter IX.

Though the law of Scotland differs from that of England and Wales in many particulars, the general principles are not dissimilar in so far as they relate to the subjects dealt with in this chapter. There are differences in legal terms but, to avoid confusion and unnecessary repetition, they are omitted. Thus the person who raises a law suit against another is described throughout as the 'plaintiff' although in Scotland he is known as the 'pursuer'.

## 2. DEFINITION OF TORTIOUS LIABILITY

Negligence is, in common law, a tort, or, in Scotland, a delict, and not an offence against statute law. A tort is difficult to define but Winfield's definition of tortious liability is as follows: 'Tortious liability arises from the breach of a duty primarily fixed by the law: this duty is to-wards persons generally and its breach is redressable by an action for unliquidated damages.'[1]

The following important points in the definition deserve to be noted:

## A. The Law of Tort is part of the Common Law

The duty which gives rise to tortious liability is fixed, from the first, by the Common Law. Thus every individual is under a duty not to slander or be negligent or to trespass upon lands, not because of any contract which may exist between individuals to prohibit such things but because the law says that it is a duty not to slander or be negligent or trespass on land or indeed to commit any other tort.

## B. The Duty is Towards Persons Generally

In respect of tortious liability the duty is towards persons generally, and not to a specific person or persons. This clearly distinguishes a tort such as negligence, from the breach of a contract entered into between individuals. If a dentist who undertakes to extract a tooth for a patient fractures the tooth in the course of the operation and fails to remove it completely, he is in breach of his contract with the patient and the latter might claim damages on that account. But the dentist, because of the skill which he professes, is bound by law, contract or no contract, to perform the operation with a reasonable amount of skill, and if the patient suffers injury through lack of such skill he may claim damages against the dentist for negligence. The patient cannot recover damages twice: he merely has, in law, the alternative means of recovery because of the duty placed upon the dentist of observing, in respect of everyone, a reasonable degree of skill.

## C. Breach of the Duty is Redressable by an Action for Unliquidated Damages

By unliquidated damages is meant a sum of money which may be awarded by the Court in its discretion, as contrasted with the term liquidated damages which, used in relation to the law of contract, signifies a predetermined and inelastic sum for which the plaintiff sues. In the case of tortious liability only unliquidated damages may be sued for, even though the plaintiff may indicate in his pleadings the sum which he thinks would compensate him for wrong he has suffered.

---

[1] WINFIELD, P. H. (1950), *Law of Tort*, 5th ed. p. 5, London, Sweet & Maxwell.
GDH

There are other general conditions affecting liability in tort but these will be considered in their special application to that particular tort called negligence.

### 3. DEFINITION OF NEGLIGENCE

In the words of Baron Alderson,[1] 'Negligence is the omission to do something which a reasonable man, guided upon those considerations which ordinarily regulate the conduct of human affairs, would do, or something which a prudent and reasonable man would not do'.

In *Heaven* v. *Pender*[2] the following definition of negligence was put forward: 'Actionable negligence consists in the neglect of the use of ordinary care or skill towards a person to whom the defendant owes the duty of observing ordinary care and skill, by which neglect the plaintiff without contributory negligence on his part has suffered injury to his person or property.'

The essential features contained in this definition are *a*) the legal duty to use ordinary skill and care, *b*) breach of that duty, and *c*) consequential injury to the person.

## A. The Legal Duty to use Ordinary Skill and Care

In its application to the dental practitioner, as to the medical practitioner, this duty obliges the practitioner to treat his patients with reasonable or ordinary skill and care, quite apart from any undertaking he may have given to the patients. There is no special law for dentists and doctors, for everyone who professes skill in a calling is bound similarly to bring to his calling a reasonable amount of skill and care.

The term 'reasonable skill and care' or 'ordinary skill and care' is not definable because what constitutes reasonable or ordinary skill and care must depend upon the circumstances in each individual case. Nevertheless, the point is of importance and is dealt with on page 93.

## B. Breach of Duty

Whether in a case of alleged negligence there has been or has not been a breach of duty to observe a proper degree of skill and care must depend upon the circumstances. The test is what a reasonable man would do or would not do in similar circumstances. It is for the Court to decide.

---

[1] *Blyth* v. *Birmingham Co.*, II Exch. 781 at page 784.     [2] (1883), II Q.B.D., 503.

## C. Consequential Injury to the Person

If there is no loss or injury, then by law there can be no liability. To be successful in a claim for damages for negligence, the plaintiff must show that he has suffered loss or injury as a direct, or not too remote, result of the negligent act. It is for the Judge (and not the jury) to decide whether the harm suffered by the plaintiff is or is not too remote a consequence of the defender's conduct.

Even if it can be proved that damage, not too remote, has been done to the plaintiff, there are other factors which may have a bearing on the issue. Three of the more important of these deserve to be considered. They are contributory negligence, inevitable accident and the maximum of *res ipsa loquitur*.

### 4. CONTRIBUTORY NEGLIGENCE

When, in the course of a dental operation, an accident occurs or when the patient suffers injury while under the care of the dentist, the patient himself, for a variety of reasons, may be partly to blame. If in the course of a subsequent action for damages for negligence, the defendant pleads that the plaintiff had materially contributed to the accident or event leading to harm, the Court must decide who is responsible. If the Court finds that loss or injury was caused by the defendant, the plaintiff may be awarded damages although he may have been partly to blame. Even if the plaintiff is found to be largely responsible, he is not debarred, as he once was, from recovering damages. The Law Reform (Contributory Negligence) Act, 1945 contains in section 1 (1) this provision: 'Where any person suffers damage as the result partly of his own fault and partly of any other person or persons, a claim in respect of that damage shall not be defeated by reason of the fault of the person suffering the damage, but the damages recoverable in respect thereof shall be reduced to such an extent as the Court thinks just and equitable having regard to the claimant's share in the responsibility for the damage.'

Contributory negligence can properly be pleaded as a complete defence against a charge of negligence and the Court may exonerate the defendant where it considers the plaintiff wholly responsible for the damage suffered.

In dental practice contributory negligence on the part of the patient may arise in a variety of ways. There may be on his part failure to follow post-operative instructions; failure to call in the dentist when post-operative trouble arises; or contribution to an accident by sudden movement during operation.

## A. Failure to Follow Post-operative Instructions

The patient's failure to carry out the dentist's instructions may and sometimes does lead to undue haemorrhage after a tooth extraction operation. In the same way, sepsis may supervene in a tooth socket because of the patient's neglect of instructions and be the cause of post-extraction pain.

## B. Failure to Call in the Dentist when Post-operative Trouble Arises

The following case is instructive.

> A claim was made against a dentist because of haemorrhage and pain after a tooth extraction operation. The Judge, in summing up the evidence, said, 'There is no case to go to the Jury. I presume that any reasonable dentist would have gone to see the patient if she had asked him. She did not call him. As there is no case, I will not call upon the defendant to defend himself and will order a non-suit.'[1]

## C. Contribution to an Accident by Sudden Movement during Operation

Unusual accidents are sometimes caused or contributed to by the patient's unexpected or sudden movement during an operation.

> A tooth was forced into the Maxillary Sinus when it collided with the forceps which were about to be applied for its extraction, the collision being due to the sudden and unexpected forward movement of the patient who desired to rinse her mouth.[2]
> A child made a movement while a bur was being used in the preparation of a tooth cavity: the bur slipped out of the handpiece of the dental engine, was swallowed and subsequently had to be removed from the stomach by a gastrotomy operation.[3]
> A patient suddenly swallowed just at the moment when the dentist was about to fix in place an artificial crown on a lower tooth root, the movement caused the crown to be dislodged from the dentist's fingers and it was swallowed by the patient.[4]

Contribution to an accident by movement on the part of the patient may not absolve the dentist from liability, as is shown in the following case:

---

[1] *Phillips* v. *Cottam* (1889), *Brit. dent. J.*, **10**, p. 204.     [2] Personal communication.
[3] PITTS, A. T. (1937), 'The Medico-legal Aspects of Dental Practice', *Dental Record* (1937), LVII, p. 485.
[4] Personal communication.

A patient sued a dentist for negligence alleging that, while preparing a tooth for a restoration, the dentist had allowed a revolving carborundum wheel to slip, thereby causing damage to the lingual artery. At the hearing the Judge said: 'If the wheel slipped, it was negligence. If the floor of the mouth rose by the patient swallowing, it was more questionable, but I find that there has been negligence because the tongue should have been kept from rising and, if this were done, the patient should have been told not to swallow and if swallowing did occur, the operation should have been immediately suspended.'[1]

In contrast to accidents such as these, which are fortunately rare, the fracture of a hypodermic needle used to inject a local anaesthetic is comparatively common. This type of accident is more liable to occur when the needle is inserted deeply into the tissues to 'block' a nerve and the risk of breakage of the needle is considerably increased by a sudden movement of the patient's head at the moment of injection.

It is again emphasized that contributory negligence of any kind by the patient does not necessarily exonerate the dentist from blame. At most it can do so: in other cases it may merely reduce the damages awarded to the patient.

## 5. INEVITABLE ACCIDENT

Pollock defined an inevitable accident as an accident 'not avoidable by any such precautions as a reasonable man, doing such an act then and there, could be expected to take'.[2] Lord Erskine, in the Institutes, put it more tersely: 'If what has brought on the damage be merely accidental, the person suffering has no remedy.'[3]

Thus it has been held that if the head of a hatchet flies off and kills or injures a bystander, the person using the hatchet is not liable so long as he was using the implement in an ordinary occupation and with due regard to the safety of others.[4] It would be logical to assume that the same principle would apply to the breakage of a hypodermic needle where it could be proved that the needle was faulty and that the fault could not be discovered by any method which a reasonable dentist would employ.

Inevitable accident is therefore a valid defence against a charge of negligence.

---

[1] *Leuw* v. *Bulleid* (1920), *Brit. dent. J.*, **41**, p. 391.    [2] POLLOCK, Torts, p. 107.
[3] ERSKINE, J. (1824), *Institutes of the Law of Scotland*, p. 592. Edinburgh, Bell & Bridfute.
[4] HAWK, P. C., c. 29. s. 2.

## 6. RULE OF RES IPSA LOQUITUR

There is another general principle affecting the law of negligence which deserves to be noted for it may occasionally apply in actions for damages against doctors and dentists.

The principle is embodied in the maxim, *res ipsa loquitur*, 'The thing speaks for itself' may be the plea put forward by the plaintiff in presenting his case and then the onus, which is generally on the plaintiff to prove negligence, is shifted to the defendant to show that the accident could have occurred in some way other than because of his negligence.

The rule has been held to apply to cases where bags of sugar fell from a crane on to a person below and where a motor-car left unattended in the street ran downhill and did damage. The presumption in such cases is that these are events which do not occur without negligence on the part of someone.

The doctrine of *res ipsa loquitur* was applied in the case of *Garner* v. *Morell*.[1]

> The plaintiff's husband visited the surgery of the defendants, dental surgeons to have some teeth extracted. During the operation the plaintiff's husband swallowed or inhaled a throat pack which had been inserted and died from asphyxia. The Court gave judgement for the plaintiff, treating the case as one of *res ipsa loquitur* and also finding that the throat pack used was too small. The Court of Appeal affirmed this judgement on the ground that there was ample evidence to support this finding and also that *res ipsa loquitur* applied, the facts calling for an explanation.

In general, it may therefore be said that if some injury results from operation which is not a natural consequence of that operation it may be regarded by the Court as being in itself evidence of negligence on the part of the operator; and the Court may hold him liable unless he can show a more probable cause of the injury than his own negligence. We cannot do better than quote Gloag and Henderson[2] on the subject. They state: 'The burden of proving negligence generally rests on the party who asserts it, and who is suing for damages for injury resulting from it. But that burden may be shifted if the facts are such that injury without negligence was extremely unlikely. The maxim *res ipsa loquitur* may then apply and the defender may be called upon to show that the accident could have happened despite the use of reasonable care.'

[1] (1953), *The Times*, 31 October.
[2] GLOAG, W. M. and HENDERSON, R. C. (1946), *Introduction to the Law of Scotland*, 4th ed., p. 390, Edinburgh, Green.

## 7. DEGREES OF NEGLIGENCE

As the terms 'gross negligence' and 'criminal negligence' are commonly used, a brief explanation regarding them deserves to be made.

The term 'gross negligence' implies that there are other less serious forms of negligence such as 'ordinary negligence' or 'slight negligence' but such is not the case. Degrees of negligence are not recognized by the law in actions for damages and when a person is alleged to be guilty of gross negligence all that is meant is that he has obviously failed to observe reasonable care and skill.

'Gross,' 'criminal' and similar epithets in relation to negligence are more commonly used in the criminal law. In order to establish criminal liability, for example in a case of homicide, a much higher degree of negligence must be proved than is necessary to enable a plaintiff to recover damages in a civil action for tortious liability.

## 8. WHAT MAY CONSTITUTE NEGLIGENCE IN DENTAL PRACTICE

Having dealt briefly with some of the principles governing the law of tortious liability and in particular with one example of it, namely negligence, attention deserves to be directed in some detail to the application of these principles to negligence in dental practice. The reader should form an idea of what may constitute negligence, keeping in mind that no hard and fast rules can be laid down because every case which arises must be judged on its own merits. In addition, the reader should know who is entitled to claim damages for negligence and against whom such a claim may be made.

In considering what may constitute negligence, it would be wise to assume at the outset, as has been pointed out by Mair,[1] that the law presupposes the prudent practitioner will observe in all his actions *a*) forethought, *b*) judgement, *c*) skill, and *d*) care.

### A. Forethought

'Look before you leap' should be the first motto. To think beforehand of the patient's welfare should be the dentist's first duty. Failure to recognize a danger which should have been recognized by a practitioner of average skill, or failure to take steps to avoid the danger, once recognized, would constitute negligence. A dentist might therefore be considered negligent if his patient suffered from severe haemorrhage after a tooth extraction when the undue bleeding was caused by

[1] MAIR, W. (1939), 'Some Legal Aspects of Dental Practice', *Brit. dent. J.*, **66**, p. 505.

some haemorrhagic diathesis which the practitioner had unreasonably failed to recognize, or, having recognized it, for which he had failed to take reasonable precautions.

The following case is illustrative of lack of forethought.

> During an extraction operation under a general anaesthetic a dentist removed the throat pack and swabbed the mouth with cotton wool held in a pair of forceps. The cotton wool became detached from the forceps, lodged in the larynx and the patient's life was saved only by a tracheotomy operation. The forceps were proved to be worn and faulty. It was alleged that using such an instrument displayed lack of forethought on the part of the dentist, who was sued for damages for negligence. The action was settled out of Court.[1]

Conversely, the following case illustrates that forethought had definitely been displayed:

> A dentist was charged with negligence because he had fractured, in the course of an extraction operation, a lower incisor tooth which was in malposition. The Court held that he was not negligent because he produced a model of the jaw made prior to the operation and a special pair of narrow-bladed forceps which he had procured specially for the operation.[2]

Another example of lack of forethought, by no means uncommon, is that which results in removal of teeth in error. The mistake usually arises by a confusion of patients' records and that implies lack of forethought and care on the part of the dentist from which he may well have difficulty in exonerating himself.

## B. Judgement

When there is a choice of course to be followed, the safer should be adopted. To make a wrong choice between possible alternatives would not necessarily be negligent but to proceed without carefully considering the alternatives might be. In carrying out treatment for a patient no one is entitled to trust to luck, so the choice of one option involving an appreciated risk rather than the safer alternative would also increase the dentist's liability.

For example, a dentist, confronted with the removal of a partially erupted lower wisdom tooth, realizes that the safer course is to remove bone from the neighbourhood of the tooth to facilitate the operation. Instead, he applies force with elevator or forceps and fractures the jaw bone. That operator would lay himself open to a charge of negligence on the ground that he should not have adopted the procedure which he knew would involve a greater risk than the alternative.

---

[1] MAIR, W. (1939), 'Some Legal Aspects of Dental Practice', *Brit. dent. J.*, 66, p. 505.
[2] McBRIDE, J. (1939), 'Some Legal Aspects of Dental Disease', *Brit. dent. J.*, 66, p. 140.

## C. Skill

The standard of skill required of a practitioner is not defined by law —nor is it definable, for every case must be decided on its own circumstances. While every person who enters a learned profession undertakes to bring to the exercise of it a reasonable degree of skill, he does not undertake to employ the *highest* degree of skill and is therefore not answerable simply because other practitioners might have displayed a higher degree of skill than he.

Furthermore, the standard of skill expected may vary according to the type of practitioner involved and with the general advance of knowledge. The practitioner of specialist or consultant rank will rightly be expected to possess a greater degree of skill than that of the average general practitioner. With the general advance of knowledge come improvements in methods of diagnosis and treatment and the dentist is expected to make use of advanced knowledge and improved methods to a reasonable extent. Failure to do so might be regarded as negligence. For example, precautions against undue haemorrhage following tooth-extraction, which a generation ago would not have been contemplated, might now be considered essential to a successful defence against a charge of negligence. Therefore to plead ,'I acted as I have always been in the habit of doing,' or 'I acted to the best of my ability,' would by itself be no answer to a charge of negligence. The test in every case where, on a point of skill, the question of negligence has to be determined, is what the ordinary prudent practitioner, exercising reasonable skill, would or would not do in similar circumstances.

## D. Care

As in the case of skill, the degree of care expected cannot be defined: it must be determined according to the circumstances. It is safe to assume that the standard of care required is not less than that displayed by the ordinary registered practitioner unless there are, in a particular case, circumstances that point to some higher standard.

In the experience of those who regulate the affairs of the Protection Societies, more claims for damages for negligence arise against dentists through lack of care than through lack of skill. The majority of such cases originate in a tooth-extraction operation after which the dentist makes no special arrangement for the return of the patient in the event of trouble ensuing. Very often in such cases the first indication of anything untoward is the receipt by the dentist of a solicitor's letter claiming damages on behalf of the patient. The prudent and careful practitioner should anticipate the possibility of post-extraction pain, undue haemorrhage or other troubles, should be solicitous after his patient's welfare and should encourage him to report immediately if complications arise. Then in the event of difficulty, its cause can be treated to the benefit of the patient who is more likely to appreciate the care bestowed upon him than to harbour a grievance and seek redress for it.

A common sequel to a tooth-extraction operation is the fracture of the tooth and the leaving behind of a tooth root. To fracture a tooth in the course of its removal is by no means indicative of negligence and it may even be advisable to leave the root *in situ*. But if the dentist does not observe due care in recording the position of the retained root and if he fails to inform the patient of the occurrence, trouble may be in store for him at a later date. While the root may remain in position without causing trouble, it may at any time produce symptoms necessitating its removal and the patient, subjected to pain and possibly involved in the expense of an additional operation, may well have a grievance against the dentist who failed to inform him of the potential source of trouble.

Numerous cases might be quoted to illustrate the variety of reasons, on the ground of lack of skill or care, which has prompted actions for damages for negligence against dental practitioners. But as no precise guidance on the standard of skill and care required of the practitioner can be gained thereby and as every case must be decided on its own circumstances, the inclusion of illustrative cases is likely to be of little assistance to the reader. Instead, we venture to proffer the following advice:

1) Be on your guard against untoward incidents for you never know when such an incident may involve you in an action for damages.

2) Do not assume that the triviality of the alleged damage to the patient will exonerate you.

3) Take reasonable precautions to prevent accidents and post-operative sequelae. For example:

i] *To reduce the risk of breakage of hypodermic needle.* Use a new needle or one that has not been sterilized by 'flaming'. Warn the patient against making a movement during injection. Have at hand an instrument suitable for grasping *at once* the projecting end of the needle if it does break.

ii] *To prevent the passage of a foreign body over the fauces.* Ensure that the throat is properly packed in all cases where teeth are to be extracted under a general anaesthetic.

iii] *To prevent fracture of the jaw.* Avoid the use of undue force when using elevators or forceps to extract teeth.

iv] *To prevent dislocation of the tempero-mandibular joint.* Support the jaw while extracting lower teeth and, if dislocation does occur, make sure that it is reduced before dismissing the patient.

v] *To prevent or minimize post-extraction pain and haemorrhage.* Give the patient explicit instructions.

vi] *To prevent injury to soft tissues.* Warn the patient against making movements when instruments (and especially revolving instruments) are being used upon a tooth.

4) Observe reasonable care for the welfare of the patient, especially after a tooth-extraction operation.

Encourage the patient to report if trouble ensues. Where there is a possibility of undue haemorrhage, make sure the patient knows where to contact you after surgery hours. Make a record at the time of any untoward incident which may arise in the course of your attendance upon your patients.

## 9. STANDARD OF SKILL AND CARE REQUIRED OF THE PRACTITIONER

From what has been already stated, the reader will have gathered that a fundamental principle of the law of negligence is that the practitioner is expected always to observe ordinary skill and care. What constitutes ordinary skill and care cannot be laid down as a hard and fast rule: it must vary between the standard expected of a newly-qualified practitioner on the one hand and of an experienced Consultant on the other. Nevertheless, it has been laid down authoritatively that to establish negligence by a practitioner in a case where deviation from normal practice is alleged, three facts require to be established:

1) It must be proved that there is a usual and normal practice.

2) It must be proved that the practitioner did not adopt that practice.

3) (of crucial importance) It must be established that what the practitioner did was something which no professional man of ordinary skill would have done if he had been acting with ordinary care.

This important statement of the law was given by Lord Clyde in the

Scottish case of *Hunter* v. *Hanley*[1] in an action for damages for negligence raised against a medical practitioner. The doctrine has been adopted in England and in both countries applies equally to the dentist and the doctor. It does much to clarify the law and dispel the belief, commonly held, that because something goes wrong in the course of treating a patient, there must have been negligence.

## 10. TIME LIMIT IN ACTION FOR DAMAGES FOR NEGLIGENCE

Prior to 3 July 1954, an action for damages for negligence could be raised in England within six years and in Scotland within twenty years from the date of the occurrence. An exception was introduced by the National Health Service Acts which stipulated that in respect of incidents happening in hospital, an action had to be instituted within one year.

The Law Repeal (Limitation of Actions) Act, 1954 makes any action for personal injuries time barred unless it is raised within *three years* of the date of the occurrence complained of, whether the incident happen-in hospital or not.

## 11. PERSONS ENTITLED TO CLAIM DAMAGES FOR NEGLIGENCE

When a dentist is alleged to have caused, through negligence, injury to a patient, he may, if in England, be sued by any person who suffers from the negligent act. The person most likely to suffer is obviously the patient and he or she may sue the dentist for damages. The feminine pronoun is purposely mentioned to make it clear that if the patient is a married woman she is entitled to sue independently of her husband. But a husband may claim damages for injury done to his spouse on the ground that the injury has deprived him of his wife's *consortium*, which means her society and service. A father has a similar right in respect of a child capable of performing duties in his household, as has also an employer in respect of injury done to his employee if the injury deprives him of the services of his servant.

In Scotland, title to sue for damages for negligence is confined to the patient himself (unless he dies, in which event certain relatives have the right). Third parties who have suffered loss through being deprived of the services of an injured person have no title to sue.

[1] *Hunter* v. *Hanley* Session Cases, (1955), p. 200.

In each country, a person who is under age has the same right to sue as an adult except that he must do so through his parent or guardian.

Another point of potential importance deserves to be noted. Within certain time limits and provided certain legal requirements are complied with, relatives of a patient who dies have the right to sue for damages for negligence alleged to have caused injury to the deceased. This right did not always exist: it was made possible by the Law Reform (Miscellaneous Provisions) Act passed in England in 1934 and by the corresponding Act passed in Scotland in 1940.

## 12. PERSONS WHO MAY BE SUED FOR NEGLIGENCE

When a charge of negligence arises from an act of omission or an act of commission on the part of a dentist, the question of responsibility may be in doubt. The dentist practising on his own account, without a partner or assistant, presents no problem for, apart from the possibility of contributory negligence by the patient, the responsibility is his and his alone. But if he has colleagues in his practice and a colleague is negligent, questions of legal responsibility are bound to arise. Is the dentist responsible for the negligence of his assistant or partner? Whose is the responsibility, if, in the dentist's absence, his *locum tenens* is negligent? Whose is the responsibility if a mishap occurs during the administration of a general anaesthetic? And what of the dentist employed in a hospital or by a local authority; do his employers share in the responsibility for his negligence? These are questions of some importance and will be considered in respect of the responsibility of *a*) the single-handed practitioner, *b*) the principal, *c*) the assistant, *d*) the *locum tenens*, *e*) the partner, *f*) the anaesthetist, *g*) the hospital authority, and *h*) the local authority.

## A. The Single-handed Practitioner

When there is no other practitioner to share the blame for an act of negligence, the question of individual responsibility does not arise but there are two points of importance affecting all dentists, whatever position they hold in a practice, that might well be mentioned here.

If a patient, under the care of a dentist, suffers injury through his negligence, the patient may sue him for damages regardless of any contract which may exist between them. Even if he treats the patient gratuitously, the dentist is liable and, if the patient is treated under the General Dental Services arrangements made by the National Health Service Acts, his right to sue for damages is in no way different from that of the patient who pays a private fee for services rendered. For all patients whom he attends, the dentist is bound to observe reasonable care and skill.

The other point relates to the Law Reform (Miscellaneous Provisions) Act, 1934 which decrees that the right to sue shall not be extinguished by death. This means that the patient may sue the legal representative of the dentist if the latter dies within a stated period of time subsequent to the alleged negligence.

## B. The Principal

By this term is meant the dentist who owns the practice and employs a registered practitioner or practitioners to assist him in it. The principal is responsible not only for his own negligent acts but also for those of his assistant for it has long been established in law that the master is liable for the negligence of his servant so long as the servant was acting in the course of his employment and in the master's interest.

If the servant was not acting in the course of his employment, the master is not liable for any harm the servant may cause. The principal would therefore not be liable if, for example, his dental mechanic performed some operation in the mouth of a patient and caused damage, for the dental mechanic is not employed to perform operations in the mouth and, if he did perform any, he would not be acting in the course of his employment.

Again, the principal would not be liable if his assistant were negligent in respect of a patient whom he had treated on his own account somewhere outside his principal's premises and without his principal's knowledge or order. In such circumstances the assistant would not be acting in his employer's interest.

The principal is liable for acts performed by the assistant within the scope of his employment even though they are undertaken in an unauthorized way. Nor does the fact that a particular act was expressly forbidden by the principal free him from liability. If, for example, the principal forbids his assistant, who ordinarily undertakes all forms of treatment, to extract a particular impacted tooth, and the assistant disobeys the order, attempts the operation and fractures the patient's jaw, the principal will be liable if the damage was due to the assistant's negligence. The test is whether the act of the assistant is within the ordinary scope and course of his employment: if it is, his principal is liable.

Subject to these rules, the principal is answerable in law for the misdeeds of his assistant: he may be sued for damages for his assistant's negligence or he may be joined in an action for damages along with his assistant.

## C. The Assistant

In spite of the rule in law that the principal is answerable for his assistant's actions so long as they are performed within the scope of his employment and in the principal's interest, the assistant, who must necessarily be a registered practitioner, may himself be sued for damages arising through his own negligence. Alternatively, an action may be raised against the principal and the assistant jointly.

## D. The Locum Tenens

Is a dentist acting as *locum tenens* for another practitioner alone responsible for his negligent acts or is the responsibility shouldered or shared by the practitioner who employs him? To these questions no definite answer can be given for they have not been the subject of a decision in a court of law. It is true that in the case of *Farquhar* v. *Murray*[1] a registered medical practitioner was held to be liable because he had left no instructions to his *locum tenens* who, in the absence of such instructions, prescribed improper treatment for a patient. But that was a particular act of omission and uncertainty remains regarding the general question of the respective liability of the employer and the *locum tenens* when the latter is negligent.

From a practical point of view, the *locum tenens* is in a different position from the assistant for he practises in the absence of his employer while the assistant usually works under the supervision of his principal. From the legal aspect, however, it is suggested that the *locum tenens* may be regarded as the agent of the practitioner employing him and, if he is the agent of his employer, he is in the same relationship to him as is the assistant to the principal.

There is no doubt that a registered practitioner acting as *locum tenens* may himself be sued for his negligent acts. It might be wise to assume that the dentist employing him can also be joined in the action for damages.

## E. The Partner

If a partner, acting in the ordinary course of the business of his firm, causes damage to a patient through negligence, he may be sued by the patient for his negligence. But his partner or partners may be sued

[1] (1901), 38, S.L.R. 642.

along with him, since each partner is the agent of the other(s). In other words, partners are severally as well as jointly liable.

In the event of a partnership firm being found liable to pay damages in respect of the negligence of one member of it, the partner who was at fault has the duty of indemnifying the other(s). If, however, the patient is unsuccessful in proving negligence and (as may well happen) is unable to pay the costs of the action, the firm cannot claim indemnity from the partner whose conduct was called in question for he has been proved by the Court not to be at fault. In such a case the costs of the action must be paid by the firm.

## F. The Anaesthetist

By 'anaesthetist' is meant, of course, the person who administers a general anaesthetic for an operation upon a patient. During or following such administrations mishaps sometimes befall the patient, causing damage or even death, and then the question may arise—who is responsible, the anaesthetist, the operator or both? The answer may depend upon the type of person acting as anaesthetist and the anaesthetist may be i) a registered medical practitioner, ii) a registered dental practitioner, iii) a person who is neither a registered medical nor dental practitioner and iv) the dentist who is also the operator. The question of the responsibility of each requires to be considered.

i] *The registered medical practitioner.* When a registered medical practitioner is employed to administer an anaesthetic he must exercise due skill and care in the course of his duties and, if he is a practitioner specializing in anaesthesia, the degree of skill required of him will be greater than that expected of the family doctor who does not specialize. Included in the duties of the doctor, whether he be specialist or not, is the duty of satisfying himself that the patient is a fit subject for the anaesthetic: it is no part of the duty of the dentist in such circumstances to do so.[1] If the patient suffers damage or dies through negligence on the part of the anaesthetist, the anaesthetist may be sued for damages but the operating dentist may not. If the patient suffers harm from injury to the mouth as, for example, dislocation or fracture of a tooth by a mouth prop or gag, or if the patient suffers because of the retention in the throat of a throat pack, the question of liability may be less certain and both anaesthetist and operator in such circumstances may be joined in an action for damages for negligence. If the patient suffers an injury solely at the hands of the dentist, when, for example, the

[1] *Warren v. White* (1935), *Brit. dent. J.*, **58**, p. 244.

jaw is fractured in the course of the operation, then the dentist alone is responsible for any negligence which may have caused the injury.

ii] *The registered dental practitioner.* The administration of certain types of anaesthetics by registered dental practitioners is common in dental practice, especially when there are colleagues such as principal and assistant or partners in the practice. The relative liability of the anaesthetist-dentist to the operator-dentist is fundamentally the same as that of the doctor and dentist in i] above. Everyone is responsible for his own wrongful or negligent acts.

But another more difficult question arises when no medical practitioner is employed. Should a dentist administer an anaesthetic without first being assured that the patient is a fit subject for the anaesthetic? That the dentist using ordinary care and skill is not competent to assure himself, by any examination which he may carry out, is generally agreed, and the question is whether he should demand from a doctor a certificate of fitness in respect of his patient. The careful dentist of course consults the doctor in any case where there is doubt about the patient's general health because of the patient's appearance or breathlessness or past history: but should the dentist insist upon a certificate in every case? From the ideal point of view the answer is 'Yes' and that view has been expressed by a Crown witness of standing in a recent inquiry into an anaesthetic death.[1] From a practical point of view, however, there are difficulties for if every dentist were to demand such a certificate, the doctors would be inundated with additional work which they would most likely not have time to undertake. It is thought to be true that only a small minority of dentists at present require a medical certificate in these circumstances, and this fact alone would make it difficult to establish that a dentist who failed to do so was guilty of negligence. There we must leave the problem and consider

iii] *A person who is neither a registered medical, nor dental practitioner.* Though the practice cannot be commended, an anaesthetic may be administered to a patient by a nurse or other employee of the dentist. If an anaesthetic is so administered, it would seem that the dentist would be wholly liable for any negligence on the part of his employee. In certain circumstances it is conceivable that the dentist might also be held to be negligent on his own account because he had entrusted this function to a person of inadequate skill whereby the patient suffered injury.

[1] *Glasgow Herald,* 20 July 1951.

HDH

iv] *A dental practitioner acting also as operator*. The dentist should never act in the dual role of anaesthetist and operator: it is against the tenets of modern teaching for it is not in the best interest of the patient. If the dentist does act in the dual capacity and some injury or harm befalls the patient, the Court may well question whether the dentist had shown reasonable care in taking upon his shoulders the responsibility of safeguarding the patient from the dangers of the anaesthetic as well as the possible mishaps of the operation.

## G. The Hospital Authority

By the rule of *respondeat superior* an employer is liable for the negligent acts of his employee so long as the acts are performed by the servant in the course of his employment and a hospital authority is no longer exempt, as it once was, from this general rule.

In the case of *Hillyer* v. *St Bartholomew's Hospital*[1] in 1909 the Court exonerated the managers of the Hospital from responsibility for injury which the plaintiff had received from a burn from a hot-water bottle. The Court's decision appeared to establish the principle that the function of hospital managers was purely administrative and that their only duty was to provide suitable accommodation, proper equipment and apparatus and a competent staff. The case may have been decided as it was because of a desire on the part of the Court to protect the funds of a charitable institution from claims for damages, St Bartholomew's and most other hospitals being then charitable institutions. The status of the professional man engaged in a hospital may also have influenced the decision, for it might have been argued that the governors could not be held responsible for persons who used professional skill in the course of their work and who were voluntary members of the staff.

The decision in the *Hillyer* case was upheld in numerous others in England and in Scotland and hospital authorities throughout the United Kingdom enjoyed exemption from the rule of *respondeat superior* and could not be sued for damages for the negligence of a professional man on their staff.

In 1942, however, the law in England was altered for in *Gold* v. *Essex County Council*[2] the Court held that a local authority administering a public hospital owes to a patient in it the duty of nursing and treating him properly and was liable for the negligence of a radiographer who was a whole-time employee even though his work entailed the

[1] (1909), 2 K.B. 820; 78 L.J.K.B. 958; 101 L.T. 368.
[2] (1942), 2 K.B. 293; 112 L.J.K.B.; (1942), 2 All E.R. 237.

exercise of professional skill. This new principle was upheld in subsequent cases and in *Cassidy* v. *Ministry of Health*[1] Lord Denning expressed the opinion that a hospital authority is liable for the negligence of the professional men whom they employ whether they were resident whole-time employees who were under contract of service or visiting consultants who were under contract for services. The range of personnel for whom hospitals are legally responsible no longer stands where *Cassidy's* case left it. In *Roe* v. *Ministry of Health*[2] Denning, L. J. said:

> I think the hospital authorities are responsible for the whole of their staff, not only for the nurses and doctors, but also for the anaesthetists and the surgeons. It does not matter whether they are permanent or temporary resident or visiting whole-time or part-time. The hospital authorities are responsible for all of them. The reason is because, even if they are not servants, they are the agents of the hospital to give treatment. The only exception is the case of consultants or anaesthetists selected and employed by the patient himself.

In Scotland the Courts were loath to depart from the *Hillyer* dictum. They adhered to the principle that the patient who suffered harm in hospital had the right to sue a member or members of the staff but had no redress against the managers of the hospital. For a time, therefore, the law in the two countries was widely divergent as it related to the vicarious responsibility of hospital authorities and it was not until 1954 that the law of Scotland was altered and brought into line with that of England and Wales.

In that year the cases of *Hayward* v. *Royal Infirmary of Edinburgh*[3] and *Macdonald* v. *Glasgow Western Hospitals*[4] were the subject of appeal to the Court of Session. In both, the hospital authorities had been absolved from vicarious liability in lower Courts but the Judges in the Court of Session overruled the decisions. In giving their opinions they stated that they knew of no reason why the law of Scotland and the law of England should differ in principle on the question of the vicarious responsibility of hospitals for the negligent acts of professional men employed in them, especially when hospitals of the United Kingdom have been brought under one scheme, varying only in minor detail, on both sides of the Border.

Thus throughout the United Kingdom the law is uniform. Hospital authorities no longer enjoy the privilege of exemption from the rule that the master is responsible for the negligent acts of his servant. A patient alleging that he has been negligently treated in hospital may

---

[1] (1951), 1 All E.R. 574.  [2] (1954), All E.R. 131.  [3] (1954) S.C. 453.  [4] (1954) S.C. 453.

therefore raise an action for damages against a member or members of the staff, against the Regional Hospital Board or Board of Governors or the Management Committee or Board of Management who administer the hospital and even against the Ministry of Health or the Department of Health for Scotland who own the establishment.

## H. The Local Authority

Just as the managers or owners of a hospital are vicariously responsible for the negligence of any member of their staff, the local authority is legally liable in respect of the negligence of an individual in their employment. If, therefore, a person suffers through the negligent act of a Public Dental Officer, that person (or his parent or guardian) may claim damages from the Officer or his employing authority or from both.

### 13. RIGHT OF RELIEF IN VICARIOUS RESPONSIBILITY

In considering who may be sued for damages for negligence, we have shown that responsibility may be direct or vicarious. In direct responsibility, the dentist causing the injury may alone be sued for his negligence whether he be a single-handed practitioner or principal or assistant, etc.

In vicarious responsibility, an action for damages may be raised against the employer instead of or as well as the wrong-doer. Examples of vicarious responsibility are to be seen when a principal is held liable for his assistant, when a partner is held responsible for his partner or when hospital managers or local authorities are held responsible for their employees.

But it matters little to the negligent dentist whether he is involved in a case in which he is held directly and solely responsible or in one where there may be vicarious responsibility, for in the latter event the employer, in law, has the right of relief against the wrong-doer. The principal who is called upon to pay damages to a patient injured through the negligence of his assistant has the right to claim relief from that assistant. The same principle applies to a partner who suffers loss through damages awarded against his partner, though a partner has no right to be compensated where loss is incurred through inability of an unsuccessful plaintiff to pay costs. Hospital managers and local authorities have the right of relief against negligent employees.

# CHAPTER IX

# Professional Fees–Consent– Confidentiality

## PROFESSIONAL FEES

### I. GENERAL

A dentist is not compelled to accept as a patient anyone who seeks his services but, whenever a person is accepted as a patient, there is brought into being between that patient and the dentist a contract for the services of the dentist. The contract whether written or unwritten, express or implied, imposes obligations on each. The dentist's main obligation is to perform services with reasonable skill and care and the patient's is to pay for the services an agreed or a reasonable fee.

If the patient seeking professional services desires to be treated under the National Health Service Acts and if the dentist agrees to treat him as such, the fee payable to the dentist is determined by the Regulations made under the Acts. The dentist recovers it in some cases from the Local Executive Council, in other cases from the patient and in still other cases from both.

The relationship between the dentist and his patient depends therefore upon whether the patient is treated privately or in accordance with the arrangements made under the National Health Service Acts. The subject is considered in this chapter in respect of both types of patient.

### 2. THE DENTIST AND HIS PRIVATE PATIENT

#### A. The Contract of Employment

Matters appertaining to professional fees are governed by the law of contract. When a dentist agrees to give his services to a patient there is set up between them a contract of some sort. It may be a definite or *express* contract, though a contract of that kind is rarely entered into in professional engagements. More often, the contract and its terms are *implied* from the conduct and words of the two parties. In the absence of an express contract, an implied contract is binding in law.

In an *express* contract the dentist undertakes to perform certain specified work in return for which he will receive a stated fee. He is obliged to carry out that work and is entitled to be paid the sum agreed to in the contract. He is entitled only to that sum even though he meets unexpected complications and even though the work involves more time than was anticipated or estimated.

The patient, on his part, is under the obligation to pay the agreed fee even though he does not derive the benefits expected from the treatment and even though he suffers detriment from it, provided that the work was performed with reasonable skill and care.

In an *implied* contract, the dentist merely indicates to the patient the work considered necessary without mentioning the precise nature of it, the materials to be used, the length of time required to complete the work or the fee to be charged. In a contract of this kind the law assumes that the dentist will perform the work with reasonable skill and care; that he will use materials such as a reasonably skilful and careful dentist would use in similar circumstances; and that he will charge a reasonable fee.

At the same time, the law implies that the patient, in the absence of an express agreement on the points, will keep appointments made with the dentist for the execution of the work and will pay him a reasonable fee, provided the work is properly performed.

## B. Liability for Breach of Contract

If either party to the contract fails to fulfil his obligations, he is answerable for any loss which the other may sustain. So if the patient fails without sufficient excuse to keep an appointment which he has made with the dentist, the latter has the right to be compensated for loss of time so long as he has not been able to utilize the time for treatment of another patient. Again, if the patient fails to pay the dentist's fee for work done, the dentist has the right to recover and may sue the patient in Court.

On the other hand, if the dentist is in breach of his contract, the patient has the right to be compensated for any loss thereby sustained. While the dentist is not compelled to accept as a patient anyone who seeks his services, he is obliged, having accepted the person as a patient, to complete the treatment agreed upon. If, without the patient's consent, he ceases treatment before it is completed or if he fails to complete treatment within the time specified, he is in breach of his contract and may be liable in damages. Failure to use proper materials for the restoration of a tooth or in the making of an artificial denture is another example of a possible breach of contract on the part of the dentist.

No sensible dentist guarantees the result of his labours and in the absence of any such guarantee a dentist could not be successfully sued for breach of contract on the ground that treatment given had not been as beneficial as he or the patient had hoped. If a dentist were sued on that ground it would normally be sufficient for him to show that he had used reasonable skill and care.

Where, however, a denture is supplied the dentist's liability is greater. In *Samuels* v. *Davis*[1] the Court regarded it as an implied term of any contract for the provision of a denture that, given reasonable co-operation by the patient, the dentist will provide a denture which fits well and which can be used by the patient for the purpose for which it was made.

Most disputes over the question of fees arise in connexion with those charged for the provision of dentures, the patient refusing to pay the dentist's fee on the ground that the dentures supplied are unsatisfactory for one reason or another. If, after reasonable steps are taken to correct faults complained of, the dentist is of the opinion that the appliance is satisfactory but the patient remains dissatisfied, an offer should be made to obtain a second opinion from a colleague. Each party should agree to abide by the second opinion, the dentist agreeing to undertake, without extra charge, any alterations suggested and the patient agreeing to pay the fee if no alterations are considered necessary.

## C. Reasons for Non-payment of Fees

When a patient fails to pay an account for services rendered, he may proffer as a defence any of the following reasons: i] the fee was unreasonable; ii] the patient is not legally obliged to pay; or iii] the treatment was wrong and the work badly performed.

i] *The fee was unreasonable.* The law sets no specific limit on the sum which the dentist may charge by way of a fee. Professional charges rightly vary with the location of the dentist's practice, with his skill and experience and with the esteem in which he is held. If the dentist and patient have expressly agreed at any stage the fee to be paid, the Court will not normally permit the patient to raise before it any questions as to the reasonableness of that fee. Where, however, in the absence of an express arrangement on the amount of the fee, a dispute

[1] (1943), 2 A.E.R. 3.

is referred to the Court, the Court will determine whether or not, in the light of all the circumstances, the charge was reasonable.

ii] *The patient is not legally obliged to pay the dentist.* This defence is most likely to be put forward by married women and children.

In the case of married women the law is substantially the same in England and Wales and in Scotland. The only important difference is noted later in this section.

A married woman living with her husband is presumed by the law to have the authority of her husband to pledge his credit for any goods and services which the law regards as 'necessaries'. Medical treatment has been held to be a 'necessary' and it seems logical to regard dental treatment in the same category provided that it does not include any items of a luxury nature.

This authority on the part of the wife is, however, only presumed by the law in the absence of facts which negative the authority. A husband will not be liable for debts incurred by his wife for necessaries if he can establish any of the following facts:

*a*) That he gives his wife an adequate allowance to enable her to pay all reasonable debts.

*b*) That he has told the dentist not to give her credit on his account.

*c*) That he has forbidden his wife to pledge his credit.

*d*) That his wife lives apart from him through no fault of his own.

But even if the husband can establish the fact stated at *c*) above, namely that he has forbidden his wife to pledge his credit, he may not be able to escape liability in certain circumstances. For if a dentist has formerly treated a married woman and her husband has paid the bill, the husband is bound to give the dentist adequate notice if he wishes to withdraw his wife's authority to pledge his credit in future. If adequate notice is not given, the husband will remain liable even though he has withdrawn his wife's authority to receive treatment at his expense.

Apart from a married woman's presumed authority to make her husband liable for the cost of her dental treatment, she is legally quite competent to make a contract in her own right if she wishes to do so. Where she seeks dental treatment and specifically agrees with the dentist that she will pay the bill, she and she alone is liable for the cost of treatment.

The difference in the law in England and Wales and in Scotland must now be stated. In England and Wales a dentist who contracts with a married woman who has in fact the authority to bind her husband for her debts is taken in law to have contracted with her as her husband's agent, even if he did not know that she was married. This means that the dentist can hold the husband liable to pay his wife's bill so far as necessary treatment is concerned but he cannot hold the wife liable.

In Scotland, however, a married woman who obtains dental treatment for herself, even with her husband's authority, may herself also be liable to pay the dentist's fees where the dentist did not know that she was a married woman at the time he made the contract. This would not free the husband from liability but the dentist in Scotland would, in such a case, have the option to hold either the husband or the wife liable for the cost of treatment.

The practical rule for dentists to follow is therefore to claim first upon the husband for treatment given to the wife. If, however, he knows that the wife has not the authority of her husband to pledge his credit, or if the married woman has agreed to be personally liable to pay the cost of treatment, the account should be presented to the wife herself.

The presumed authority of the wife to obtain necessary treatment at her husband's expense extends also to treatment for children of the marriage. Thus, if a married woman authorizes a dentist to treat her children, the husband will be liable to pay the cost if in the same circumstances he would have been liable for the cost of his wife's treatment.

In England and Wales a child is an 'infant' in law and until he attains the age of twenty-one he can make a valid contract only for what the law regards as necessaries, which would presumably include dental treatment of a reasonable nature. When necessary treatment is given, the infant himself is liable upon his contract for treatment. A parent or guardian is not normally liable to pay any debt incurred by the infant under his care, whether it is in respect of necessaries or otherwise. The parent or guardian is liable, however, if he has agreed expressly or by implication to pay the child's bills or has authorized the child to incur a particular debt.

In Scotland, children under twenty-one are divided into two classes. Up to the age of fourteen, if a boy, or up to the age of twelve, if a girl, a child is a 'pupil'. From twelve or fourteen, as the case may be, the child is a 'minor'.

A pupil has no separate legal persona and is incapable of entering a binding contract. His guardian may, however, enter into obligations on his behalf. The child's father is normally his guardian and is under obligation as father to maintain the child and supply him or her with necessaries. It will seldom happen that a dentist will undertake dental treatment for a pupil without prior consultation with the child's father, or mother acting as agent for the father, and in these cases the father will be liable for the dentist's fee. If the child has estate of its own, that estate will be liable for necessary treatment if the father cannot pay.

The legal position of a minor in Scotland is somewhat different. His father, so long as the minor is living in family with him, is not married and is unable to support himself, has still the obligation to supply him with necessaries. Apart from this obligation of the father, the capacity of a minor to enter into a binding contract depends on whether or not he has a curator. If he has a curator, the minor can enter into most forms of contract with the curator's consent. Without such consent the contract would be void, with this proviso that the minor would be liable to pay a fair price for any goods and services of the nature of necessaries supplied to him. If a minor does not have a curator, his capacity to contract is the same as that of a minor who has a curator and contracts with the curator's consent.

iii] *The treatment was wrong or the work badly performed.* The patient may refuse to pay the dentist's fee on the ground that the treatment he received was substantially useless owing to the dentist's negligence. The patient may also raise a counter claim for damages for negligence. A considerable proportion of claims for damages for negligence against dentists arise in this way, primarily in an attempt to evade payment of the dentist's bill. This is particularly so where the service rendered has been the provision of artificial dentures.

## D. Steps for Recovery of Fees

Ordinarily, the professional man is reluctant to sue for recovery of fees but there is no reason, legal or ethical, why the dental practitioner should not do so. Before taking this step, he may appeal directly to the patient for payment or he may employ a solicitor or a debt-collecting agency to collect the debt for him.

If the dentist does decide to sue for recovery, he should employ a solicitor who will guide him regarding the right person to proceed against, the correct court in which to bring the action and other important details. He should satisfy himself that the debtor has the means to pay because if he has not the means to pay, the dentist may be called upon to pay his own costs in the action. He should also remember that there is a time limit beyond which he may not sue and that limit is usually six years in England and three years in Scotland.

### 3. THE DENTIST AND HIS PATIENT IN THE NATIONAL HEALTH SERVICE

## A. Nature of the Contract

In private practice the relationship between the dentist and the patient is clear: a contract exists between them which requires the dentist to treat the patient with a reasonable standard of skill and care and the patient to pay an agreed or a reasonable fee for the services rendered to him.

When a dentist treats a patient under the National Health Service, the fee for the treatment is determined in accordance with a scale laid down by Regulations. This scale lays down fixed fees for certain kinds of treatments, and for others provides that the fee payable shall be approved by the Dental Estimates Board. Under the National Health Service Act, 1946 (and the corresponding Act in Scotland), all treatment which was necessary for the patient's dental fitness was paid for by the State and payment for all such treatment was made to the dentist by the Local Executive Council upon the authorization of the Dental Estimates Board. The National Health Service Acts, 1951, 1952 and 1961 require the patient to pay the whole or part of the cost of treatment in certain circumstances.

The dentist therefore receives payment of fees in accordance with the scale or of fees approved by the Dental Estimates Board, and may receive payment wholly from the patient, wholly from the Local Executive Council or partly from the patient and partly from the Local Executive Council. Where a charge is payable by the patient, the Regulations provide that the dentist may recover it as a simple contract debt, that is, if necessary by suing for it in the Courts. The reader will keep in mind what has been said on pages 108 and 109 regarding the person who is liable when the dental treatment is given to a married woman or a person under twenty-one.

The dentist is in contract with the patient whom he treats under the National Health Service arrangements, but the contract is modified by the transfer to the Local Executive Council of the obligation to pay the dentist part or all of the fee to which he is entitled. In respect of a particular patient, the dentist is consequently in contract with that patient and with the Local Executive Council.

The dentist is also in contract with the Local Executive Council in a general way. He enters into this contract when he has his name placed on the Dental List of the Local Executive Council for, when he signs the requisite form of application, he undertakes to provide general dental services under the National Health Service Acts on the terms in operation in the area of the Council.

No contract exists between the dentist and the Dental Estimates Board. This statutory body acts as an intermediary between the dentist and the Local Executive Council: its authority is required before the dentist can proceed with certain forms of treatment and before the Local Executive Council can pay the dentist his fee in respect of work completed. At no stage does the dentist enter into a contract with the Board.

## B. When the Contract Commences

Under the National Health Service Acts and Regulations the dentist is free to accept or reject any particular person who applies to him for treatment under the Health Service arrangements. The dentist's obligations to the patient, under contract and under the Regulations, do not come into existence until he has accepted the patient for treatment as a Health Service patient.

The questions as to what constitutes acceptance of a patient for treatment under the Health Service is therefore an important one and one that may cause some difficulty. It seems clear that it is not necessary for such an acceptance to be made in writing in order to be binding on the dentist. The National Health Service Regulations do require that in accepting an applicant for treatment the dentist must complete a part of form E.C.17. But the patient may be deemed to be accepted even before this form has been completed. If, for example, a person asks the dentist whether he will accept him as a patient for treatment under the Health Service and the dentist replies that he will, it would appear that at that moment a valid contract is made for the giving of the treatment and the patient is accepted for the purpose of the Regulations.

Moreover, it is possible for the dentist to be bound in this way by the action of his employee. Thus, where the dentist authorizes his receptionist to decide whether particular patients will be treated under the Health Service, a decision by the receptionist in respect of a particular patient would bind the dentist. Even in cases where specific authority has not been given by the dentist in this way, it is possible that the employee may have what the law recognizes as 'ostensible authority'. If the public can reasonably assume from the status and duties of the dentist's employee that he or she has the employer's authority to accept patients for treatment under the Health Service, the dentist will be bound by any acceptance made by the employee, even though he has given to that employee no such authority. If the dentist wishes to avoid all risk of his employees being regarded as having ostensible authority for this purpose, he must give notice to his patients that no authority to accept patients is in fact vested in his employees. This could be done, for example, by means of a notice in the dentist's waiting room, but such a notice would protect the dentist only in the case of persons who saw, or should reasonably have seen, the notice *before* an employee accepted them as patients of the dentist.

## C. Persons Under Age

However a person is accepted as a patient under the National Health Service, he is required by the Regulations to sign form E.C.17 to show that he desires to be treated under the Service, that he undertakes to pay the dentist whatever fee he may be liable to pay and finally that, to the best of his belief, the treatment has been completed. Every patient who is over the age of sixteen is required to sign in this way whether in England or in Scotland. If the patient is under the age of sixteen, the statutory form must be signed on his behalf by his parent, guardian or other authorized person.

## D. Disputes Over Fees and Treatment

Where a patient is required to pay the dentist part or all the cost of his treatment, it is permissible for the dentist to decline to proceed with that treatment until he has received payment from the patient. If the dentist does not require the patient to pay the fee before proceeding with the treatment and if the patient subsequently fails to fulfil his obligation, the dentist may proceed just as if the defaulter had received treatment as a private patient. The dentist may sue the patient in Court.

The patient who is dissatisfied with treatment received from a dentist, or who has any other grievance against the dentist, may lodge a complaint with the Local Executive Council. The procedure under which these complaints are dealt with is fully explained on pages 78 to 79. After full investigation in accordance with the procedure described on those pages, the Executive Council has power either to exonerate the dentist or to find him at fault. In the latter event, the Council has the power to impose certain penalties, including a recommendation that money be deducted from the dentist's remuneration.

#### 4. OWNERSHIP OF X-RAY FILMS

Before leaving the subject of professional fees, an attempt should perhaps be made to clarify the question of the ownership of X-ray films. When a private patient has his mouth X-rayed, he is rightly charged a fee for the resulting radiographs. Do these radiographs become the property of the patient or do they remain the property of the dentist who produced them or had them produced by a radiographer?

It might be contended that the patient who is charged a fee for radiographic service should be offered or given the films. But it might also be contended that the radiographs are obtained merely as a means to an end—namely to assist the dentist in diagnosis or treatment or to enable him to furnish a report on the dental condition of the patient. On that contention the patient appears to have no more right to the radiographs than he has to models of his mouth made in preparation of some restoration or artificial denture.

The question of the ownership of X-ray films has never been decided in a Court of law and, until it is, it must remain in doubt in those cases where no express contract is made between the dentist and the patient concerning it. This generalization applies equally to the patient treated under the National Health Service.

## CONSENT TO OPERATION

#### 1. IN GENERAL

Everyone has the right of freedom from interference with his person, a right which forbids the dentist, doctor or anyone else, as a general rule, to do anything which involves the physical touching of the patient without the patient's consent. Infringement of this right constitutes in England the tort of trespass to the person, commonly called assault, and the crime of battery. In Scotland, the term assault is used loosely to mean any act of violence to the person.

Consent to operation must be given by the patient who is in possession of his faculties and who is able to be consulted: it is a prerequisite to any operation (unless in an emergency) for, in the absence of consent, the operator who performs the operation or the person who administers an anaesthetic to the patient is liable.

To do anything to the person of another without his consent is an assault, even though the person receives no actual harm, and the offender may have to pay damages. Thus the mere examination of a person without his consent constitutes an infringement of his right and renders the examiner liable for damages. Furthermore, the doctor or dentist who uses physical force to correct a 'difficult' child patient lays himself open to an action for assault.[1]

## 2. NATURE OF CONSENT

Consent need not be expressly given: it may be implied. An example of implied consent is seen in everyday dental practice when a patient makes an appointment for periodic inspection and treatment: in respect of such persons the making of the appointment implies consent for the usual filling or scaling operations necessary to maintain dental fitness. Such consent does not permit the practitioner to undertake any additional operation as, for example, the extraction of a tooth or the provision of a more expensive type of restoration. For such procedures, consent must be expressly given by the patient. The validity of implied consent was brought out in a case where the Court held that a patient who had not objected to puncture of the spinal cord for the purpose of diagnosis could not recover damages for assault.[2] Submission to an operation may therefore be taken to imply consent.

When a patient agrees to the extraction of a tooth, his consent covers the laceration of the gum and the spilling of blood which are consequent upon the operation. When, however, consent is given to the extraction of a particular tooth, that consent does not extend to the removal of another—either instead of or in addition to the tooth designated. As a general rule, the right to extend an operation is no greater than the right to operate in the first instance, though the rule must obviously be modified or ignored in cases where extension is necessary for the preservation of life (a circumstance seldom likely to arise in dental practice). The plaintiff was awarded £250 damages in a case where the dentist had extracted more teeth than had been agreed to by the patient.[3]

To be valid, consent must be freely given and this presupposes, among other things, that the patient is made fully aware of all the relevant facts. When, for example, removal of an impacted tooth is

---

[1] KITCHEN, D. H. (1941), *Law for the Medical Practitioner*, p. 47. London, Eyre & Spottiswoode.
[2] *Donald v. Swann* (1931), 137 So. 178.
[3] *O'Shea v. Moyce and Donston*, The Lancet, 20 June 1936, p. 1433.

advised, the dentist should explain the nature of the proposed operation and not allow the patient to assume that its removal can be affected as simply as that of a normal tooth.

Consent to an operation may be given in writing or orally and, although written consent is not legally essential, it obviously has greater value than the oral. For that reason the usual custom in hospital is to obtain the patient's signature to a statement giving his permission for the operation proposed. The Defence Societies[1] recommend for this purpose the following:

*Form of Consent for operative treatment*

To the Medical Staff and Committee of                          *Consent by patient*
Management of the                          Hospital.
I, ............................................................... of ...............................................................
hereby consent to undergo the operation of ...............................................................
the effect and nature of which has been explained to me.

I also consent to such further or alternative operative measures as may be found to be necessary during the course of such operation and to the administration of a local or other anaesthetic for any of the foregoing purposes.

I understand an assurance has not been given that the operation will be performed by a particular surgeon.

Dated this                          day of                          19  .
                                        (signed) ...............................................................

                                                                         *Consent by relative*

I ............................................................... of ...............................................................
the ............................................................... of the above named ...............................................................
hereby also consent to such operation.

Dated this                          day of                          19  .
                                        (signed) ...............................................................

It should be noted that, in that part of the form to be signed by the patient, provision is made for consent to an extension of the operation should the necessity arise and to the operation being performed not necessarily by a specified member of the staff. These provisions, along with the arrangement whereby the form is also signed by a relative, are designed to prevent those troubles which, in the experience of the Defence Societies, are apt to arise.

### 3. VICARIOUS CONSENT

Consent is a prerequisite to examination and treatment of every patient but it may not be possible for the consent to be given by the patient

---

[1] The Medical Defence Union, the Medical Protection Society and the Medical and Dental Defence Union of Scotland Ltd.

himself. He may be of unsound mind and incapable of understanding, in which case consent should be obtained from someone having authority to give it. He may be unconscious or too ill to consent to an operation considered essential for his welfare. In dental practice the necessity for an emergency operation of this nature is a rare event but the dentist confronted with it should endeavour to obtain consent from a relative of the patient.

By contrast, the problem of giving treatment to a person of tender years commonly confronts the dental practitioner. A person under twenty-one years of age is, generally speaking, debarred from entering into a contract so it may be logical to argue that he is incapable of giving consent to any operation upon himself. To this general rule there is an exception: the person over sixteen years of age is entitled to choose in the National Health Service his doctor or dentist and to sign statutory documents. He may therefore be deemed to be competent to give his own consent to an operation though this important point does not appear to have been tested in any Court of law.

For practical purposes persons under twenty-one years of age may be divided into the following classes:

## Class 1. *Persons under sixteen years of age*

A person in this class has no legal right to give consent and the practitioner who treats such a person without the consent of that person's parent of guardian runs the risk of being sued for assault.

## Class 2. *Persons between sixteen and twenty-one years of age and living at home*

As has been pointed out, the National Health Service regulations permit a person who is over sixteen years of age (whether living at home or not) to enter into a contract with a dentist of his choice and to sign the Form E.C. 17. From this, it may be assumed that he has the right to give consent to an operation upon himself. It should be emphasized, however, that this is only an assumption for the question has not been before the Courts and until the contention is supported by a legal decision, the safe rule is to obtain consent of parent or guardian for every person under the age of twenty-one. Especially should this rule be observed in respect of young persons who are living at home and dependent upon their parents. There exists some doubt as to their legal right generally to give consent, whatever their right under the National Health Service Acts.

Class 3. *Persons between sixteen and twenty-one years of age living away from home and earning*

In Scots law a person in this class is said to be 'forisfamiliated' and can give his own consent to any operative procedure including the administration of a general anaesthetic. In England a similar right probably extends to this class of person.

In spite of this, consent of parent or guardian should be obtained before the administration of a general anaesthetic in view of the risks which are generally recognized to be attendant upon that procedure. The wise practitioner should also obtain consent of parent or guardian when any treatment is contemplated of an expensive nature. If the parent were called upon to pay the fee for that treatment he might refuse to do so on the ground that he had not given his consent.

Class 4. *Children of any age attending an Education Authority School*

By the Education (Scotland) Acts, 1946 and 1956, and the Education (Miscellaneous Provisions) Act, 1953 a child in this class is compelled to undergo dental examination but the child's parent or guardian has the right to refuse treatment by the School Dental Officer. Consequently, the practice adopted by most, if not all, Education Authorities is to arrange that a child will be treated by the School Dental Officer only after the written consent of the parent or guardian has been obtained.

Class 5. *Children of any age at boarding school*

Headmasters can act *in loco parentis* and give consent for an operation to be performed upon a pupil at his school. Hospital Authorities, however, insist on getting the consent of parent or guardian and in some instances the parent or guardian is asked to sign a general consent to necessary operations and anaesthetics when the pupil enrols in the boarding school.

## CONFIDENTIALITY

Authoritative statements concerning professional secrecy in dental practice are few. It seems to be taken for granted that the dentist, like the doctor, must treat as confidential facts which he learns in the course of his attendance upon the patient, and must not divulge them to anyone else without the patient's consent.

It is generally agreed that medical practice cannot be conducted efficiently and honourably unless the rule of secrecy is observed. From the earliest times medical men engaged in the healing art were guided by the golden rule having its origin in that part of the Hippocratic Oath which read, 'Whatsoever in my professional practice or not in connexion with it, I see or hear in the life of man which ought not to be spoken of abroad, I will not reveal as reckoning that all such should be kept secret.'

Nowadays, some universities and corporations invite those about to receive a medical degree or licence to sign a modified form of the Hippocratic Oath. Some adopt the Sponsio Academica which contains the following: 'I promise that I will not make public without serious reason those things seen or heard in my practice upon which it is fitting to be silent.' Others make use of wording of their own. The oath subscribed to by medical graduands in St. Andrews University (and recently adapted for graduands in Dentistry) is in these terms:

'To-day I acknowledge with gratitude the distinction to be conferred upon me and I solemnly promise that as a graduate in Medicine I will abide steadfast in all loyalty and endeavour always to promote the welfare and to maintain the reputation of the University of St. Andrews.

'Further, in the exercise of my profession I will ever have in mind the care of the sick and the well-being of the healthy and to this end will use all my knowledge and judgement.

'Lastly, I will keep silence on any matters I may see or hear in the course of my professional work which it would be improper to divulge.'

At some universities the medical student, on the eve of graduating, is *invited* to subscribe to some form of oath containing the promise not to divulge professional secrets. In the unlikely event of a person refusing to subscribe to the oath, his degree would not be withheld and for that reason the oath in modern usage can perhaps best be regarded as a survival of an excellent custom. It remains a good custom if for no other reason than that it draws the attention of those on the threshold of a medical career to the existence of a code of ethics which includes the rule to observe professional secrecy.

Failure to observe the rule would constitute a breach of the ethical code and the offender might be called upon to answer for it to his professional brethren. But the offence, if flagrant, might have a more serious consequence for it might be regarded as 'infamous conduct in a professional respect' and anyone found guilty of such conduct runs the risk of being struck off the medical register. There is yet another factor which conduces to confidentiality. Divulgence of professional matters on the part of a doctor may be a breach of contract between the doctor and his patient for it may be implied that the contract includes the promise by the doctor not to divulge information without the patient's consent. This has been pointed out by Kitchen[1] who cites the dicta of the Judges in *Tournier* v. *National Provincial and Union Bank*[2] and in *A.B.* v. *C.D.*[3] in support of the contention. There is no legal decision on the question as to whether failure to observe secrecy is a tort in law and, in the absence of a decision, that question must remain an open one.

The position of the doctor in respect of professional secrecy appears to be that he must observe the rule regarding it lest he be charged with unethical conduct by his professional brethren, infamous conduct by the General Medical Council or breach of contract in a court of law. What of the dental practitioner? Is he bound, like the doctor, to keep to himself information which he learns about his patient?

It would seem safe to state that, where the information in his possession is of a serious nature, the dentist is bound to keep it secret. For example, the dentist, because of oral manifestations, may be the first to recognize the presence of venereal disease; in such a case the patient would be entitled to rely upon his dentist's confidence and, on the analogy of the position of doctors quoted above, the disclosure of such information by the dentist might well be regarded as unethical, might make him answerable to the General Dental Council for infamous conduct in a professional respect or even cause him to face a charge of breach of contract in a court of law.

On the other hand there is the type of information relating to patients which is quite unimportant, as, for example, information that a patient has undergone a routine examination. It is difficult to imagine any adverse consequences arising from the disclosure of information of this sort.

The practical difficulty of the dentist may well be to decide what is his duty with regard to information which lies between these two extremes of importance. The only safe rule is for the dentist to regard *all* information relating to his patients as confidential. Most of his patients will appreciate his courtesy in so doing.

There is one important exception to the rule regarding professional secrecy and that exception applies to doctor and dentist alike. When

---

[1] KITCHEN, D. N. (1941), *Law for the Medical Practitioner*, London, Eyre & Spottiswoode.
[2] (1924), I.K.B. 461.     [3] (1851), 14 Dunlop 177.

called upon to give evidence in Court, the doctor or dentist must answer any question put to him even though the answer involves violation of the rule of professional secrecy (so long as it does not incriminate himself). He may appeal to the presiding judge to disallow the question but, if the latter decides that the question and its answer are necessary to assist the Court, the question must be put and answered. Refusal to answer questions renders the professional man liable to punishment for contempt of court. In other words, the doctor or dentist giving evidence in Court is not privileged, in contrast to the lawyer who is not permitted to divulge matters communicated to him by a client unless the client gives his consent.

This legal duty imposed on doctors and dentists is not universal. In some American states statutes have been enacted which forbid physicians or surgeons to testify on matters which are confidential between them and their patients. It is not without interest that at least in one instance the enactment necessitated a legal decision as to whether the term physicians and surgeons included dentists. The decision in that case[1] was that it did not and the dentist was compelled to give evidence relating to his patient. This American decision apart, it is reasonable to regard the obligations of the dentist as being similar to those of the physician or surgeon. The golden rule for all should be never to divulge, without the patient's consent anything to anybody except when giving evidence in Court.

[1] *People* v. *De France* (1895), 104 Mich. 563.

CHAPTER X

# Relationship with Colleagues in the Same Practice

In his relationship with professional colleagues in the same practice and practitioners outside it, the dentist may be confronted with a variety of problems and potential difficulties. Some of these are of a legal nature: others are ethical. Both are dealt with in this chapter in respect of the dentist's colleagues in the same practice, and in Chapter XI in respect of his other dental colleagues and his medical colleagues.

## I. ASSISTANTSHIPS

When disputes arise between a principal and his assistant, as they sometimes do, they more often than not arise because of the absence of a written agreement between the parties. It is therefore highly desirable that, when a practitioner arranges to employ an assistant, an agreement should be drawn up and signed by him and his assistant.

Assistantship Agreement Forms are available to members of the British Dental Association and the Defence Unions or Societies. It is, however, always advisable to seek the advice of solicitors before drawing up the final agreement, even where the model agreement supplied seems to meet the needs of the particular case. It is also desirable where solicitors are employed that the two parties employ different firms. In this way the interests of both parties can be fully and equally protected.

In general, an assistantship agreement should contain clauses to include the following provisions:

1) The duration of the agreement—e.g. 'from.......... to ......... and thereafter to continue until ...... months' notice is given in writing by either party'. In addition, provision should be made to enable either party to give notice to the other of his intention to terminate the agreement before the date specified (except in circumstances stated in 12) below). When notice is given in writing, it should be sent by registered post.

2) The amount of the salary, to be paid in equal monthly sums, and the day of the month on which payments are to be made.

3) The hours during which the assistant is to work per day and per week.

4) The holidays to which the assistant is to be entitled with full pay.

5) Arrangements appertaining to the assistant's absence from duty due to sickness or other unavoidable cause.

It is customary for the assistant to be paid in full during an absence not exceeding three weeks consecutively and to receive half pay for three months thereafter.

In the event of the assistant being absent for a period exceeding three months consecutively or for an equivalent aggregate period of working days in any year, the principal should have the right to terminate the agreement by giving one week's notice in writing at the expiry of the period.

6) The assistant to have full use of the principal's professional books, instruments, appliances and drugs.

7) The assistant to undertake to keep accurate records of work performed by him and to account for all money received.

8) The assistant to undertake to obey the directions of the principal, to work diligently and in the interests of the principal and to conform to the laws, customs and ethics of the profession.

9) The assistant to agree not to disclose during or after his employment the professional secrets of the principal nor (without the consent of the principal) to attend to any patient of another practitioner or engage in practice on his own account or to accept any appointment.

10) The assistant to undertake at his own expense to join and remain a member of a recognized Defence Society providing legal aid or assistance in respect of claims for damages for alleged professional negligence.

To the assistant, the benefit of this requirement is obvious. A claim for damages for alleged negligence may be threatened or brought against him in respect of any patient whom he has attended. From the principal's point of view, the requirement is even more important for not only may he be proceeded against for any wrongful act of his assistant but the Defence Society of which he is a member may refuse to assist him unless his assistant is himself a member of a Defence Society, though not necessarily the same organization.

11) The assistant, in anticipation of the termination of the agreement, to undertake not to inform the patients whom he attends of

his departure from the practice or the address at which he may subsequently intend to practise.

12) In the event of the assistant contravening anything contained in clauses 7, 8, 9 or 10, or being guilty of any serious misconduct which would be prejudicial to the practice, the principal to have the right to terminate the agreement without giving notice or paying salary in lieu of notice.

13) The assistant to undertake, for a specified number of years after the termination of the agreement, not to practise on his own account, or in association with another practitioner, within a specified number of miles.

> Five years is the period usually stipulated and is a reasonable one in most circumstances.
> The distance to be specified depends upon the nature and situation of the employer's practice. A high-class practice commonly attracts patients from a wider area than does a practice which caters for the population of an industrial area. In country districts any practice may draw its patients from a wide area around it. The distance imposed must therefore vary with the circumstances and should only be so much as is reasonably necessary to prevent the assistant from taking an unfair advantage of his knowledge of the employer's patients. The employer cannot protect himself absolutely against all competition from his assistant and the Courts will be ready to declare invalid any binding-out clause which goes beyond the bounds of reasonableness.

14) In the event of a dispute or difference of opinion arising between the parties over any matter contained in the agreement, there should be provision for the matter to be referred to an arbitrator who should be named along with a substitute.

## 2. EMPLOYMENT OF LOCUM TENENS

When a *locum tenens* is employed for a short period there is little need for an agreement to be drawn up on the lines of an assistantship agreement. It should be recognized, however, that, the longer the period of employment, the greater becomes the danger of the *locum tenens* establishing himself in practice in competition with his employer. In contemplation of such a possibility, it would be reasonable for the employer to insist upon the *locum tenens* signing a restrictive covenant to prevent him from practising dentistry within a stipulated area for a stipulated period. If such a covenant is taken it should be done at the beginning of the locumship when the terms of employment are settled. Whatever the period of employment of a *locum tenens*, there arises the question of his liability in law for any negligence arising in respect of a patient whom he treats on behalf of his employer. As the question has never been tested in a Court, the answer must be a matter of opinion. Unlike an assistant, a *locum tenens* works independently and it might be argued that he alone is answerable for any act of negligence of which he might be found guilty. It is by no means certain, however, that in such an event the employer would not be joined as in an action for damages. Consequently, it is highly desirable that the employer should ask the *locum tenens* to furnish evidence of his membership of a Defence Society.

### 3. PARTNERSHIPS

The Partnership Act of 1890 defines partnership as 'the relation which subsists between persons carrying on a business in common with a view of profit'. Notwithstanding this definition, the question as to whether a partnership exists may not be easily determined. A partnership may exist without any written agreement and may even exist in spite of a written agreement to the contrary.

So far as the individuals comprising a firm are concerned, it may be of little moment whether they are or are not in legal partnership. But if a dispute arises between an outside person and a member of the firm the question of its status immediately assumes importance. For, if a partnership exists, a claimant can recover against the firm as a whole and each partner in the firm is liable jointly with the others notwithstanding any written agreement which may exist to the contrary.

Though the Partnership Act was designed chiefly for commercial partnerships, it governs dental partnerships like all others. The rules set forth governing the rights and obligations of partners, one to another, may be varied or set aside in an agreement, but, if the partners agree not to vary or negative the rules, or if the rules are not clearly varied or negatived by the agreement, then the partners must act in accordance with the rules set forth in the Act. Included in the rules are the following:

*a)* The partners are entitled to share equally in the capital and profits of the business and must contribute equally towards any losses.

*b)* A partner must be indemnified by the firm for expenses incurred in conducting the business of the firm but no partner shall be entitled to remuneration for acting in the partnership business.

*c*) A partner is entitled to receive interest on sums advanced as capital in excess of what he has agreed to subscribe.

*d*) Every partner may take part in the management of the business.

*e*) The partnership books are to be kept at the place of business and be available for inspection by any partner.

*f*) If there are more than two partners and they disagree on the ordinary matters of partnership business, they must abide by the decision of the majority, but any change in the nature of the partnership (including the introduction of a new partner) requires the consent of all the partners.

*g*) No partner may carry on business in competition with the firm without the consent of the other partner or partners.

*h*) No partner can be expelled unless the agreement expressly permits of it.

The Act also includes rules for dissolution by termination of agreement, death, bankruptcy, etc.

The rules set forth in the Partnership Act, framed as they are in a general way, may not suit the circumstances of a particular case so that a carefully compiled agreement should be drawn up with such modifications of the rules as may be considered desirable.

Those contemplating entry into partnership should be guided by the same principle which governs assistantship agreements: they should sign a written agreement not because any of the parties is concerned lest he be cheated by another but because an agreement in writing greatly minimizes the possibility of difficulties and disputes arising at any time in the future. A written agreement is even more advisable in the case of a partnership than for an assistantship, for a partnership usually lasts longer than an assistantship and is often by the terms of the agreement between the parties more difficult to terminate. A partnership agreement might justifiably deal with the following points:

i] *Duration of the partnership*. It is customary to stipulate the date of commencement and of termination of the partnership, though the latter may be omitted. In addition provision is sometimes made for the dissolution of the partnership at any time at the wish of one of the partners. If the agreement states the date of termination and the partners continue, as they may, to act together, then, as Kitchen[1] puts it, 'the law will presume that they intend still to be bound by the conditions of the agreement and have the same rights and duties. This is a "partnership at will". Any partner may dissolve it when he

---

[1] KITCHEN, D. H. (1941), *Law for the Medical Practitioner*, London, Eyre & Spottiswoode.

chooses, but he must do so in good faith; he will not be allowed to benefit by any unfair advantage he may have gained by the dissolution. An expulsion clause in the original agreement does not apply to a partnership continued at will, but a provision that the surviving partners shall buy the share of a dead partner . . . probably continues in force'.

ii] *Name of the partnership.* Usually, the name of the firm is the name of the partners, with or without christian names or initials thus 'A. Smith and B. Stewart' or 'Smith and Stewart'. When any other designation is used, as, for example, 'Smith and Company' or 'Stewart and Sons', the firm's name must be registered in accordance with the Registration of Business Names Act, 1916.

In the event of Smith ceasing to be a partner and the business being carried on by Stewart alone or with a new partner, it is legally permissible for the business to be carried on under the original name.

From an ethical point of view, however, it is preferable that the names of the partners be always indicated so that the proper plan to adopt is, for example, to style the business 'B. Stewart and C. Thomson'. The words 'formerly A. Smith and B. Stewart' may be added if it is thought desirable to make use of any good will attached to the name of Smith.

iii] *Provision of capital.* The proportion in which capital is to be provided by each partner should be clearly stated as well as the dates on which any contributions of capital sums are due to be paid.

In a clause dealing with this matter it would be equitable to include a provision whereby any partner who contributed capital in excess of his agreed proportion would receive $x$ per cent. interest on the excess.

It might also be wise to include a provision permitting a junior partner to acquire an increased share in the business after a stated interval.

iv] *Ascertainment and division of profits, etc.* All fees received in respect of patients (or in respect of appointments held by a partner with the consent of his partner or partners) should be stipulated to be the property of the partnership. Net profits are the moneys received less the expenses and, unless specially arranged for, are to be divided equally between the partners. If the profits are to be divided in other proportions these must be clearly stated and, in either case, the sum which each partner may draw each month from the business ought to be stipulated.

Under this heading should also be inserted a requirement that all moneys received shall be deposited regularly in a Bank to be named, that the books of the partnership shall be properly made up to a definite date each year and duly audited and be available to any partner for inspection at any time.

v] *Ownership of partnership property.* A partner need not own any part of the premises in which the business is carried on. The business may be conducted in premises leased or rented, or belonging to each partner in proportion to his share in the business or owned by one partner solely. In the last named event, provision may justifiably be made for payment to the partner owning the property of an annual sum in respect of rent.

When property owned by one partner is to be taken over by the partnership, it should be valued at the commencement and taken over in accordance with the valuation. Similarly all furnishings, appliances, instruments and books should be valued and sold to the partnership.

vi] *Obligations of partners, one to another.* The utmost good faith should exist between partners and each should be trusted to contribute to the common effort by regular attendance at business and by taking no more than his share of holidays. It is advisable, however, that clear provision should be made in the agreement on the following points:

> No partner to engage in business in competition with the firm.
>
> No partner to accept an appointment without the consent of his partner or partners.
>
> No partner to introduce an additional partner without the consent of his existing partner or partners.

It may also be considered advisable to include a provision that, when a partner is absent from duty through illness extending beyond a stated period, he should provide a *locum tenens* at his own expense or otherwise.

In this connexion it would not be unreasonable for the agreement to require each partner to insure himself against sickness.

There remains one other requirement which is so important that it should never be omitted from an agreement: it is the requirement for each partner to join and remain a member of a reputable Defence Society. The arguments in favour of its inclusion in an agreement have been stated on page 123 and need not be repeated.

vii] *Relation of partners to outside persons.* In England, each partner is

liable jointly with the other partner or partners for all debts which
the firm incurs while he is a partner in it. If a partner is sued for a
partnership debt he may therefore apply to have his fellow partner(s)
joined with him as defendant(s) so that the liability shall be shared
by each partner or all the partners. In Scotland, a partner is severally
liable and must be sued alone.

In either country all the partners in a firm are liable in law for the
wrongful act or omission of any partner acting in the ordinary
course of business. In the event of damages and costs being awarded
against a partner, the plaintiff may claim these from the firm or
from the partner. Even though a plaintiff may lose his action and
be found liable for costs, he may, through lack of means, be unable
to pay the costs. Those costs would then fall upon the firm and the
firm would have no claim against the partner who had successfully
defended the action raised against him. It may happen, therefore,
that serious financial embarrassment may result whether an action
succeeds or fails and this fact alone makes it imperative that every
member of a partnership should belong to a reputable Defence
Society.

viii] *Expulsion of a partner.* When there are more than two partners,
the inclusion of a clause empowering expulsion of a partner might
be considered, for, unless they specify accordingly in an agreement,
they have no legal right to expel one of their number. Even if a
clause designed for the purpose is included in an agreement, there
may be difficulty in putting it into effect, in which case the alternative
is to take advantage of any provision contained in the agreement for
the dissolution of the partnership.

ix] *Restraint of practice by outgoing partner.* A partnership agreement
may justifiably include a clause to restrain an expelled or retiring
partner from practising in competition with his former partner or
partners. Any such clause should be carefully worded to ensure that
the restrictions imposed as to radius and period of enforcement are
not unreasonable.

x] *Dissolution of partnership.* A partnership may be dissolved by:

*a*) Retirement of a partner who retires on the date specified in
the agreement. A partnership need not be terminated then for the
partner due to retire may, with the consent of his colleague or
colleagues, continue in 'partnership at will' after the date specified.
If, subsequently, he desires to retire or if no date for terminating
the partnership is stated in the agreement, he must give notice of
his intention to do so. Where no period of notice is specified in

the agreement the notice given must be reasonable having regard to all the circumstances of the case. (See *Duration of the partnership*, page 126.)

*b*) Mutual consent of the partners, usually by one partner giving the other or others notice in writing to terminate the agreement. In a clause covering this eventuality it may be laid down that the partner who gives the notice is required to purchase the share of the outgoing partner or partners. Alternatively, it may be arranged that each partner may submit to an arbitrator a sealed offer for the purchase of the business.

*c*) Death of any partner which automatically entails dissolution of a partnership, subject to the provisions of the partnership agreement. Provision is usually made in the agreement that the deceased partner's share will be bought over by the surving partner or partners who will pay to his representatives an agreed sum over a period of time to be stipulated.

In the case of a junior partner having a small share in the business, it might be unfair if he were called upon to pay in full for the share of his dead partner on the ground that he would have little guarantee that the patients of his late partner would continue to visit the practice. To meet this point, it might reasonably be arranged that a certain sum should be payable if the senior partner dies within one year, an increased sum if he dies within two years and so on until the full sum is reached.

*d*) Bankruptcy of a partner which legally dissolves a partnership, subject to the provisions of the partnership agreement.

*e*) Permanent incapacity of a partner which may result in dissolution of a partnership if the partners have previously agreed that it shall be so. If no such agreement was made between the partners and one becomes permanently incapacitated the partnership can be dissolved only by application to the Court.

*f*) Conduct of a partner seriously prejudicial to the partnership which is good ground for dissolution and might reasonably be included in an agreement. If a partner were guilty of an act which resulted in his name being erased from the Dentists Register or from the list of an Executive Council (see page 77) he would obviously cease to be able to contribute a fair share to the partnership effort. If he were guilty of 'infamous conduct in a professional respect', for example committing adultery with a patient, his presence in the practice would have an adverse effect upon it. If he were guilty of wilful and persistent breach of the articles of the partnership agreement, proper co-operation between the partners would become impossible and if the partner could not be expelled the only course would be to dissolve the partnership. If there is no provision in the agreement for dissolution in these circumstances, the Court has power to order dissolution provided it can be shown that the partnership business has been substantially prejudiced.

xi] *Arbitration.* Arbitration should be provided for on the principle that it is infinitely better to refer matters in dispute to an arbitrator than to engage in litigation, which might be the only alternative.

### 4. SALE OF PRACTICE

The transfer of a practice by sale raises questions of importance to the buyer and seller alike. When the purchase of a practice is contemplated the prospective buyer should investigate carefully:

The gross receipts of the practice over a period of years.
The expenses.
The amount of work required to earn the income of the practice.
The question of the ownership of the property and the possibility of acquiring the premises.
The prospects of increase or decrease in the practice.

He would be well advised to consult a local lawyer and qualified accountant and be guided by them in arriving at a fair price to offer for the practice. The seller should make available information on all questions raised by the prospective buyer, including the certified accounts of the business.

The seller should also satisfy himself regarding the *bona fides* of the prospective buyer and his character and capabilities but should obtain the buyer's consent before instituting enquiries on these matters.

Disputes not infrequently arise following the sale of a practice and they arise chiefly because of difficulties relating to the introduction of patients to the buyer and restriction of practice imposed on the seller. To reduce the possibility of such disputes, a written agreement should always be insisted upon, and it should contain the following:

i] *Price to be paid.* The date upon which the practice is to be transferred and the price to be paid to the seller should be set forth at the outset. If, as is usual, the sum due is to be paid in instalments, the amount of these and the dates upon which they fall due should be stated.

If an arrangement is made whereby the buyer agrees to pay for the practice by handing to the seller a proportion of the profits over a period of years, the buyer should undertake to continue to practise for the period stipulated or pay the balance of the original sum agreed to. It should be noted that payment of a proportion of profits does not constitute a partnership between the buyer and seller.

The asset of a practice is the goodwill attached to it—something of a nebulous nature. As Henderson[1] puts it, 'The sale of a practice is in law the selling of the introduction of the dentist who sells to the dentist who buys it.' It by no means follows that patients introduced to the buyer will seek his services, so much depending on the personality of the dentist. Furthermore, the value of a practice may depend upon its nature and site and the possibility or likelihood of its being subjected to competition from other practitioners establishing themselves in practice in the neighbourhood, which in turn depends upon the availability of premises suitable for the conduct of dental practice. One year's gross receipts or one and a half times the annual profit (each calculated on the average of three years) was formerly regarded as a fair estimate of the value of a practice. Whichever formula is used as a *basis* for negotiation between the parties, the true value of any practice can only be arrived at by mutual consent in the light of all the circumstances prevailing.

ii] *Premises and contents.* If the premises are owned by the seller it may be stated in the agreement that they will be taken over at valuation by the buyer. If the premises are not owned by the seller, then arrangements must clearly be stated for the transference of the lease of the premises to the buyer.

The clause should also contain the provision that the furnishings, instruments, appliances, books, etc., may be acquired by the buyer at valuation.

iii] *Introduction of patients to the buyer.* The personal introduction of patients and their recommendation to the buyer place a moral, if not a legal, obligation upon the seller and are of such importance that details concerning them should be clearly set forth in every agreement.

The clause should define the period during which introduction is to be given by the seller and how it is to be effected, and should also provide that there will be an agreed reduction in the purchase price in the event of the seller failing to implement his promise.

[1] HENDERSON, P. B. (1914), Appendix to *The Science and Practice of Dental Surgery*, edited by Bennett, N. G., London, Hodder & Stoughton.

If there is no agreement between the parties concerning the personal introduction of patients, the buyer has no redress in Court in the event of introduction not being given. If the seller wilfully fails to implement his promise it is doubtful whether he could be compelled by law to do so, but the Court would protect the buyer in such an event in accordance with the provision for a reduction of the purchase price. If the seller, through illness or death, is unable to fulfil his part of the bargain, that part of the clause permitting a reduction in the purchase price would equally apply.

iv] *Book debts.* Book debts, valued preferably by an accountant, may be included in the assets sold to the buyer, or may remain the property of the seller who will himself collect debts incurred up to the date of the transfer of the business. A third alternative, whereby the buyer agrees to collect outstanding debts on behalf of the seller, is not to be recommended. In whatever manner the book debts of the practice are to be dealt with, the manner should be agreed and clearly stated in the agreement.

v] *Restriction on the seller not to practise in competition.* The value of the goodwill of the practice would be seriously affected if the practice were subjected to competition by the seller practising in the area. The parties should accordingly agree upon a restrictive covenant on this point and incorporate it in the agreement. Apart from such legal provision there is also a moral obligation upon the seller to do nothing to lower the value of the goodwill he has sold.

As in the case of assistantship and partnership agreements, the restrictive covenant should be carefully worded to avoid ambiguity and ensure equity. To stipulate that the seller must retire from practice altogether would not be equitable but it would be reasonable to restrain him from engaging in any form of dental practice within a defined area and to impose upon him the further restriction that he should not attend to any of his former patients in the event of his practising beyond the area.

The area in which total restriction is imposed on the seller should be determined by the local conditions affecting the practice, but it must be reasonable in extent. If a dispute regarding it is referred to the Court, the Court on finding the restriction unreasonable will not amend it but will declare the covenant invalid.

It is customary and proper to include a penalty which the seller will be liable to pay to the buyer in the event of a breach of the restrictive agreement. It should be noted, however, that the outgoing practitioner would be in breach of the agreement if he merely tendered the sum stipulated in respect of the penalty and proceeded to engage in practice in the restricted area. In an action in respect of the breach the Court would not regard itself as bound by the penalty stipulated in the agreement but could award more or less damages if it thought fit.

vi] *Arbitration*. In spite of a carefully drawn up agreement disputes may arise between the buyer and seller. To have disputes settled in Court is likely to be harmful to the practice and unpleasant to the individuals. Provision should therefore be made for disputes to be settled by an arbitrator, mutually agreed, who should be named. A substitute should also be nominated.

# CHAPTER XI

# Relationship with other Dental Colleagues and with Medical Colleagues

In a variety of ways the dental practitioner, directly or indirectly, consciously or unconsciously, comes into relationship with his professional colleagues. His methods of conducting practice should be in accordance with generally accepted ethical principles and, if he transgresses the ethical code in any particular, it is his professional colleagues who will criticize his action or take steps to have it rectified. The inexperienced or the unwary may get into difficulties with professional colleagues over such matters as setting up in practice; professional announcements; advertising; engagement of employees; dealing with new patients; consultations; criticism of fellow practitioners and the splitting of fees.

## I. SETTING UP IN PRACTICE

A dental practitioner may practise his profession anywhere he chooses so long as he does not select a particular place through knowledge acquired in abortive negotiations with a practitioner in the area over entry into partnership or the purchase of a practice. Nor should a practitioner 'put up his plate' anywhere within an area from which he might be bound out in terms of any assistantship or other agreement which he has signed. Such action, apart from constituting a breach of his agreement, would be highly unethical.

Having selected legitimately a location for his practice, the dentist would be well advised to introduce himself to other dental practitioners in the neighbourhood. His object should be to establish and maintain friendly relationship with all his colleagues.

## 2. PROFESSIONAL ANNOUNCEMENTS

To indicate his whereabouts to those who may seek his services is fit and proper—provided that in so doing the dentist observes certain ethical rules.[1]

If the dentist is entering into partnership or is buying a practice either fact may be announced to the patients of the practice by a simple statement under cover of an envelope bearing no indication of the name of the sender. It is customary for this announcement to be made in the name and with the consent of the senior partner or vendor as the case may be. Similar announcements are permissible on change of address.

The press may not be used for any announcement of this kind. To intimate a change of address, the patients of the practice may be informed by letter enclosed in an envelope. Alternatively, a notice may be inserted in the local press but if this method is employed, care must be taken to ensure that it contains no indication whatever of the nature of the advertiser's profession. The following wording would be suitable:

> 'Mr. ........................... begs to
> announce that he has moved
> from.....................................
> to ......................................'

No letters indicative of his qualifications should appear after the name.

With regard to a name-plate on his premises, the dentist should be guided by the custom generally adopted in the neighbourhood and to some extent by the situation and nature of his premises. His name-plate should be neither larger nor more conspicuous than is necessary for easy identification[2] and should contain no letters implying qualifications to which he is not entitled. The smaller the name-plate and the simpler the lettering upon it, the more dignified and therefore the more desirable it will be.

When a dentist carries on the practice of a former practitioner, it is proper for the predecessor's name to appear on the name-plate provided that the word 'late' or 'formerly' is added to the predecessor's name.

Similar principles should guide the dentist in his choice of letter-heading for his professional stationery.

### 3. ADVERTISING

Advertising in any form is unethical and should be assiduously avoided.

[1] See Appendix III.          [2] See Appendix IV.

To engage in any blatant form of advertising would be an infringement of the rules propounded by the General Dental Council and would render the advertiser answerable to that body. But there are indirect ways in which the name of a practitioner may be publicized and the dentist should be on his guard to avoid such publicity. In articles in or letters written to the lay press, he should be careful to avoid any laudatory statements of himself and should not permit the publication of his photograph. He should take steps to ensure that a report in the lay press of any activity in which he has engaged should omit any mention of his qualifications or laudatory statement regarding his professional work.

A dentist who takes part in sound or television programmes should insist on anonymity: failure to do so might lead to an infringement of the Notice issued by the General Dental Council.[1]

On no account should the dentist permit his name to appear in heavy type in a directory nor should he agree to the insertion of his name in any directory where a charge is made for the insertion.

He should be careful to avoid the use of postcards or envelopes bearing his name and qualifications.

## 4. ENGAGEMENT OF EMPLOYEES

There is a right way and a wrong way to go about the business of engaging employees such as dental technicians and dental surgery assistants. The right way is to make use of the local press to advertise for the type of employee required or to insert or answer advertisements in the dental press. When inserting an advertisement, especially in a newspaper, the dentist should do so over a box number and should not publish his name and address.

If to any advertisement an application is received from a person already in the employment of a dental colleague in the same town or district, the dentist should inform his colleague. It is ethically wrong for a dentist to entice in any way into his employment anyone who is at the time employed by another practitioner.

The guiding principle should be 'do unto others as you would have them do unto you'. Neglect of the principle is apt to lead to disputes between professional men and disputes should be avoided.

## 5. DEALING WITH NEW PATIENTS

It is over the procedure adopted in dealing with new patients that most

[1] See Appendix II, page 286.

disputes arise between dental colleagues. While every dentist has the experience of losing patients for a variety of reasons, he is naturally much disturbed when he discovers or suspects that the reason for his loss is that his patient has been enticed away by another practitioner. All patients have the right to chose or change their dentist but any enticement or even encouragement for them to do so by another practitioner is highly unethical. When consulted by a patient for the first time, the dentist should always ascertain the reason for the consultation and should act accordingly. The patient's reason for consulting the dentist may be:

i] *That he is not under the care of any other practitioner.* In that case the dentist is at liberty to accept him as a patient.

If, however, the dentist has previously seen the patient in consultation with a colleague, or while acting as a deputy for a colleague, he should undertake only emergency treatment and should not accept the patient for further treatment until he has communicated with the colleagues and unless the colleague consents to the transfer of the patient.

ii] *That he does not desire to return to his former practitioner.* In that event, the dentist is entitled to accept the patient and no useful purpose is served by informing the former practitioner of the patient's decision.

iii] *That his usual practitioner is unable, through absence or illness, to attend to him.* For that type of patient the dentist should undertake any emergency treatment which may be necessary and should inform the patient's usual dental practitioner of what has been done. The dentist should not accept the patient for further treatment or advice.

iv] *That he desires advice or treatment regarding some special condition.* The dentist should not give the advice or treatment sought before consulting the patient's usual dental practitioner.

v] *That he has been recommended by his usual dental practitioner to seek advice or treatment.* In this type of case it is proper for the dentist to give the advice or treatment asked for and to report afterwards to the patient's usual dental practitioner what has been said or done.

Under no circumstances and at no time should the dentist consulted accept the patient for ordinary dental treatment.

## 6. CONSULTATIONS BETWEEN DENTAL PRACTITIONERS

When a dentist desires an opinion from a dental consultant regarding his patient, he should be present at the consultation or should send to the dentist consulted all relevant information concerning the patient and the condition upon which advice is being sought.

The dentist consulted should report fully to the patient's usual dentist his findings and advice and to the patient may give such information as he thinks appropriate.

The dentist consulted should not undertake any treatment for the condition about which he has been consulted, unless at the express wish of the patient's usual dentist. Under no circumstances and at no time in the future should the dentist consulted undertake any other treatment for the patient. In other words, he should never accept the patient who has been referred to him for consultation as one of his ordinary patients.

The rules governing consultations between the dental and medical profession are dealt with on pages 140 and 141.


## 7. CRITICISM OF FELLOW PRACTITIONERS

An excellent rule, issued for the guidance of its members by the British Dental Association[1] reads thus:

> 'When a dentist is consulted by a patient who has been previously treated by a colleague, it is his duty to avoid, as far as possible any word or action which might disturb the confidence of the patient in his previous dentist.'

The dentist would be wise always to observe this rule. When he sees work previously done for the patient he may think it of low standard, only to find that his own work, subsequently performed, is even less satisfactory because of difficulties presented by the patient. To voice any criticism of work performed by another would therefore be foolish but it might also be dangerous for two reasons. In the first place, criticism of the work of a colleague might encourage the patient to threaten or bring an action for damages against the former practitioner and the critic might easily become involved as a witness in the action. In the second place, there is the risk of an action being raised against the critic on the grounds of defamation. The dentist should also realize that in the National Health Service condemnation of work previously performed by another will inevitably lead to an investigation by the Dental Estimates Board.

[1] See Appendix III, page 293.

### 8. SPLITTING OF FEES

Any arrangement entered into between members of the dental profession or between members of the dental and medical professions whereby part of the fee received by one in respect of the attendance upon or treatment of a patient is passed to the other is known as *fee-splitting* or *dichotomy*. The practice cannot be too highly condemned for not only is it extremely unethical, it is also a legal offence, being an infringement of the Prevention of Corruption Act of 1906. A dentist reported to the General Dental Council and found guilty of the offence would run a grave risk of having his name erased from the Dentists Register.

### 9. RELATIONSHIP WITH MEDICAL COLLEAGUES

The dentist enters into relationship with a medical colleague through consultations and when he enlists the services of a doctor to administer a general anaesthetic for his patient. In both instances certain ethical rules should be followed and these are set forth below. Questions concerning the liability for accidents which may arise during a dental operation under a general anaesthetic administered by a doctor are discussed on page 100.

## A. Rules Governing Consultations

In outlining rules which should be observed when a dentist calls a doctor into consultation regarding a patient or when a doctor similarly refers a patient to a dentist for an opinion, we acknowledge the good advice contained in the British Dental Association's *Guidance for Professional Conduct*.[1]

### i] *Dentist requiring medical opinion*

*Rule* 1. When a dentist considers it necessary to obtain a medical opinion concerning a patient he should advise the patient to consult his usual doctor, and, with the patient's consent, should furnish that doctor with any relevant information about the patient.

*Rule* 2. If the dentist desires a further medical opinion, he should inform the patient's doctor before making any arrangement for obtaining the second opinion.

*Rule* 3. If the patient has no family doctor, the dentist should advise the patient to select a doctor for the purpose of the consultation and should inform the patient that, subject to the patient's consent, he will

[1] See Appendix III, page 293.

be pleased to communicate with the doctor selected on receiving from the latter a request for information.

*Rule 4.* If the patient has no family doctor and specifically requests the dentist to recommend one, the dentist may do so.

*Rule 5.* The doctor consulted should communicate his opinions to the dentist.

## ii] *Doctor requiring dental opinion*

*Rule 6.* When a doctor considers a dental opinion advisable, he should normally advise the patient to consult his usual dentist to whom the doctor should send relevant particulars of the patient.

*Rule 7.* If the patient has no dentist, he should be advised to select one and the patient should inform the doctor whom he has chosen so that there may be collaboration between the professional men for the patient's benefit.

*Rule 8.* If, for any reason, the patient consults a dentist who is not his usual dentist, the dentist consulted should report his findings not only to the doctor but also to the patient's usual dentist.

*Rule 9.* When a patient consults a dentist who is not his usual dentist, the dentist consulted should not undertake any treatment (except emergency treatment) for the patient without the consent of the patient's usual dentist.

*Rule 10.* In all cases the dentist consulted should furnish without delay a report of his findings to the doctor concerned with the case.

## B. Relationship with Anaesthetists

The practitioner's first duty is to his patient. When a dentist decides that a general anaesthetic is necessary for a patient, his duty is to enlist from those available the services of the person who he thinks can best administer the anaesthetic. The conduct of the dentist must depend upon the circumstances of the case but he should be guided by the following rules:

*Rule 1.* If the anaesthetist selected is not the patient's family doctor, the dentist should inform the latter of the arrangements made.

*Rule 2.* If the operation to be performed is of a minor nature (for example, to be undertaken in the dental surgery) the dentist need not invite the patient's family doctor to be present unless he knows that the patient is under medical care. The *patient*, however, may invite his family doctor to be present at the operation.

*Rule 3.* If the operation to be performed is of a major character (for example, to be undertaken in a nursing home) the dentist should invite the family doctor to be present.

*Rule* 4. In every case, the dentist should instruct the patient to consult him in the event of post-operative trouble arising and should take all reasonable steps to facilitate such consultation.

Too often the family doctor is called out to arrest haemorrhage and, if the above rules have not been observed, that may be the first he knows of his patient having undergone a dental operation under a general anaesthetic administered by another doctor.

## PART II

# Forensic Dentistry

# CHAPTER XII

# Courts of Law and Legal Procedure

A dental practitioner may be required to attend a Court of Law in order to give evidence as an ordinary or as an expert witness in a civil or a criminal action; in order to defend an action of negligence brought against him; or to sue a patient for payment of a fee due to him. It is therefore desirable that he should have some knowledge of Courts of Law and legal procedure in England and Wales or in Scotland and it is proposed in this Chapter to deal briefly with this subject.

## I. COURTS OF LAW IN ENGLAND AND WALES

### A. The Coroner's Court or Coroner's Inquest

The office of Coroner is a very ancient one, its origin being lost in obscurity. His name derived from the title *custos placitorum coronae*— 'Keeper of the King's pleas.' In mediaeval times he fulfilled certain judicial functions but these are no longer part of his duties. In place of acting as a judge the Coroner has become an inquirer or accuser.

i] *Qualifications and duties of Coroner.* The qualifications and duties of a Coroner are laid down in the Coroners Act of 1887 and the Coroners (Amendment) Act of 1926. By the 1926 Act, a Coroner must be a barrister, or a solicitor, or a legally qualified medical practitioner of at least five years' standing.

The Coroner still retains the ancient duty of being responsible for inquiry into treasure-trove. In the City of London he must investigate non-fatal fires but the main duty of the Coroner is to inquire into all cases of violent, sudden, suspicious or unexplained deaths which occur within his jurisdiction.

It was formerly necessary for the Coroner to hold an inquest in all cases of sudden death which he investigated but the Act of 1926 provides that he may order a post-mortem examination, a written report of which may satisfy him that death was due to natural causes. In that event the Coroner may issue a certificate for disposal of the body and dispense with the holding of an inquest. An inquest must be held, however, in all cases where there is reasonable cause to suspect that the deceased person has died a violent or unnatural death, or has died in prison or has died in such place or circumstances as to necessitate the holding of an inquest in accordance with any Act other than the Coroners Act of 1887. On application by the Attorney-General, the High Court may order an inquest or a new inquest if the interests of justice so require.

ii] *Juries in Coroners' Courts.* The Jury in a Coroner's Court consists of not less than seven and not more than eleven persons. The Coroner may accept the verdict of the majority so long as the minority is not more than two.

In accordance with the Schedule to the Juries Act, 1870 certain classes of persons are exempt from jury service. By the Dentists Act; 1957, s. 32 registered dentists are excused from serving on any jury if they desire to be.

The Coroner may hold an inquest with or without a jury. He is empowered to summon a jury in any case if he thinks fit, but *must* do so if there is reason to suspect that the death being investigated:

*a*) was due to murder, manslaughter or infanticide;
*b*) was due to accident, poisoning or disease, notice of which is required to be given to any Government Department under any Act;
*c*) was due to accident arising out of the use of a vehicle in a street or public highway;
*d*) occurred in a prison or in such circumstances as to require an inquest under any Act other than the Coroners Act.
*e*) occurred in circumstances the continuance of which or possible recurrence of which is prejudicial to the health or safety of the public, or any section of the public.

iii] *Post-mortem and special examinations.* The Coroner may request a registered medical practitioner to conduct an autopsy or may request a qualified person to conduct a special examination. When it is alleged by a statement made on oath to the Coroner that a person died as a result of negligent treatment at the hands of a doctor, dentist or other person, that doctor, dentist or other person may not attend the post-mortem examination ordered by the Coroner although he has the right to be represented at such examination if he so desires.

iv] *Procedure at Coroner's inquest.* The procedure in a Coroner's Court even where there is a jury, is less formal than in other judicial inquiries or courts of law. The Coroner may question anyone who may care to give evidence. All witnesses are examined on oath; the strict legal rules regarding the giving of evidence do not apply; and a solicitor, though permitted to be present to look after the interests of a client, has no *locus standi* and therefore can defend his client by cross-examining witnesses only with the consent of the Coroner.

In spite of the informality of the Court, evidence given before a Coroner should always be given as carefully as in other legal proceedings. The evidence is usually taken down in writing and signed by each witness. If he wishes, it can be read over to him and he will be given the opportunity of correcting or amending his statement. It is most desirable for a witness to ensure that this is done. The signed statement is known as a deposition. If the case goes to a higher Court, the depositions made before the Coroner are sent to that Court, and the persons making them may be required to attend that Court where they are liable to be cross-examined on the statements contained in their depositions.

The main object of the Coroner's Court is to bring in a verdict as to the cause of death, and its criminal function is only to accuse and not to try. The verdict may charge a person with causing the death, in which case the Coroner has the duty of issuing a warrant for the arrest of that person if he is not already in custody. The Coroner has power in certain cases to grant bail.

## B. Magistrates Court of Petty Sessions

Often referred to as the Police Court, this is a Court of summary jurisdiction in criminal cases and is presided over by at least two Justices of the Peace, or by a Stipendiary Magistrate, sitting without a jury. A large number of petty offences are by statute punishable on summary conviction, that is, after trial without a jury before two or more justices. Some more serious offences which are indictable may also be tried at Petty Sessions in certain circumstances.

The Magistrates Court of Petty Sessions tries most cases of minor crimes such as drunkenness, small thefts, motor-car offences and the like. The Court may impose fines of varying amounts but seldom punishes by imprisonment for periods exceeding three months.

An appeal against a decision of the Court can be taken to Quarter Sessions and, on a question of law, from there to the High Court.

In addition to trying minor offences, the Magistrates Court investigates more serious cases by conducting a preliminary examination of prisoners charged with indictable offences. Indictable offences (which comprise the more serious crimes) must be tried before a jury except where the prosecutor, accused and magistrates agree to trial at Petty Sessions. The object of the preliminary examination is to discover whether there is such evidence against the accused as to raise a probable presumption of his guilt and thus justify the case being sent to a higher Court.

When the Court tries or investigates any case, the accused person must be present and the presiding justices have power to compel witnesses to attend. The Magistrates' Courts Act, 1957, permits a plea of guilty to be taken in the accused's absence. This may be done for a summary offence not being *1)* an offence also triable on indictment, or *2)* an offence for which there is liability to imprisonment for a term exceeding three months, or *3)* an offence specified by order of the Secretary of State. Witnesses give their evidence in accordance with the laws of evidence and where the Court is investigating an indictable offence the evidence is taken down in writing and signed by the witness after he has been given the opportunity of making any corrections. These written statements form the basis of the charge against the accused if he is committed for trial at the Quarter Sessions, the Assizes or the Central Criminal Court, and any witness at that trial is liable to be cross-examined on the contents of the statement which he has signed.

## C. Quarter Sessions

This is a Court held at least once a quarter in some boroughs and in each County in England and Wales. In the case of county Quarter Sessions at least two Justices of the Peace are required to constitute a Court and the chairman of the Court is usually a person with legal qualifications. The judges in borough Quarter Sessions are called Recorders, are appointed by the Crown and must be barristers of at least five years' standing.

The functions of the Quarter Sessions may be summarized thus:

i] It can try all indictable offences committed to it for trial except certain of the more serious crimes such as treason, murder and manslaughter. It does not deal with certain cases likely to involve difficult questions of law, these being referred to the Assizes. Indictable offences coming before the Quarter Sessions are tried by jury.

ii] The Quarter Sessions acts as a Court of appeal from convictions of the Courts of Summary Jurisdiction and from decisions regarding licensing and other matters. These are heard without a jury.

iii] In addition, Quarter Sessions has jurisdiction in certain miscellaneous cases under special statutes.

## D. The County Courts

The County Courts are the principal lower Courts for the trial of civil disputes. They are divided into sixty-three circuits and are presided over by County Court judges, who usually sit without a jury.

They may try a wide variety of cases but their jurisdiction is limited. In general they can try only cases in which the amount involved does not exceed £400.

## E. The Assizes

The Assizes are sittings of the judges of the High Court for the trial of cases out of London. There are seven circuits in England and Wales and sittings are held periodically at which both civil and criminal cases are tried. Usually two judges attend, one to preside over criminal and the other over civil cases.

## F. The Central Criminal Court

The Central Criminal Court which sits at the Old Bailey acts as Court of Assize for London, Middlesex and part of the Home Counties. It sits every month and there may be several Courts sitting simultaneously each presided over by a judge of the High Court, or the Recorder of London, or the Common Serjeant, or a Judge of the City of London Court.

## G. The Court of Criminal Appeal

This Court was established in 1907. It consists of the Lord Chief Justice of England and the judges of the Queen's Bench Division. Three judges preside at a sitting of the Court. The Court has the power to hear appeals against convictions and sentences passed at Assizes or Quarter Sessions. Appeals on a question of law must be heard; appeals on a question of fact or against sentence may be heard only by leave.

## H. The High Court of Justice

The High Court of Justice consists of three Divisions, a Queen's Bench Division, a Chancery Division and a third for Probate, Divorce, and Admiralty.

In the Courts of the Queen's Bench Division are tried civil actions, usually actions where the amount of a claim is too great or the question of law involved too important to be dealt with by a County Court.

The Division has jurisdiction in common law, which covers, for example, actions for libel, slander, breach of promise, and breach of contract. In certain cases there must be a jury: in other instances the presiding judge may sit with or without a jury. The Courts of the Chancery Division try cases concerned with matters of equity, e.g. partnerships, marriages, trusts, and the administration of deceased persons' estates. There is no jury in the Chancery Courts.

The Probate, Divorce, and Admiralty Divisions deal with the granting of probate of wills; maritime matters, such as collisions at sea, and divorce business. In some cases the judge acts alone, in others with a jury.

## I. The Court of Appeal

The Court of Appeal is in practice drawn from the Master of the Rolls and a number of Lords Justices of Appeal. The Court hears appeals in civil matters from any Division of the High Court, from the Assizes, and from the County Courts.

## J. The Privy Council

Through its Judicial Committee, the Privy Council exercises the functions of a Court of law, one of its duties being to hear appeals made to it from some Dominion and all Colonial Courts. Its findings are recommendations and not judgements and they require confirmation by Her Majesty in Council.

## K. The House of Lords

The House of Lords is the highest court of appeal in the United Kingdom. It hears every class of appeal, civil and criminal, though the latter more rarely. In its capacity as a Court, it consists mainly of the Lord Chancellor and the Lords of Appeal in Ordinary.

The following summary may help to make the positions of these Courts clear:

### Courts having criminal jurisdiction

House of Lords
Court of Criminal Appeal
Assize Courts
Central Criminal Court
Quarter Sessions
Petty Sessions (Magistrates Court)

Courts having civil jurisdiction
House of Lords
Court of Appeal
High Court
Assize Court
County Courts

## 2. COURTS OF LAW IN SCOTLAND

At the head of the criminal administration in Scotland is the Lord Advocate, the principal law officer of the Crown, who has full power to prosecute all crimes committed in the country. His subordinates are the Solicitor-General and four Advocates-Depute to each of whom the Lord Advocate may delegate his powers in the prosecution of crimes. In the High Court prosecutions are conducted by the Lord Advocate, the Solicitor-General or by an Advocate-Depute: in the Circuit Courts of Justiciary an Advocate-Depute conducts the prosecution of criminal trials while in the Sheriff Courts the Procurator-Fiscal or his Depute acts as the prosecutor.

## A. Duties of the Procurator-Fiscal

There is no Court in Scotland corresponding to the Coroner's Court in England and Wales. The duties which the Coroner undertakes in England and Wales are included in the duties of the Procurator-Fiscal in Scotland and these duties must be mentioned here to give a clear picture of legal procedure in Scotland.

The Procurator-Fiscal is the chief executive officer of the Crown within the division of a county. He is a qualified solicitor and is appointed by the Lord Advocate. He may be assisted by deputies. While the prosecution of crimes and offences committed within the area of his jurisdiction is the main part of the Procurator-Fiscal's duty, it is not the only part. His varied duties may be summarized thus:

i] *As Public Prosecutor.* Breaches of the law occurring within his district are investigated by the Procurator-Fiscal. In all his investigations he has the assistance of the police and, where necessary, of special reports such as the report of a post-mortem examination. In carrying out his investigations he may require to take precognitions from witnesses. That is to say he may request witnesses to appear before him whom he examines privately. If a person called before him as a witness refuses to disclose information, that person may be judicially examined before a magistrate in Court. The questions put to witnesses and the answers given are written down and these precognitions are sent along with the Procurator-Fiscal's report to Crown Counsel for instructions. The Procurator-Fiscal is advised in due course by Crown Counsel whether there is to be a prosecution and, if so, whether it shall be on indictment or on summary complaint. If on indictment, the case is tried by the Sheriff sitting in his Court with a jury, unless Crown Counsel directs to indict the case for the High Court of Justiciary, which he may do if he regards the offence as a serious one. Where the prosecution is on summary complaint, the case is tried by the Sheriff sitting without a jury. In cases tried in the Sheriff Court the Procurator-Fiscal acts as prosecutor, though in exceptional cases his place may be taken by an Advocate-Depute.

ii] *As Coroner*. The Procurator-Fiscal has the duty of investigating all sudden, suspicious and accidental deaths occurring within his area. His investigations are made privately and confidentially and nothing concerning them is published unless there follows a public inquiry or criminal proceedings. After completing his inquiries, the Procurator-Fiscal in certain cases makes a report to Crown Counsel who may instruct i] no further action, ii] a public inquiry or iii] a charge against some person or persons.

When the Procurator-Fiscal is satisfied that a sudden or suspicious death has not been caused by foul play or by negligence, he issues the necessary certificate for disposal of the body.

When a public inquiry is ordered, it takes place before the Sheriff and a jury of seven who return a verdict setting forth the time, place, and cause of death. They may add to their verdict a finding of fault against a person or persons or in the system of working which contributed to an industrial accident.

iii] *As Crown Inquiry Agent*. It is the duty of the Procurator-Fiscal to investigate the circumstances of all fires and explosions occurring in his district and in suspicious cases to report the results of his investigations to Crown Counsel. The Procurator-Fiscal also acts in various matters affecting the interests of the Crown, for example, by reporting to the Queen's and Lord Treasurer's Remembrancer estates falling to Her Majesty as *Ultimus Haeres* and treasure trove discovered in his district. He also carries out investigations of certain complaints brought to the notice of the Lord Advocate by Government Departments, Members of Parliament or private individuals.

## B. Justices of the Peace Court

The civil jurisdiction of Justices of the Peace is confined to actions for the recovery of debts not exceeding £5 in amount: the criminal jurisdiction to all breaches of the peace and various minor offences. The principal administrative duties of the Justices of the Peace deal with licensing. The quorum of the Court is two.

## C. The Burgh Court

The Burgh Court, colloquially the Police Court, is presided over by a Magistrate or Baillie who has a civil and criminal jurisdiction similar to that of the Justices of the Peace. Burghs have the power to appoint stipendiary magistrates. Prosecutions in the Burgh Court are usually undertaken by the Burgh Prosecutor who is appointed under statute.

## D. The Sheriff Court

The Sheriff Court is the principal local court in a county or division of a county and the Sheriff-Principal or the Sheriff-Substitute who presides exercises a very wide civil and criminal jurisdiction. A Sheriff-Principal must be an advocate or a sheriff-substitute of at least five year's standing; a Sheriff-Substitute must be an advocate or a solicitor of standing for the same period. Both are appointed by the Crown.

The civil jurisdiction of the Sheriff in his ordinary Court extends to nearly all actions, the exceptions being actions involving status such as divorce, legitimacy and the like. Actions which do not exceed £50 in value must be raised in the Sheriff Court and not in the Court of Session but actions exceeding £50 in value may be raised in the Sheriff Court or in the Court of Session.

In a Summary Action (which is one not exceeding £50 in value) the right of appeal varies depending on whether or not the evidence has been recorded. If the evidence has been recorded, there is a right of appeal to the Sheriff-Principal on fact and on law—otherwise, there is a right of appeal on points of law only. There can be no appeal beyond the Sheriff-Principal unless, after giving judgement, he certifies the case as one suitable for appeal to the Court of Session. In an Ordinary Action (where the value exceeds £50) there is full right of appeal either to the Sheriff-Principal and from him to the Court of Session *or* direct to the Court of Session.

In addition to the civil actions which he hears in his ordinary Court, the Sheriff deals with cases in the *Small Debt Court*. Actions in that

Court concern the recovery of debts, actions for the delivery of moveables and for sequestration for rent, provided that the amount involved does not exceed £20 in value. The decision of the Sheriff is final, the only possible appeal being to the High Court of Justiciary on grounds of corruption of the judge, oppression, etc.

In criminal jurisdiction the Sheriff is a competent judge in all crimes except treason, murder, attempt to murder, or rape. He may try cases summarily without a jury and in these he may award punishment to the extent of six months' imprisonment. In indictable cases the Sheriff sits with a jury numbering fifteen persons and, when sitting with a jury, he may award punishment up to two years' imprisonment. When the gravity of an alleged offence appears to be such that the maximum penalty of the Sheriff Court would be inadequate, criminal proceedings are taken in the High Court of Justiciary or the case is remitted there by the Sheriff.

Appeal against the finding of the Sheriff Court in a criminal cause may be made to the High Court of Justiciary.

### E. High Court of Justiciary

This is the supreme criminal Court in Scotland and is constituted by the Lord President (under the title of the Lord Justice General), the Lord Justice Clerk and the other Judges of the Court of Session. It sits in Edinburgh but provision is made for Circuit Courts to be held in the large cities. It has a universal jurisdiction in all cases of crime except in minor offences where its original jurisdiction is excluded by statute. Prosecutions before the High Court are conducted by the Lord Advocate, the Solicitor-General or by an Advocate-Depute.

When sitting in Edinburgh the High Court of Judiciary also has jurisdiction to hear appeals from inferior criminal Courts where the proceedings have been initiated by summary complaint and not by indictment.

### F. The Court of Appeal

This Court, constituted by three Judges of the High Court of Justiciary, may hear appeals from that Court. By the Criminal Appeal (Scotland) Act, 1926 an appeal may be made against a conviction obtained on indictment on any question of law and, by leave of the Court, on any question of fact or mixed fact and law. An appeal may also be made against the sentence pronounced unless the sentence was one which was fixed by law. A decision of the Court of Appeal is final, there being no right of appeal from it to the House of Lords.

## G. The Court of Session

The Court of Session is the supreme civil Court in Scotland. It consists of the Lord President, the Lord Justice Clerk and twelve other judges. The total number of judges may be fifteen. It is divided into an Outer House and an Inner House. The Outer House is a Court of first instance, having an exclusive jurisdiction in certain matters as, for example, in actions relating to status. From the Outer House appeals may be taken to the Inner House or to the House of Lords.

The Inner House has two divisions. The First Division is presided over by the Lord President sitting with three Lords Ordinary: the Second Division is presided over by the Lord Justice Clerk sitting with three Lords Ordinary. The Inner House acts mainly as an appeal Court hearing appeals from the Outer House or from inferior civil Courts.

## H. The Privy Council

The Judicial Committee of the Privy Council has no judicial functions in Scotland except under particular statutes such as the Dentists Act, 1957 and the Medical Act, 1950.

## I. The House of Lords

The ultimate appeal in a civil case originating in Scotland is to the House of Lords, which inherited the jurisdiction exercised by the Scots Parliament before the Union in 1707. A case in the House of Lords must be heard by at least three Lords of Appeal. There is no appeal to the House of Lords from the High Court of Justiciary or from the Court of Appeal.

The following is a summary of the Scottish Courts of law:

### Courts having criminal jurisdiction

Court of Appeal
High Court of Justiciary
Sheriff Court
Burgh Court
Justices of the Peace Court

### Courts having civil jurisdiction

House of Lords
Inner House of the Court of Session
Outer House of the Court of Session
Sheriff Court

Small Debt Court
Burgh Court
Justices of the Peace Court

### 3. VERDICTS IN COURTS OF LAW

The law differs in England and Scotland in respect of the verdicts possible in criminal trials and in the manner in which verdicts may be reached in all trials by jury.

In England only two verdicts are possible in criminal trials, 'Guilty' or 'Not Guilty'. In Scotland there is a third possible verdict namely, 'Not Proven'.

In trials by jury in both civil and criminal cases, the verdict in England must be unanimous. If the jury are not unanimous they are sent back to reconsider their verdict; if they cannot agree, they are discharged and the case has to be retried before a new jury. In Scotland, the jury may reach its verdict unanimously or by a majority.

### 4. EVIDENCE IN COURT

The dentist may be called upon to give evidence in any Court of Law. While he need not be expected to have a profound knowledge of the Rules of Evidence, complete ignorance of the procedure adopted by the Courts in examining witnesses places him at a distinct disadvantage in the witness box. For this reason there is included in this chapter a brief note of the subject.

When in a law Court legal rights or liabilities have to be determined and when facts are in dispute, four questions arise, namely:

1) What facts must be proved?
2) What is the nature of the evidence to be given?
3) By whom may evidence be given?
4) How must the evidence be given?

## A. What Facts must be Proved?

Relevant facts which are in dispute must be proved. Facts are said to be relevant when in law they can be deemed to prove or disprove in whole or in part matters required to be proved or disproved. In determining what facts are relevant and admissible the law adopts stricter rules than suffice for most people in everyday life, and certain kinds of facts which might appear to be relevant are, however, not admissible.

These include:

i] *Similar but unrelated facts.* Thus if a man is charged with theft it is inadmissible to state that he had formerly committed theft. It would be unfair to call upon him to 'defend every action of his whole life in order to explain his conduct on a particular occasion'.

ii] *Evidence as to character.* This is generally inadmissible but there are exceptions to this rule. For instance, in a criminal case the accused may produce evidence of his good character with the object of showing that he is unlikely to have committed the offence with which he is charged; and in certain civil cases the fact that a person is of bad character may be given in evidence in reduction of damages.

iii] *A fact asserted by a person not called as a witness.* Hearsay evidence is the oral or written statement of a person who is not in Court conveyed to the Court either by a witness or in writing. Hearsay evidence is not admissible because it is not the best evidence; the real observer of the fact is not giving evidence so that the veracity of his statements cannot be tested by cross-examination.

There are exceptions to this rule, one being that dying declarations by the victim are admissible in trials for murder or manslaughter, subject to certain conditions.

iv] *A fact that is not within the knowledge of a witness.* The rule is that a witness must confine his evidence to facts within his own knowledge and not speak as to matters of opinion or inference. This rule does not apply to an expert witness who is permitted to express an opinion on given facts in the light of his special knowledge, skill or training in the matter in question. (See page 159.)

## B. What is the Nature of the Evidence to be Given?

The best evidence of which the nature of the case admits must be produced if it can possibly be obtained; if not, then the next best evidence that can be obtained is admitted. Thus, for example, as a general rule:

i] where a written document is to be used as proof the original document must itself be produced;

and

ii] where a fact can be proved by persons who actually saw or heard it they must be called.

Only if it is proved that this best evidence cannot be obtained is secondary evidence admissible.

## C. By Whom may Evidence be Given?

i] *Competence of witnesses.* As a general rule any person may give evidence as a witness provided he is of sound mind and capable of appreciating the nature of the oath or affirmation. Children too young to understand the nature of an oath or affirmation may not give evidence in civil cases. In criminal cases, however, such children may give unsworn evidence but it requires corroboration. Husbands and wives may not give evidence for the prosecution in the case of criminal charges against their spouses but there are exceptions to this rule, e.g. in cases of bigamy. In Scotland a child under twelve years of age is not put on oath but a child of any age may be examined in Court at the discretion of the Judge. It depends on his intelligence and whether he understands the duty of speaking the truth.

A competent witness may be compelled to attend the Court in answer to a summons which in England is in the form of a *Subpoena* and in Scotland a *Citation*. If a witness fails to answer his summons to attend Court, his failure may result in his imprisonment for contempt of court, unless, for example, a medical certificate is produced to prove that illness provided an adequate reason for his absence.

ii] *Privilege of witnesses.* Though a person may be a competent witness he may decline to give certain evidence on the ground that he is protected by privilege. This applies in the case of certain kinds of confidential relationships, or where a witness may incriminate himself, or where the welfare of the State is involved. Thus the following are privileged:

*a)* Communications between husband and wife. A husband cannot be forced to give evidence on any communication made to him by his wife during their marriage and the rule applies equally to the wife in respect of her husband.

*b)* Communications between a counsel or solicitor and client. These may not be disclosed unless the client consents.

*c)* State officials. Evidence which would be injurious to the welfare of the State.

*d)* Any witness who by answering a question might incriminate himself and make himself liable to a criminal charge. The privilege applies only to questions of this character.

Doctors, dentists and clergymen are not privileged to refuse to disclose communications between themselves and their patients or flock.

In practice, however, clergymen are not compelled to go against their conscience in this matter.

iii] *Expert witnesses.* A witness called as an expert is one who from his special knowledge, skill or training, is able to guide the Court by giving his opinion on technical or scientific subjects. It is for the Court to determine whether a person has the requisite qualifications or experience to make his opinion as an expert admissible. It should be noted that, though an expert witness may be called by either side in an action, his duty is to the Court. So that his opinion may be most useful to the Court, an expert witness may:

*a*) ascertain the facts in dispute in the case;

*b*) relate statements which he has obtained from the parties and others bearing on his investigations so as to show the grounds for his opinion;

*c*) relate the result of his observations on other cases or describe experiments made outwith the presence of the parties;

*e*) include in his evidence the opinions of writers of authority on the subject;

*f*) by permission of the Judge, be present in Court to hear evidence of facts in dispute, though in Scotland he may not hear opinion evidence given by other skilled witnesses.

An expert witness may *not* express any opinion which is the direct answer to the issue to be tried by the judge or jury.

## D. How Must Evidence be Given?

i] *Oaths and affirmation.* In general all oral evidence given in any proceeding before the courts must be given upon oath or by means of a solemn affirmation.

In England the witness is sworn in the following way: He holds the New Testament (or if a Jew, the Old Testament) in his hand which is uplifted, and says:

'I swear by Almighty God, that the evidence which I shall give shall be the truth, the whole truth and nothing but the truth.'

In Scotland the oath is administered by the judge, immediately before the evidence of a witness is commenced. With the right hand uplifted the witness repeats these words after the judge:

'I swear by Almighty God as I shall answer to God at the great day of Judgement, that I will speak the truth, the whole truth and nothing but the truth.'

Where a witness objects to taking an oath on the ground that he has no religious belief or that taking an oath is contrary to his belief, he may make a solemn affirmation in the following terms:

'I, A . . . B . . . , do solemnly and sincerely and truly declare and affirm that the evidence which I shall give shall be the truth, the whole truth and nothing but the truth.'

ii] *Examination of witnesses.* Evidence is taken from a witness by means of question and answer. The plaintiff or prosecutor commences his case by placing his witnesses each in turn in the witness-box, and by means of questions put to these witnesses he elicits all the information he can in support of his case. This is called examination-in-chief, and during this examination no leading questions may be put to a witness. A leading question is one which suggests the answer. Cross-examination by the opposing counsel or solicitor follows and the witness may be asked questions to test his veracity, accuracy or his knowledge of the subject. In cross-examination the rule excluding leading questions does not apply. When the cross-examination is over, the counsel or solicitor who examined-in-chief may re-examine to clear up any doubts which may have arisen in cross-examination. At any time in the proceedings, questions may also be put to a witness by the Court or by a member of the jury through the Court.

In giving evidence, a witness should bear in mind the following axioms:

1) He should have the subject matter clearly in his mind and should consider it in all its aspects before entering the witness-box.

2) He should speak slowly, audibly and distinctly.

3) He should be on his guard against complicated questions.

4) He should give a direct answer to every question but should confine himself to answering the questions and should not volunteer additional information.

5) He should use simple, non-technical language wherever possible.

6) He should not argue with his examiner nor should he lose his temper. This may not be easy sometimes under cross-examination when questions are put to discredit him as a witness.

iii] *Use of notes by a witness.* A witness may make use of notes in the witness-box provided that:

1) The notes were made at the time of the event or shortly after it.

2) The notes were made by the witness himself.

3) The notes are used only for the purpose of refreshing the memory of the witness.

Such notes may be in the form of case-sheets, record-cards, diaries or memoranda, etc., and their value depends on their being genuine and concurrent with the matter recorded.

iv] *Presence in court during the examination of other witnesses.* In Scotland the rule is that an ordinary witness is not permitted to hear the evidence of other witnesses before giving his own testimony. Failure to observe this rule may be a ground for the exclusion of evidence. An expert witness, on the other hand, is allowed to hear the evidence of ordinary witnesses unless, in criminal cases, an objection is raised by an accused person when the Court may disallow the presence of an expert to hear evidence as to facts.

In England, a greater latitude is permitted, but the Court will order out of Court all witnesses awaiting examination on the application of either party.

### E. Fees Payable to Witnesses

A person called into Court for the purpose of giving evidence is entitled to a fee, and to travelling and subsistence expenses where necessary.

i] *As witness as to facts.* The fees payable to witnesses giving evidence of fact vary according to the status of the witness and the kind of Court in which the evidence is given. In some Courts a scale of witness fees is prescribed, the scale being varied from time to time: in other Courts there is no such scale. In every Court, however, it is the practice to pay a professional man who is giving evidence on professional matters a higher fee than lay witnesses. A dentist giving evidence on matters connected with dentistry would, therefore, be entitled to the professional witness fee: but as a witness in other matters, for example, as the observer of a robbery, he would receive only the layman's fee.

ii] *As expert witness.* It is not the practice to compel persons to give evidence as expert witnesses against their will. On being approached with a request to give expert evidence in Court, a dentist accordingly may refuse with perfect propriety. If he does agree he should name his fee, which should be paid or agreed to by the party calling him before he appears in Court. If the fee is not paid or agreed to before he is sworn, the amount of his fee may be decided by the Court. Having been sworn he has no right to object to giving evidence on the ground that his fee has not been paid or agreed to by the party who called him.

# CHAPTER XIII

# Identification by Teeth and Jaws

## 1. NECESSITY FOR PROVING IDENTITY

Identification of living persons or of human remains may become necessary for a variety of reasons. It may prevent or reveal imposture; it may enable proof of death to be established and so permit payment of insurance moneys or inheritance to relatives who would otherwise be debarred from benefiting for a period of seven years from the date of presumed death.

In the Civil Courts identity of living persons has to be proved where questions or disputes arise in connexion with claims to property or succession to title. In the Criminal Courts identity of a person charged with a crime must be established and will obviously become a matter of prime importance when the person charged pleads in defence that he has been mistaken for another. Where murder has been committed, identification of the victim is almost essential for it greatly helps the police in their investigations and may indeed be the first step in bringing the criminal to justice.

A serious fire occurred in the premises of a builder named Furness and in the debris there was found the charred remains of what was at first presumed to be the builder. Investigation proved, however, that the remains were those of an employee and Furness was subsequently found guilty of murder. Failure to identify the body might well have resulted in the criminal escaping the punishment he deserved.

## 2. METHODS EMPLOYED FOR IDENTIFICATION

Though we were concerned chiefly with the teeth and jaws as aids to identification, other methods commonly employed deserve to be mentioned. Smith and Cook[1] describe more than twenty ways by which identity can be proved, some of which are brought into everyday use by the police or can be sworn to by any observant witness, while others can be used only by those having special knowledge and experience.

[1] Smith, S. and Cook, W. G. H. (1934), *Taylor's Principles and Practice of Medical Jurisprudence*, 9th ed., 1, p. 106, London, Churchill.

Articles of clothing, laundry marks thereon, keys or other articles in pockets are reliable and useful aids in identification. On the other hand, identity of a person based on likeness of features, speech or gait may be entirely unreliable and handwriting characteristics have also been known to result in mistaken identity. Tattoo markings on the skin may be helpful though they can be altered or obliterated and tend to fade with the passage of time. Operation or wound scars are more valuable for they cannot be eradicated. The discovery of a scar in a piece of abdominal skin in Dr. Crippen's victim played an important part in the medical evidence in his trial for the murder of his wife.[1]

Even the more scientific methods of proving identity have their limitations. Thus the Bertillon system of Anthropometry which were adopted by the French authorities in 1882 has at least two disadvantages —it requires special apparatus and, depending as it does on the personal factor in recording measurements, it allows of the introduction of serious errors.

Dactylography, identification by finger-prints, was officially introduced into this country in 1894. As no two persons have identical finger-prints the method is rightly regarded as infallible but it too has its limitations. In the British Isles, at least, records are kept only of persons who have been convicted and this therefore restricts the scope of the method. Furthermore, the fact that the skin is quickly destroyed after death confines the usefulness of dactylography as a means of identification to the living or the recently dead.

By contrast, the teeth are the least destructible of the human tissues and for that reason, though it is not the only one, they offer valuable aids to identification. Their utilization in this direction is not a new idea but more importance tends to be placed on dental evidence now-adays than formerly, possibly because proof of identity was established largely or entirely by dental evidence in such cases as those of Ruxton, Dobkin and Haigh. These and other cases in which teeth and jaws have played a part in providing identity are recorded in this chapter.

### 3. DIFFICULTY OF PROVING IDENTITY

In spite of the numerous methods available, the difficulty which is sometimes experienced in proving the identity of even a living person may be very great and should be recognized. Smith and Cook[2] give as an example the inmates of an American prison, Will West and

[1] BROWNE, D. G. and TULLETT, E. V. (1951), *Bernard Spilsbury*, London, Harrap.
[2] SMITH, S. and COOK, W. G. H. (1934), *Taylor's Principles and Practice of Medical Jurisprudence*, 9th ed., 1, London, Churchill.

William West who bore an extraordinarily close resemblance one to the other, and were found to have identical bodily and facial measurements as recorded by the Bertillon method. They differed only in their finger-prints and to have identified Will from William without the aid of finger prints would have been a matter of the greatest difficulty.

The famous Tichbourne case[1] illustrates as well as any other in this country how difficult it may be legally to prove, or disprove, the identity of a living person.

Orton, a butcher born in Wapping, emigrated to Australia and claimed to be the missing heir to the Tichbourne estates, who was known to have been shipwrecked. Returning to England, Orton raised an action to prove his claim. In this he was unsuccessful but the hearing occupied 102 days and was estimated to have cost the defendants no less than £91,000. Two years later, in 1873, the claimant was tried for fraud and was finally proved to be an imposter, but the trial lasted 188 days at a cost to the Crown of some £50,000.

There have also been recorded instances of persons who, because of mistaken identity, have been wrongfully punished for alleged crimes. Throughout the annals of British legal history no case is more notorious than that of Adolph Beck.[2]

In 1887, John Smith was sentened to seven years penal servitude for a series of thefts from women. In 1896 there was an outbreak of similar crimes and a man who gave his name as Adolph Beck was arrested and identified as John Smith by the numerous victims. Beck was sentenced to a term of imprisonment on the expiry of which he set about trying to prove that he had been falsely accused but during these endeavours he was again arrested on a similar charge and, having again been 'identified' as the perpetrator of the crimes, was found guilty. Sentence was postponed and in the interval the real John Smith, who was at the time a prisoner under arrest for the same type of crime, was recognized by a police official. Beck was immediately released, granted free pardons and given a solacium of £2,000 by the Treasury. Though the trouble arose largely through a legal point by which evidence of an alibi was disallowed, the fact remains that the unfortunate man was 'identified' by quite a number of women who swore that he was the man who had robbed them.

It seems likely that in cases such as these much suffering and expense would have been saved if more scientific methods had been employed to prove the identity of the persons involved.

Difficult though proof of identity of living persons may sometimes be, that of dead bodies and of human remains must necessarily present a greater problem. Each year a surprising number of persons are reported missing: each year in our large cities bodies are discovered of

[1] MAUGHAM, Lord F. H. (1936), *The Tichbourne Case*, London, Hodder & Stoughton.
[2] O'DONNELL, B. (1935), *The Trials of Mr. Justice Avory*, London, Rich & Cowan.

persons drowned or killed in street accidents and a proportion of them remained unidentified. Because of the changes in appearance liable to occur in such circumstances, identification of a body by relatives and others is often unreliable. Keith Simpson, for example, instances the case of the body of a woman murdered in Luton in 1943. The body was identified positively by eleven people as being four different persons—but not one was right.[1]

The National Registration Act, 1939, which required every individual to be given a registration number, reduced very considerably the proportion of bodies which remained unidentified, but neither this Act nor any other can have any effect upon the difficulty of identifying a body when steps have been taken to prevent identification by mutilation.

In cases of murder, identification of the victim is of vital importance in enabling the police to investigate the crime and failure to identify may account for some murder mysteries. In *Rex* v. *Rouse*,[2] Rouse was found guilty of murder although his victim was never identified. Again in *Rex* v. *Camb*,[3] the accused was found guilty although the body of his victim was never found, having been slipped through a port-hole of the ship on which the murder was committed. Such cases are exceptions to the general rule that identification of the victim goes a long way towards bringing the criminal to justice. Because of this, it is not surprising that murders sometimes dismember and mutilate the body of the victim.

What is surprising is that identity can be established in any case where there has been gross mutilation. In the *Ruxton*[4] case, for example, the problem of identifying the victims was almost insurmountable and it reflects credit on those responsible for the conduct of that case that it was brought to a successful conclusion. It is questionable whether that would have been reached had not Dr. Ruxton's victims been identified. The dental evidence went a long way in bringing about the identification. In view of the difficulty which may attend the business of proving identity, every aid should be made use of including that which teeth and jaws may offer. The value of teeth and jaws as aids in identification is discussed below and some cases are recorded in which practical use was made of such dental evidence.

---

[1] SIMPSON, K. (1951), 'Dental Evidence in the Reconstruction of Crime', *Brit. dent. J.*, 91, p. 234.
[2] NORMANTON, H. (1931), *The Trial of Alfred Rouse*, London, Hodge.
[3] ROBERTS, G. D. (1948), *Rex* v. *Camb*, *Med. legal J.*, 16, p. 147.
[4] GLAISTER, J. and BRASH, J. C. (1937), *Medico Legal Aspects of the Ruxton Case*, Edinburgh, Livingstone.

## 4. TEETH AND JAWS AS AIDS IN IDENTIFICATION

Dental evidence can be useful as an aid in establishing identity for the following reasons:

### A. The Teeth are Characteristic of the Individual

The normal complement of permanent teeth in the human being is thirty-two. Each tooth has a characteristic shape and marking of its surface from occlusion with teeth in the opposing jaw. In size and general arrangement, the teeth show wide variations; cavities in teeth caused by decay may be restored by filling materials of different kinds; teeth may be missing and missing teeth may be replaced by a variety of crowns, bridges or artificial dentures. No two dentitions are exactly alike and the dentition of an individual is therefore as characteristic of the individual as are his finger prints.

### B. Marks Made by Teeth Offer a Certain Means of Identification

When, for example, a suspected person leaves the marks of his teeth on a piece of cheese and the marks are found to coincide with a model of his teeth, the evidence of identity is conclusive. Criminals have been convicted on such evidence. Sadists have been identified by the marks which their teeth have left on their victim's body. Conversely, Rhodes[1] records a case where a girl bit the man who assaulted her and where the identity of the assailant was proved by the discovery that marks on his hand corresponded with marks made by the girl's teeth. One case is recorded where the marks made by teeth on a cigar-holder were of importance in a murder investigation.[2]

The Odontoscopic method of identification was introduced by Sorup in Germany where attacks by criminals with sadistic traits appear to have been not uncommon.

By this method plaster casts of the teeth are obtained, dried and varnished, after which the incisal edges and occlusal surfaces are coated with printer's ink. Upon this inked surface moistened paper is pressed and after the ink has dried a print is taken from it on to transparent paper. The final print is placed over a lifesize photograph and compared with the marks on the body.

Humble[3] suggests a modification in which the inked plaster casts are photographed and from the negative a positive is made on flat

[1] RHODES, H. T. F. (1937), *The Criminals we Deserve*, London, Methuen.
[2] SCHIRNDING, H. (1934), 'The teeth and their significance in forensic medicine', *Dental Cosmos*, **26**, p. 856.
[3] HUMBLE, B. H. (1933), 'Identification by means of teeth', *Brit. dent. J.*, **54**, p. 528.

film. This transparent positive is placed over the photograph of the tooth marks and compared.

## C. The Teeth are Relatively Indestructible

Although in the living, the teeth so readily decay, in the dead, they outlast every other tissue in the body. This somewhat ironical fact gives to the teeth a special importance in matters relating to identification. The explanation of the indestructibility of teeth as compared to that of bone is that the teeth have relatively little organic matter capable of alteration after death. The enamel which covers the crowns of the teeth is almost entirely composed of calcified tissue.

## D. The Teeth Offer Valuable Evidence of Age

Determination of age may be of primary importance in establishing identity. Particularly within certain age groups the teeth offer a means of estimating age which is as reliable as any other method. The subject is considered separately on page 169.

## E. The Teeth may Serve as a Guide to Habits and Occupation

In a mouth the state of the teeth and their supporting structures may act as an index of the care, or lack of care which the person has employed in oral hygiene. Even examination of a skull can give similar assistance from the presence of decayed teeth, or roots buried in the bone of the jaw or absorption of bone indicative of an abscess at the root of a tooth or of paradontal disease. The presence or absence of fillings or other restorations in the teeth and the presence or absence of tartar deposits on the teeth may also be indicative of the care bestowed on the mouth and therefore an index of the individual's habits.

Wearing down of teeth in one situation may justify the assumption that the individual was a pipe-smoker while attrition of all the teeth may point to the habit of tobacco chewing.

Occasionally, teeth may offer evidence of occupation from wearing of the cutting edge of the upper central incisor teeth. This sometimes occurs in the seamstress who is continually biting thread and in the upholsterer who, after filling his mouth with tacks, expels them one by one with his tongue in such a manner that they pass over the edge of the front teeth and wear them down. Keith Simpson[1] has drawn attention to a unique case of deep grooving of incisor teeth in a hairdresser whose habit it was to hold hairpins with his teeth.

[1] SIMPSON, K. (1951), 'Dental Evidence in the Reconstruction of Crime', *Brit. dent. J.*, **91**, p. 232.

## F. The Jaw Bones may Offer Valuable Evidence

Sex cannot be determined by teeth alone, except perhaps in the Esqui-maux in whom attrition, or wearing down of the teeth, tends to be more pronounced in the females because it is the custom of the females to soften animal skins by chewing them in preparation for their use as articles of clothing. The jaw bones, on the other hand, may be some guide to sex for, generally speaking, those of the males are larger and exhibit greater bony prominences where the stronger muscles of masti-cation have been attached

The alveolar bone is that part of the jaw which surrounds the developing teeth and supports the teeth after they have erupted. It is dependent upon the presence of teeth so that when a tooth is extracted the neighbouring alveolar bone is gradually absorbed. The degree of this absorption can give a rough indication of the period of time which has elapsed since the extraction of a tooth (see page 170).

In addition to this gradual absorption of bone certain well-defined changes occur in the healing process which takes place after tooth extraction. A microscopic study of these changes will reveal the stage reached in the healing process and this may assist in identification in certain circumstances. For example, in the Second World War the identification of bodies of airmen killed in battle was assisted in some instances by comparing the evidence contained in the jaw with the known date of tooth extraction. Mangos[1] has carried out a limited investigation in this field. His findings are tabulated in Fig. 1 to give the reader an idea of the potentialities of such an investigation rather than to suggest that the data is sufficient to enable scientific deduction to be made. Further research deserves to be undertaken to discover the average period at which definite changes are to be expected.

Apart altogether from evidence dependent on bone absorption and changes inherent in the healing process after tooth extraction, the general shape of the jaws may be distinctive, as was revealed, for example, in the case of *Rex* v. *Dobkin* (page 175).

## G. Artificial Dentures may Establish Identity

Since the Parkman case in 1850 in which the discovery of a part of his artificial denture established his identity and did much to hang his murderer, many instances have been recorded of identity being proved by the artificial dentures worn by a deceased person. Some of these are referred to below, including what may be regarded as the modern

[1] MANGOS, J. F. (1940), 'The healing of extraction wounds', *Brit. dent. J.*, **21**, p. 10.

classic example in the case of *Rex* v. *Haigh*, where the identity of his victim was determined by artificial dentures alone (page 185).

Identity from evidence supplied by artificial dentures can be proved either by some distinguishing mark on the denture or by comparing it with the model of the mouth in possession of the dentist who made the appliance. Among general dental practitioners the marking of artificial dentures is not a common practice. If it were, it would help to facilitate identification. When a denture is made of metal a distinguishing mark or number can easily be stamped upon it. When vulcanite is the material employed, marking or numbering presents a greater difficulty though the inclusion of a distinguishing mark on the lines of the white spot in a certain make of tobacco pipe could be undertaken with benefit and without difficulty. Jeffreys[1] has suggested a method by which distinctive markings can be incorporated in dentures made of acrylic resin material and the plan, or a similar one, has been adopted by the dental departments of the American Armed Forces and by that of the Royal Air Force in this country.

To prove the identity of a person by means of an artificial denture without distinctive markings, or without comparison of the denture with the model for which it was made, must be a difficult matter. This is borne out by the experience of the Bureau of Police in New Rochelle who, in 1942, in an endeavour to secure identification published in a dental journal the photograph of the artificial denture found on a body. In addition, they exhibited the denture for five days during an Annual Dental Convention, which was attended by some ten thousand dentists and one thousand dental technicians. In spite of such wide publicity, the denture remained unrecognized.

### 5. DETERMINATION OF AGE BY TEETH AND JAWS

To determine even the approximate age of an unknown person whose dead body is discovered or the approximate age revealed by human or skeletal remains may be of great importance in establishing identity. Indeed, it may be a fundamental step in an investigation for without such information identification may be impossible. Nowhere was this more clearly shown than in the investigation which led to the trial of Dr. Ruxton for the discovery of the ages of his victims indicated a line of inquiry which might not otherwise have been followed (page 182).

There are several ways by which an estimation of age may be arrived at. Tables of averages are available from which age may be deduced

[1] JEFFREYS, F. E. (1944), *Dental Digest*, 50, p. 64.

| Period after extraction | Periodontal Membrane | Surface Epithelium | Organization of blood clot | Inflammation cells | New bone deposits in socket | Bone absorption around socket |
|---|---|---|---|---|---|---|
| 3 days | Bundles of torn fibres | Commencing | Fibroblasts at edges | In evidence | None | None |
| 7 days | Undergoing degeneration | Proceeding | Fibrous tissue forming | do. | None | None |
| 10 days | do. | Almost across socket | Fibrous tissue well marked except in centre | Leucocytes near surface of clot | Osteoblasts in evidence | Osteoclasts in evidence at crests of socket |
| 2 weeks | No trace left | Completely covers the clot | Organization nearly completed | do. | Spicules of bone appear | do. |
| 3 weeks | do. | do. | Organization complete | Round cells appear | Cancellous bone at base and sides of socket | do. |
| 5½ weeks | do. | Well healed | Dense fibrous tissue in upper part. Less dense in lower part | Round cells evident | Bone deposit rapid | do. |
| 8 weeks | do. | Intact | Fibrous tissue being replaced by bone | No trace of round cells | Bony trabeculae in evidence | Crest of socket resorbed |
| 10 weeks | do. | Normal appearance | do. | do. | Bone in 2/3 of socket | do. |
| 15 weeks | do. | do. | Fibrous tissue replaced by bone | do. | Bone completely fills socket | do. |

Fig. 1. Table of changes which occur in the healing process after tooth extraction

by comparison with measurements of the height of the body or length of the long bones of the arm or leg. Such tables are more accurate in the very young and become less reliable as age advances. Bone development is another useful guide and, within limits, a fairly accurate one. Epiphyses appear at regular times so that their presence in the body is a good guide up to the age of thirteen years, while the union of these epiphyses to the long bones gives an indication of age from about fifteen to twenty-five years. The fusion of certain bones, one to another, is a further example of the assistance which may come from an investigation of bone development. In the soft tissues the changes which occur in both sexes at the time of puberty may be useful guides between the ages of thirteen and sixteen years.

The teeth can be of real assistance in determining age. They are calcified with remarkable regularity so the stage reached in their calcification is an accurate indication of age in the young.

The times at which the teeth erupt into the mouth cavity are more liable to variation and the progress of eruption, though helpful, is less reliable as a means of determining age.

The chronology of tooth development has been studied in many quarters and tables have been produced to show the extent of calcification and eruption at given ages in the normal child and young person. The details evolved by Schour and Massler are generally accepted as being accurate, especially as regards calcification. These details, in diagrammatic form, are reproduced in Figs. 3 and 4. From diagrams such as these or from tables an investigator who has obtained X-ray negatives of a skull can quickly arrive at an approximate age of the subject. If, for example, he discovered that the crowns and most of the roots of the permanent incisor teeth and of the first permanent molar were formed; that the crown and one-third to one-half of the roots of the permanent canine and of the premolar teeth were calcified; that the crown only of the second permanent molar was calcified and that only the cusps of the wisdom tooth appeared, he could by comparison with the diagram estimate the age at about nine years. Examination of the mouth would reveal in the normal child the presence of the temporary canine and temporary molar teeth (unshaded in the diagram) and reverting again to the X-ray negatives the investigator would observe that the roots of these teeth had undergone absorption to about half their extent in preparation for being shed in due course. Of the permanent teeth, only the central and lateral incisor and the first molar would be observed to have erupted.

But it is not only in the young person that teeth can assist in determining age. In the adult, and even in the adolescent, changes occur in the teeth as age advances and these changes have been used by Gustafson[1] to evolve a scientific basis for estimating age. Briefly, these changes concern:

i] The wearing down of the tooth or attrition due to mastication.

ii] The deposit of secondary dentine in the pulp chamber.

iii] The gum attachment to the tooth which in the normal young tooth should be at the point where the enamel ceases.

iv] The deposit of additional cementum on the root.

v] The translucency of the root due to supercalcification of the dentine.

vi] The resorption of the root.

$A_0$ = no attrition
$S_0$ = no secondary dentine
$G_0$ = no recession of gum
$C_0$ = no thickening of cementum
$T_0$ = no translucency
$R_0$ = no resorption of root (apex open)

$A_1$ = attrition of enamel only
$S_1$ = slight deposit of secondary dentine
$G_1$ = slight recession of gum
$C_1$ = slight thickening of cementum
$T_1$ = translucency in apical third
$R_1$ = very slight resorption of root (apex closed)

$A_2$ = attrition involving dentine
$S_2$ = secondary dentine half fills chamber
$G_2$ = gum recession distinct
$C_2$ = thick layer of cementum
$T_2$ = translucency beyond apical third
$R_2$ = resorption of root distinct

$A_3$ = attrition reaching pulp chamber
$S_3$ = secondary dentine fills or nearly fills chamber
$C_3$ = gum recession two-thirds down root
$C_3$ = very thick layer of cementum
$T_3$ = translucency in two-thirds of root
$R_3$ = marked resorption of dentine and cementum

FIG. 2. Point values of age changes (after Gustafson)

[1] GUSTAFSON, G. (1950), 'Age determination on teeth', *J. Amer. Dent. Ass.*, **41**, pp. 45-54.

# DECIDUOUS DENTITION

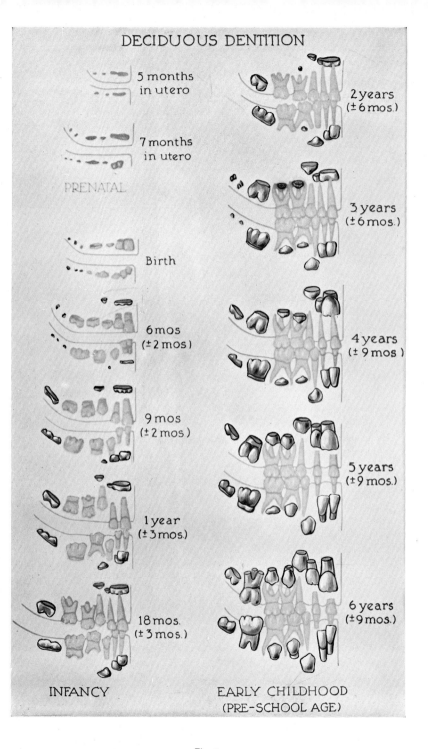

5 months in utero

7 months in utero

PRENATAL

Birth

6 mos. (±2 mos.)

9 mos. (±2 mos.)

1 year (±3 mos.)

18 mos. (±3 mos.)

INFANCY

2 years (±6 mos.)

3 years (±6 mos.)

4 years (±9 mos.)

5 years (±9 mos.)

6 years (±9 mos.)

EARLY CHILDHOOD (PRE-SCHOOL AGE)

Fig. 3

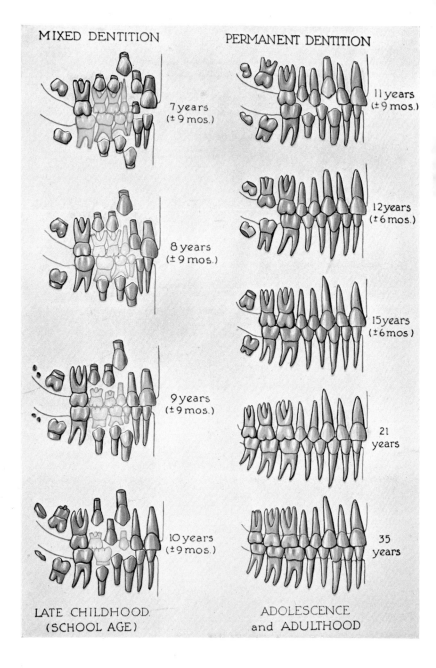

MIXED DENTITION

PERMANENT DENTITION

7 years
(±9 mos.)

8 years
(±9 mos.)

9 years
(±9 mos.)

10 years
(±9 mos.)

11 years
(±9 mos.)

12 years
(±6 mos.)

15 years
(±6 mos.)

21
years

35
years

LATE CHILDHOOD
(SCHOOL AGE)

ADOLESCENCE
and ADULTHOOD

Fig. 4

These changes are diagrametically represented in Fig. 2. Some are to be seen by the naked eye but most require examination under the microscope of a ground section of the tooth. The first step in examining a tooth for age is therefore to obtain a thin section of it. The second step is to allot no points, one point, two points or three points for each feature, depending on the degree of departure from the normal. It is scarcely possible to make a sharper distinction, nor indeed is it necessary. The third step is to compare the total points allotted with those of teeth of known age. This can best be done by means of a graph having on it what Gustafson calls the 'regression line', which is a line showing the relation between the point values of teeth removed from persons of known age (Fig. 5). It is determined on a statistical basis, for the details of which the reader is referred to Gustafson's article.

So long as points for each of the changes are taken into account, and assuming that a suitable graph with an accurate regression line is used, this method of age determination is one in which the margin of error is remarkably small. The necessity for taking every change into account will be appreciated when it is realized that any one of them can occur through pathological conditions independent of age. To omit the points value of any one change would increase materially the margin of error.

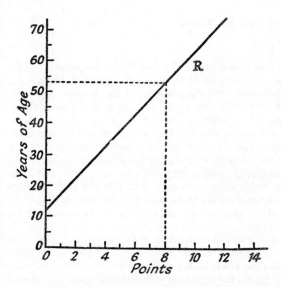

FIG. 5. Graph of age relationship to point value. Where point value is 8 dotted line meets regression line R opposite age 53

## 6. CASES ILLUSTRATING THE VALUE OF DENTAL EVIDENCE IN IDENTIFICATION

A brief survey of cases in which dental evidence has been of value in proving or helping to prove identity is of interest if for no other reason than to reveal the variety of ways in which teeth and jaws have been of use in this direction. These cases are classified thus:

*a*) Evidence furnished by teeth:
    i] By presence of teeth.
    ii] By presence of roots of teeth.
    iii] By missing teeth.
    iv] By peculiarity in the arrangement of teeth.
    v] By peculiarity in the shape of teeth.
    vi] By the general condition of the teeth.
    vii] By fillings in teeth.
    viii] By crown and bridge work.

*b*) Evidence furnished by jaws.
*c*) Evidence furnished by marks made by teeth.
*d*) Evidence of age furnished by teeth.
*e*) Evidence furnished by artificial dentures.

## A. Evidence Furnished by Teeth

i] *By the presence of teeth*

In 1831 an elderly Irish person named Caroline Walsh disappeared and the woman with whom she had gone to reside was charged with her murder. On the evening following the disappearance, an old woman, also Irish, giving the name of Caroline Welsh, was found lying in an exhausted condition in a nearby street. The prisoner claimed that this was the same woman who had disappeared and whom she was accused of having murdered. Identification became, therefore, a matter of primary importance. It was proved chiefly by the fact that while it was known that Caroline Walsh had, for her age, surprisingly good front teeth, no teeth were present in the mouth of Caroline Welsh and there was no indication that teeth had been recently extracted. It was therefore proved that Caroline Welsh was not the missing woman and the prisoner was found guilty of the murder of her lodger, Caroline Walsh.[1]

In 1873, the Goss-Udderzook case was tried in the American Courts. Goss was supposed to have perished in a fire which destroyed his house in Baltimore in 1871. Mrs. Goss raised an action against the insurance companies who refused to pay up the insurance policies because of doubt expressed at the inquest that the body was not that of her husband. While the case was

[1] *Rex* v. *Ross*, C.C.C., December 1831.

still pending, Udderzook, who had been the principal witness of the fire in Baltimore, was charged with the murder of a man in Pennsylvania. The murdered man was proved to be Goss and Udderzook was found guilty of his murder. The case hinged upon the identity of the victims. Goss was known to have most of his natural teeth (and in good condition). Evidence was given which proved that the exhumed body of the fire victim revealed only fifteen teeth, more or less neglected, while the body of the murdered person had twenty-eight, all in good condition.[1]

ii] *By the presence of roots of teeth.* In the case of *Rex* v. *Dobkin*[2] the identity of the body which was alleged to be that of Dobkin's wife became a matter of primary importance because the defendant claimed that it was the body of an air-raid victim and not that of his spouse. Identity was proved almost entirely by the dental evidence at the trial. Among British trials it is the first in which dental evidence played a primary part so that in the field of forensic dentistry it may rightly be regarded as a classic case.

On 12 April 1942, the London police were informed that Rachael Dobkin had disappeared. Two days later, an unexplained fire broke out in the cellar of the Kennington Baptist Church in the precincts of which Harry Dobkin, the woman's husband, acted as fire-watcher. In this capacity he acted literally for it was proved that he watched the conflagration without raising an alarm or calling the fire brigade. Suspecting that there might be some connexion between the mysterious fire and the disappearance of Mrs. Dobkin, the police made an investigation of the premises. The search revealed a quantity of partially burnt straw and a freshly dug hole measuring approximately six feet by two, but no trace of a body. Suspicion subsided and the police investigation ceased, but fifteen months later a workman, engaged in demolition, discovered beneath a stone slab a partially burnt, dismembered body. The question which immediately arose was obvious, was this the body of the fire-watcher's wife and how had she come by her death?

In order to keep down the offensive smell of decomposition, the body had been covered with slaked lime which, in contrast to quick lime, has the effect of preserving rather than destroying. From those parts of the body which had been thus preserved, the Crown Pathologist was able to prove that the body was that of a female who had died twelve to eighteen months previously and that death was due to strangulation. This disposed of the defendant's plea that the body was that of the victim of an air-raid, and disproved the theory, also put forward in defence, that an ancient grave had been disturbed.

Owing to the advanced state of decomposition, and to the fact that the body had been mutilated, it was possible by the usual means to establish only the sex, stature, approximate age and colour of hair of the deceased. Fortunately, the dentist who had attended Mrs. Dobkin was traced and found to be an exceptionally careful recorder of his work. From his case sheets, he

[1] GARRISON, C. G. (1887), *The American System of Dentistry*, **3**, pp. 969–74, Philadelphia, Lea Brothers.
[2] ROBERTS, C. E. B. (1944), Editor, *The Trial of Harry Dobkin*, Old Bailey Trial Series, London, Jarrolds.

was able to draw a diagram of the upper jaw (the lower jaw was never found) showing its peculiar shape, the teeth which were standing and the fillings which he had inserted in the teeth.

The dentist further revealed that, when in 1934 he extracted the premolar teeth, the roots fractured and were left in the jaw bone. The expert dental witness who was called revealed, in X-ray films which he had taken of the skull, the presence of these roots in the situations indicated by the dentist and even demonstrated that with the aid of a magnifying glass, the roots could be seen peeping through the bone at two places.

The details given by the dentist were found to correspond exactly with those found in the skull and the discovery of the tooth roots embedded in the jaw bone finally clinched the matter and removed from the minds of the jury any possible doubt that the remains found in the cellar of the Baptist Church were those of Mrs. Dobkin. The prisoner was found guilty of murder and sentenced to death.

In the Court of Appeal, to which the case was taken, dental evidence was again prominent and Kelsey Fry[1] records the statement made by Mr. Justice Humphreys. Referring to the dental evidence the Judge said, 'It was very remarkable evidence . . . and might well be of itself sufficient to justify a jury and, for aught we know, has been in this case sufficient to justify the jury in saying that these were the remains of Mrs. Dobkin.'

The appeal was dismissed and the prisoner paid the supreme penalty.

iii] *By missing teeth.* According to Humble[2] the earliest recorded case of identification by means of teeth was in 1477 when, after the battle of Nancy, a body, supposed to be that of Charles the Bold, was found in circumstances which made identification uncertain. Identity was established mainly by the discovery that certain teeth were missing and by the knowledge that these teeth had previously been lost as the result of an accident.

iv] *By peculiarity in the arrangement of the teeth*

A man named Guérin was murdered in France and his body was buried beneath a cellar floor where it remained undiscovered for three years. The teeth in the skull assisted in proving that the remains were those of the murdered man because the lower canine teeth projected considerably in front of the neighbouring teeth.[3]

The dentist who attended the children of the late Tsar of Russia was able to prove that a person who claimed to be one of them, the Grand Duchess Anastasia, was an imposter. This he did by examining models of the claim-

---

[1] Kelsey Fry, W. (1943), 'The Baptist Church Cellar Case', *Brit. dent. J.*, **25**, p. 157.
[2] Humble, B. H. (1933), 'Identification by means of teeth', *Brit. dent. J.*, **54**, p. 528.
[3] Smith, S. and Cook, W. G. H. (1934), *Taylor's Principles and Practice of Medical Jurisprudence*, 9th ed., **1**, p. 177.

ant's mouth and declaring her teeth and jaws to be quite different in general arrangement from those of his former patients.[1]

v] *By peculiarity in the shape of teeth.* To cite only the shape of teeth in dental evidence brought forward to establish identity must be uncommon and relatively unimportant but the following case is included if only for its uniqueness.

There are few historical mysteries more intriguing or baffling than that which surrounds the Little Dauphin, son of Louis XVI, King of France. Did he, while still a boy, die in prison as was alleged, or was he released by his captors who substituted another body for the inspection and certification by the doctors? Was he rescued from the Temple prison by Royalist partisans and, if so, what became of him?

As was to be expected in the circumstances, several claimed to be the son of Louis XVI and heir to the Throne, the most serious and persistent being Charles Louis, Duc de Normandie, alias Karl Naundorff. The likelihood that the latter was in fact the King's son is borne out by the testimony of Madame de Rombard who had acted as the Little Dauphin's governess and who had met him after his supposed demise. She satisfied many that Naundorff and the Dauphin were one and the same, basing her belief on certain marks on the skin, a characteristic thickness of the neck and *the peculiar shape of the front teeth.* Naundorff staked his claim in the French Courts but was exiled and died eventually in Delft in 1848. The fact that he was unsuccessful in his legal action does not necessarily indicate that his former governess was mistaken in her identification of the famous French figure.[2]

vi] *By the general condition of the teeth*

In Berkeley, California, in 1925, a small laboratory used by a chemist called Swartz blew up and became a blazing ruin from which there was eventually taken a charred body. This was identified by Mrs. Swartz and by an employee as the body of the chemist who was thus supposed to have been the victim of an appalling tragedy. Suspicion arose that the laboratory had been deliberately set on fire and that led to a closer investigation of the body. It was discovered that the two teeth missing in the upper jaw had been recently extracted and that the remainder had been neglected, being broken, disscoloured and decayed.

Swartz was known to have possessed a perfect dentition, with the exception of two teeth missing in the upper jaw, and the contrast in the dental conditions proved that the body was not that of the chemist who had meanwhile disappeared but was arrested later and charged with murder of a person unknown. It was established at the trial that Swartz had in fact removed two teeth from the victim's jaw in the hope that the body might be mistaken for his own. There was evidence of other deliberate mutilations made in an attempt to support the assumption that the body found after the fire was his.

[1] Newspaper report, *Daily Mail*, 16 October 1818.
[2] MADOL, H. G. (1951), *The Shadow King*, p. 166, London, Allen & Unwin.

The dental evidence did much to prove that the chemist was the murderer and not the victim of the fire.[1]

The *Noronic* disaster created a problem in identification on a scale seldom met with. The evidence relating to the general dental state of the natural teeth in the bodies of the victims greatly assisted in solving the problem.

In the early hours of 17 September 1949, a disastrous fire broke out in the S.S. *Noronic* while the ship was in Toronto harbour. As a result, 118 persons lost their lives and identification of the majority of the victims presented a difficult problem because of the intensity of the fire which caused extensive disfiguration and partial destruction of the bodies. Apart from the few who were drowned, in their attempt to escape the flames, only one body had recognizable facial features. A team of dentists, doctors and radiologists, assisted by the Canadian Red Cross and other organizations, got quickly to work and succeeded in identifying all but three of the bodies, though the task extended over four months. The dental members of the team made an investigation first of all and recorded in great detail particulars of natural (and artificial) teeth which, when compared with charts, X-rays and other details supplied by victims' dentists and relatives, enabled twenty bodies to be positively identified. But the dental investigation played an even more important part in the general plan. From the dental evidence, lists were drawn up to show on the one hand which bodies were excluded from identification and, on the other, which bodies could be those of the persons sought. The dentists who conducted the investigation were thus able to 'screen' the cases and this greatly facilitated the medical and other investigations which followed.

The 'crossword' system of charting proved invaluable. By it, body numbers were placed on the horizontal and names of missing persons on the vertical and the corresponding squares were blacked out or shaded out when the dental, medical and radiographic evidence pointed to elimination. One of the charts is reproduced in Fig. 6 and from it the reader will quickly see the method which was employed.[2]

vii] *By fillings in teeth.* Though a dentist might be able, by some special feature of shape or contour, to recognize a filling or an inlay which he had inserted in a tooth cavity, it is mainly by their position and the materials employed that fillings or inlays in teeth can be of assistance in identification.

When the French Prince Imperial was killed in the Zulu War, there was difficulty, because of certain circumstances, in identifying his body. Identity

[1] GRIBBLE, L. R. (1946), *Great Detective Feats*, p. 83, London, Burke.
[2] GRANT, E. A., PENDERGAST, W. K. and WHITE, E. A., 'Dental Identification in the *Noronic* Disaster', *J. Can. Dent. Ass.*, 18, p. 3.

was established by the presence in the molar teeth of four gold fillings which he was known to have had inserted.[1]

John Hamilton was the right hand man of Dillinger, described in America at the time as 'Public enemy No. 2'. In a fight with 'G' men, Hamilton was fatally wounded and his companions in crime applied lime to the face and

| 18 NOV. '49 | B 12 | B 19 | C 1 | C 2 | C 11 | C 19 | D 4 | D 5 | D 11 | D 15 | D 19 | D 21 | D 22 | E 19 | E 20 |
|---|---|---|---|---|---|---|---|---|---|---|---|---|---|---|---|
| J. DOERING | ● | | | | | | | | | | | | | | |
| J.M. THOMAS | | | | | | | ● | | | | | | | | |
| R. ZIMMERMAN | | | | | | | | | | | | | | ● | |
| H.H. KOHN | | | | ● | | | | | | | | | | | |
| T.J. MALLOY | | | | | ● | | | | | | | | | | |
| D. KEDDIE | | | | | | | | | | | | | | | ● |
| C. BELTZHOOVER | | | | | | | | | | | | | | | |
| M. BERKE | | | | | | | | | | | | | | | |
| L.H. BLAKE | | | | | | | | ● | | | | | | | |
| J.L. CALIHAN | | | | | | | | | | | | | | | |
| B. FUREY | | | | | | | | | | | | ● | | | |
| F.S. JEWELL | | ● | | | | | | | | | | | | | |
| A. LEYBOURN | | | | | | ● | | | | | | | | | |
| W.J. PASCOE | | | | | | | | | ● | | | | | | |
| A. PRICE | | | ● | | | | | | | | | | | | |

Horizontal squares = Noronic victims    Vertical squares = Bodies

■ Dental exclusion    ▨ Medical and X-ray exclusion
⊡ Body identified    ☐ Body not identified

Fig 6

hands and secretly buried the body in a gravel pit. The attempt to prevent identification was unavailing because, when it was ultimately discovered, the body was definitely identified by the police by comparison of the fillings in the teeth with the dental records in their possession.[2]

The Pyjama Girl case is instructive from a dental point of view.

In 1934, the dead body of a young female, clad in pyjamas, was found in a

[1] HUMBLE, B. H. (1933), 'Identification by means of teeth', *Brit. dent. J.*, **54**, p. 528.
[2] HOOVER, J. E. (1939), *Persons in Hiding*, London, Dent.

sack at Albury in Australia. Identity could not be established and the police circulated photographs of plaster casts of the jaws along with a description of the fillings which had been inserted in the teeth. For ten years the body remained unidentified, but, after a lengthy inquest in 1944, identity was proved when a dentist in Sydney described the work he had carried out which was identical with the fillings found in the teeth of the corpse.

The reason for the extraordinary delay in establishing identity was that, in the statement circulated by the police, some fillings had been omitted in error, thus giving a false record of the dental work which had been performed.[1]

viii] *By crown and bridge restorations in the mouth*. Because of the greater scope for originality in the design and construction of crowns and bridges, it would be reasonable to suppose that restorations by such means would provide evidence of identity even more valuable than that supplied by fillings in the teeth. The paucity of recorded cases is therefore somewhat surprising, only two cases being known to the authors.

Curnock[2] describes how a London dentist was able to establish the identity of a body found in a harbour in New Zealand. He sent a description of the method he had employed, some time previously, in repairing a Richmond Crown for the person and investigation revealed in the body a crown repaired in the manner described.

Bullock[3] cites a case where in 1927, a body was found floating off Brooklyn Pier. The body had been immersed for over eight months but it was identified by the bridge work in the mouth which was traced to the dentist who had made it. The dentist gave the name and address of the mother of his patient and she eventually identified the body as that of her daughter.

## B. Evidence Furnished by Jaws

In three ways the jaws may offer evidence helpful in identification; they may present some peculiarity of shape; they may show varying degrees of absorption depending on the extraction of teeth, and jaws may be compared with models made by a dentist for the purpose of fitting artificial dentures.

From the point of view of its importance in forensic dentistry, one of the earliest cases occurred in American in 1850.

Webster, the professor of chemistry in Harvard University, was arrested following the disappearance of Dr. Parkman, one of his colleagues with whom he was known to be on terms which were anything but friendly. He was charged with murder and at the trial it was alleged that he had killed

---

[1] CLELAND, J. B. (1944), 'Teeth and Bites in History, Literature, Forensic Medicine and otherwise', *Aust. J. dent.*, **48**, p. 107.

[2] CURNOCK, G. L. (1928), *Brit. dent. J.*, **49**, p. 492.

[3] BULLOCK, F. (1932), 'Dental Jurisprudence', *Brit. dent. J.*, **53** (1), p. 508.

Parkman and had attempted to get rid of the body in a furnace in his chemical laboratory. From the ashes of the furnace there were retrieved numerous small pieces of jaw bone, three blocks of artificial teeth and some melted gold. When the pieces of bone were assembled, they were found to comprise most of one half of the lower jaw and to *reveal a peculiar shape in the alveolar portion of the bone*. The deceased's dentist testified that he had recently made new artificial dentures for Dr. Parkman and that the *peculiar conformation of the jaw had presented some difficulty in their construction*. He also demonstrated that the reconstructed lower jaw corresponded exactly with the model of Parkman's jaw which was in his possession. The remains of the artificial denture retrieved from the furnace also played an important part in the evidence given at the trial which ended in a verdict of 'Guilty' and Webster was sentenced to death. It is doubtful whether, in the absence of the dental evidence, that verdict would or could have been reached.[1]

A somewhat remarkable case is reported from Australia where in 1923 the remains of a decomposed body were identified in great part on the dental evidence.

In describing this case, Cleland[2] states: 'The teeth were missing but the jaws showed that the deceased had worn upper and lower dentures, and expert examination of the alveolar ridges of the jaws disclosed that they were not evenly absorbed, indicating intermittent extraction of teeth over a period of years. By checking the dental history of the murdered girl and comparing it with the evidence of the remains, the recorded extractions were found to agree precisely with the ridge absorptions both as to locality and age.'

In *Rex* v. *Dobkin* the importance of the dental evidence, by which alone identity of the victim was proved, has been referred to (page 175). The shape of the victim's upper jaw was one of the dental details of importance.

On both sides the posterior part of the jaw showed a marked enlargement. Mr. Kopkin, the dentist who had attended the deceased, drew a plan of the jaw showing the bilateral enlargement towards both the midline and the cheek and this was found to correspond exactly with the jaw of the victim's skull.

Even though there may be no abnormality of shape in the jaws, they may furnish valuable evidence, as is illustrated in the following case.

A wild-game hunter was killed and buried in Central Africa. In due course application was made to the Probate Court for assumption of death but the petition was dismissed as the evidence of identity was insufficient to satisfy the Court. The body, now reduced to a skeleton, was subsequently brought to England and the jaws were compared with models in the possession of the dentist who was known to have made artificial dentures for the deceased. The comparison satisfied the Probate Court regarding the deceased's identity.[3]

[1] DILNOT, G. (1928), *The Trial of Professor Webster, Famous Trials Series*, London, Bles.
[2] CLELAND, J. B. (1944), *Aust. J. dent.*, 48, p. 107.
[3] MAGGS, W. A. (1932), 'Arnold Rogers and his Sons—a family of dentists', *Dental Record*, 52, p. 291.

## C. Evidence Furnished by Marks made by Teeth

Instances are reported from time to time of criminals who are brought to justice following their identification by marks which their teeth have made on articles of food and, less frequently in this country, on the skin of the victim of a sadistic assault. Keith Simpson[1] records a case in the latter category.

> In 1949, a young woman was found dead at the rear of the police station in Tunbridge Wells. She had been strangled and violently assaulted and there were tooth marks on the exposed right breast. The woman's husband was detained on suspicion and an impression taken of his incisor teeth. The cast which was constructed was compared with the marks on the breast. When they were found to coincide, the suspect was arrested. He was subsequently tried and convicted of murder.

## D. Evidence of Age Furnished by the Teeth

Estimation of age from an examination of human remains is sometimes of primary importance for it may be an essential step in proving identity and teeth may furnish evidence enabling that to be made. Illustrative cases occur from time to time but none is more illuminating than that of *Rex* v. *Ruxton*.[2]

> In September 1935, there were reported missing from Lancaster two women, the wife of Dr. Ruxton and Mary Rogerson, her maid. The doctor declared that they had left his house, and said he thought they had gone to Edinburgh. Two weeks later, some human remains were found in a ravine by the road-side near Moffat, some 170 miles north of Lancaster. Further search resulted in the discovery of more human fragments, some being found nine miles away. In all, 68 portions were discovered and, when assembled, they were found to represent parts of two female bodies.
>
> Severe mutilation had been carried out to defy identity, the victim's hands, scalp, eyes, ears and some teeth being removed. Because of this, it was realized at the outset that identification would be a matter of great difficulty, but the forensic experts succeeded in proving that the bodies were those of Mrs. Ruxton and Mary Rogerson though there was nothing at that stage in the investigation to connect the bodies with the missing women from Lancaster. The first step which led to identification was the assessment of age of the victims and this was determined largely by the dental evidence available. This was as follows: In Head No. 1

$$8 \text{ teeth } \frac{64 \mid 6}{76 \mid 567} \text{ had been extracted some time previously (the gums had healed completely)}$$

---

[1] SIMPSON, K. (1951), 'Dental Evidence in the Reconstruction of Crime', *Brit. dent. J.*, **91**, p. 234.

[2] WILSON, G. H. (1936), *The Trial of Buck Ruxton, Notable British Trials*, London, Hodge.

```
          1│1
2 teeth ──┼── had been recently extracted (open sockets with no blood
                clots)

          2│235
5 teeth ──┼── displayed carious cavities
          4│

          │
1 tooth ──┼── showed mottling of the enamel
          1│
```

4 teeth unerupted

There were no fillings in the teeth and there was no evidence that a denture had been worn.

X-ray films of the unerupted wisdom teeth showed that the roots were not fully calcified and Dr. Hutchinson, the dental expert in the case, estimated from this evidence the age to be between eighteen and twenty.

It was subsequently ascertained that Mary Rogerson was twenty years of age and, at the trial, two dentists testified that they had extracted four teeth in 1932 and two in 1934.

In Head No. 2 the dental condition was as follows:

```
            864│2346
15 teeth ──────┼────── had been extracted some time previously
           7653│5678

          75321│17
14 teeth ──────┼────── had been recently extracted
            421│1234

               │58
2 roots ───────┼────── were present

               │
1 tooth ───────┼────── was present which was very carious
              8│
```

All the wisdom teeth had erupted and two of them had been extracted some time previously. The crown of the lower right third molar was almost completely destroyed by caries and all that remained of the upper tooth was a loose root. It was therefore a safe assumption that the age in this case was over twenty-five. Mrs. Ruxton was thirty-five at the time of her death.

It was also assumed that an artificial denture had been worn by the deceased. It was unlikely that she would have tolerated a gap in the front of her mouth; Dr. Ruxton, in the description he gave to the police of his missing wife, said: 'Wears false teeth left upper jaw, gold clasp shows when smiling'; the root of the upper premolar tooth had the appearance of being ground level with the gum with an abrasive wheel as if the tooth had broken from caries or abrasion as a result of a denture clasp around it.

No artificial denture was ever found nor was a model of the mouth discovered in the possession of any dentist. If either had been discovered and found to correspond with the mouth of the victim, the question of identity would have been settled beyond all doubt.

The dental evidence was nevertheless important for it was proved at the trial to correspond in every detail with the history given by the dentists who had attended the deceased. It therefore assisted in establishing identity. Other factors which satisfied the jury included marks on clothing, evidence of a bunion, casts of feet fitting shoes worn by the women and, for the first time in any trial, the superimposing of photographs of the skulls on life-size photographs of the dead women.[1]

Dr. Ruxton was found guilty of murder and condemned to death.

## E. Evidence Furnished by Artificial Dentures

As has been pointed out on page 169, the evidence supplied by artificial dentures is likely to *prove* identity only when there are distinctive marks or features on the dentures or when they can be shown to fit a model of the jaw for which they have been constructed.

Numerous cases are recorded where evidence from artificial dentures has *assisted* in identification. Thus a dentist, when shown an artificial denture discovered on a dead body in Yorkshire said, 'I most definitely identify it as the denture I made for F . . . C . . . I recognize it by the repair I did.'[2] A dentist in London was able to recognize dentures he had made for a patient who was killed in a street accident, and this he did by the special type of gum-section teeth he had employed.[3] In the Carron murder case in Australia dental evidence helped to identify the victim whose body had been destroyed by fire. Careful search of the ashes was rewarded by the discovery of some human and some 'diatoric' artificial teeth and a dentist testified that he had made for the victim a denture and had used this type of tooth in its construction.[4]

Following the *Noronic* disaster (page 178), evidence obtained from artificial dentures of the victims was carefully tabulated and proved to be of great assistance in the general plan adopted for the mass identification. In at least two instances the denture evidence was sufficient to prove identity: in one because of the peculiar construction of the denture and in the other because of the unusual type of artificial tooth used in the making of the denture.

In the Parkman case (page 180), the outstanding features of the dental evidence were the peculiar shape of one half of the lower jaw and the details of the prosthetic appliance which had been made for Dr. Parkman a short time before his death. Only part of the artificial denture was found but it was sufficient to prove that it had been made to fit the peculiarly shaped jaw and the models in possession of the

[1] GLAISTER, J. and BRASH, J. C. (1937), *Medico-legal Aspects of the Ruxton Trial*, Edinburgh, Livingstone.
[2] Newspaper report, *Daily Telegraph*, 26 May 1939.
[3] Report (1945), *Brit. dent. J.*, **28**, p. 76.
[4] CLELAND, J. B. (1944), *Aust. J. dent.*, **48**, p. 107.

dentist. The latter further stated that his patient had experienced difficulty in wearing the appliance because of interference with his tongue, so that he had had to grind away a portion of the denture. There was evidence of this grinding in the portion of artificial denture which was found, and this added further proof of the identity of the victim. The Parkman case remains an outstanding one in the field of forensic dentistry, superseded in importance, from the point of view of 'denture' evidence, only by the case of *Rex* v. *Haigh*,[1] where identity was proved on the evidence of artificial dentures alone.

John George Haigh and Mrs. Olive Durand-Deacon were two of the guests living in an hotel in Kensington. Outside the hotel they were seen together on an afternoon in February 1949 but, from that moment, Mrs. Durand-Deacon disappeared. The police were informed and Haigh, whose past history revealed him as a bad character, was questioned about the disappearance of the wealthy widow. At the fourth interview he became boastful, like many another criminal before him, and, though duly cautioned, admitted having killed Mrs. Durand-Deacon, adding, 'I have destroyed her with acid. You will find the sludge that remains at Leopold Road. Every trace has gone. How can you prove murder if there is no body?'

At the address indicated there was found a quantity of sludge and ample evidence that a body had been dissolved in sulphuric acid. Careful sifting of the debris brought to light three human gall stones, part of a left foot, some eroded fragments of human bones and a full upper and lower artificial denture. The Crown Pathologist was able to state only that the remains were human and those of a female and it fell to a dental surgeon to prove that the remains were those of Mrs. Durand-Deacon. Miss Mayo showed at the trial that the dentures fitted the models in her possession which she had made two years before; stated that the patient had been an exacting one, anxious about her appearance so that the dentures had required building up on several occasions, and demonstrated how the plates had been altered. Referring to the dentures, Miss Mayo said in evidence, 'I could describe them from my notes before I saw them.' This unshakable evidence was accepted as clear proof that Haigh's victim on this occasion (there were probably others) was Mrs. Durand-Deacon and he was found guilty of her murder.

Without the evidence furnished by the dentures, identity of the victim could not have been proved and it was fortunate that they were found at the time they were, for they were made of acrylic resin material which is not resistant to acid. If Haigh had not made, when he did, the statement to the police and, if examination of the sludge had not been undertaken when it was, it is probable that the invaluable dental evidence would have disappeared. As it was, the dentures were discoloured, indicating the commencement of attack by acid, and they were found fourteen days after the disappearance of Mrs. Durand-Deacon. Had they not been found then, they might well have suffered the same fate as the body itself for an acrylic resin denture when immersed in strong sulphuric acid will completely disappear in about three weeks.

✱     ✱     ✱

[1] SIMPSON, K. (1950), *Rex* v. *John George Haigh*, *Medico-legal Journal*, **43**, p. 38.

## 7. THE APPLICATION OF FORENSIC DENTISTRY IN IDENTIFICATION

If due recognition is to be given, as it deserves to be, to the part which dental evidence can play in crime investigation and in identification generally, consideration should be given to the expert examination and report, the recording of details by general dental practitioners and statistical possibilities.

## A. The Expert Examination and Report

When a dentist is called upon to assist in identification, he should bear in mind the variety of ways in which dental evidence can be of value. After a careful examination of the subject, whether a living person, a dead body or human remains, he should include in his report the following:

i] The number and names of the teeth and roots present.

ii] The number and names of the teeth missing.

iii] An estimate of how long the missing teeth have been absent.

iv] The position of any extra teeth.

v] The general arrangement of the teeth—whether regular or irregular, spaced or crowded, prominent, rotated or tilted.

vi] Peculiarities in the size and shape of the teeth—whether any are extra large, peg-shaped, notched or hypoplastic.

vii] The general condition of the teeth—whether there is discoloration, mottling or tartar deposit; broken teeth; attrition or abrasion; carious cavities.

viii] Description of dental work performed—the position and nature of fillings and inlays, of crowns and bridges and of artificial dentures.

ix] X-ray findings to reveal the presence of buried roots, unerupted teeth, other evidence of pathological conditions and the degree of calcification as an indication of age.

x] The shape and condition of the jaw bones with special reference to the presence and degree of alveolar absorption.

xi] Estimate of age from observation of degree of calcification or extent of changes in adult teeth.

## B. Recording of Details by Dental Practitioners

It is obvious that the expert's evidence alone may be of little value without the co-operation of the general dental practitioner, at least in those cases where dental treatment of any kind has been undertaken, and they are vastly in the majority. If every dentist made and preserved a careful record of the dental state of each patient whom he treated and recorded equally carefully the nature of the treatment given and if, in addition, he marked in some distinctive way every artificial denture which he provided, the value of dental evidence would thereby be greatly enhanced. This ideal, from a forensic point of view, has become more possible of achievement by the introduction of the National Health Service Acts for the Regulations made under them require the dentist to chart and record work done for all patients treated within the Scheme.

## C. Statistical Possibilities

Welty and Glasgow[1] have suggested that, by employing the modern method of statistical control, dental data might be used to establish a complete method of identification. An example of this modern system is the Hollerith System of the British Tabulating Company. Briefly, the system consists of i] transferring to a special card such details as may be considered necessary, for example, missing teeth, the position of fillings and so forth; ii] punching, by means of a mechanical key puncher, holes in the card to respond to the information on the card; iii] the arrangement of the punched cards in sequence by a sorting machine; and iv] the collation or selection by special machines of particulars of any desired information.

There would appear to be little doubt that a system such as the Hollerith System is capable of increasing very materially the value of dental characteristics as a means of identification. Its adoption by some central agency might lead to the universal use of the dental tissues in this direction and revolutionize the whole business of identification.

[1] WELTY, L. G. and GLASGOW, R. R. (1946), *J. Amer. Dent. Ass.*, **33**, p. 714.

## PART III

# Income Tax and Superannuation for the Dentist

# CHAPTER XIV

# Income Tax for the Dentist

## I. INTRODUCTION

The income of a dentist may be taxed in one of two ways:

1) By deduction at the source.
2) By direct assessment.

Wherever possible the Inland Revenue prefer the former method as it is a sure, quick method of gathering in the tax. It is economical in operation and reduces tax evasion to a minimum.

1) *Deduction of tax at source.* With a few exceptions, interest, dividends and annuities are normally received less a deduction for income tax, and from 6 April 1944, when the 'Pay As You Earn' system commenced, salaries and wages were brought into this category also. It is worth noting that, where the tax should have been deducted but has not been deducted, the person receiving the interest may be assessed under Case III of Schedule D (*Glamorgan Quarter Sessions* v. *Wilson* (1910) 1 K.B. 725).

2) *Direct Assessment.* On the other hand, a dentist in practice is taxed by direct assessment on the profits he earns from his practice, as well as any untaxed interest he may receive from War Loan, Defence Bonds, and all interest and dividends of any amount derived from United Kingdom Government securities held on the Post Office Register. The same procedure is adopted where interest has been received from a deposit account with a Joint Stock Bank and discount on Treasury Bills. From 1956/7 interest in excess of £15 in any year received from the Post Office Savings Bank or from a deposit in the ordinary department of a Trustee Savings Bank is directly assessed. All interest received from the Special Investment Department of the Trustee Savings Bank is taxable in like manner.

In assessing income, the Board of Inland Revenue do not in every case take the actual income of the fiscal year ending 5 April. In certain circumstances the income of the preceding year may be used. A dentist's *Statutory Income* is therefore arrived at by taking the actual income arising in the tax year from certain sources and the income arising in the year preceding the year of assessment from other sources, according to the nature of the income, and then deducting annual charges such as mortgage interest, ground rents, etc.

## 2. ALLOWANCES AND RELIEF

No matter how he is taxed, the dentist, like all tax-payers, is entitled to certain allowances and relief. These allowances, with the exception of Earned Income Relief, are not granted automatically. They must be claimed, and it rests with the dentist to fill in the appropriate claim sections in his Income Tax Return form. These allowances are set out briefly as follows:

## 1. Earned Income Relief

A dentist is allowed as a deduction from his statutory total income a sum equivalent to two-ninths of his earned income up to a maximum earned income of £4,005. In addition there is an allowance of one-ninth of earned income in excess of £4,005 on a further £5,940. This means that the limit at which earned income relief ceases is £9,945. The maximum amount of earned income relief will be £890 at the full rate and £660 at the half rate, making a total of £1,550.

If his total income includes any earned income of his wife additional relief will be given amounting to seven-ninths of the wife's personal earnings up to a maximum of seven-ninths of £180. Earned income includes:

*a*) Remuneration from employment, including the wages received by a married woman who acts as her husband's receptionist, secretary, etc.

*b*) Pensions, including old age and widow's pensions granted to survivors of a deceased person in respect of past services of the deceased.

*c*) Director's remuneration.

*d*) Income from property taxable under Schedule A where the right to occupy the property forms part of the emoluments of the office or employment.

*e*) Profits from a practice.

*Notes regarding earned income.* The following points should be noted with regard to earned income relief:

*a*) The share of profits due to a sleeping partner is unearned income, but very slight action on his part will be sufficient to entitle him to relief.

*b*) Each dentist in a partnership receives relief up to the limit of £1,550. This means that the aggregate earned income relief in the firm's assessment may exceed £1,550.

*c*) Limited companies do not receive relief.

*d*) It was decided in the case of *Frame* v. *Farrand* (1928) 13 T.C. 861, that, where expenses are properly deductible from remuneration, the earned income relief must be calculated on the net amount of the remuneration after deducting allowable expenses.

## 2. Age Relief

In substitution for earned income relief, where the dentist or his wife, who must be living with him and maintained by him, is sixty-five years of age or over at any time during the year of assessment, he may deduct from his statutory total income an amount equal to two-ninths of his total income, whether earned or not, provided the total income from all sources does not exceed £800. Marginal relief is given where the income slightly exceeds £800 per annum, in which case he can elect to pay:

1) The amount of tax payable assuming his income is £800, plus
2) Eleven-twentieths of the amount by which his income exceeds £800.

The sum remaining after deducting from the total statutory income, the amount of the earned income relief or age relief, whichever is appropriate, is known as the Assessable Income.

## 3. Age Exemption

In 1957 the Government felt that some special relief should be given to persons over sixty-five years of age with small incomes, and the Finance Act of that year gave certain old persons exemption from Income Tax altogether. These provisions have since been amended on more than one occasion. The present position is that for a single person who is sixty-five years of age or over exemption is given if his total income does not exceed £275. A married man is exempt where either the husband or the wife is sixty-five or over and their total income is not more than £440. A system of marginal relief also operates here. Where the income is slightly in excess of the figures mentioned, the liability is restricted to one-half of the amount by which the income exceeds £275 or £440 as the case may be.

## 4. Small Incomes Relief

When a dentist is not entitled to Age Relief and his total income does not exceed £300, whether earned or unearned, he is entitled to an allowance of two-ninths of his income. Here again there is marginal relief. If the income exceeds £300 but not £405, the tax payable is not to exceed the total of *a*) tax on £300 plus *b*) two-fifths of the excess over £300.

## 5. Personal Relief

The allowance given to an unmarried dentist or a separated or divorced person or a widower is now £140. The allowance for a married man is £240 provided his wife is living with him or is wholly maintained by him during the year of assessment.

## 6. Child Relief

A dentist is given an allowance in respect of each child born during the tax year, each child under sixteen at the beginning of the tax year, and each child over sixteen who is receiving full-time instruction at any university, college, school, or other educational establishment, in or out of the United Kingdom. The allowance is also given where a child is undergoing training by an employer for any trade, profession or vocation, for a period of not less than two years. This relief is given on the following scale:

    i] Child not over the age of eleven                   £100
    ii] Child over the age of eleven but not over sixteen   £125
    iii] Child over sixteen years of age               £150

If a child's income in his own right, excluding income from any scholarship or bursary, or other similar educational endowment, exceeds £100 per annum, the parent is not entitled to a child allowance for him. Children include stepchildren. In the case of an adopted child, the allowance applies only if he is maintained by and in the custody of the taxpayer, and provided the allowance is not claimed by the child's own parents. Incapacitated children who are over sixteen years of age and not receiving full-time instruction are treated as dependents for whom the allowance of £75 may be claimed.

## 7. Relief for Dependent Relatives

If the dentist maintains at his own expense a relative of his own or of his wife, and if the relative is incapacitated by old age or other infirmity from maintaining himself or herself, he is entitled to an allowance of £75 for each such relative. In addition, if his widowed mother or mother-in-law, whether incapacitated or not, is maintained by him, a similar allowance is granted. For this relief to be granted in full the relative's income must not exceed £210 per annum, but it will be partially granted if the income is between £135 and £210 per annum.

## 8. Relief for Daughter's Services

Should the dentist maintain a daughter who lives with him because he is old or infirm he may claim an allowance of £40.

## 9. Relief for Housekeeper

A widower (or a widow) may claim relief of £75 in respect of a female relative of his or of his deceased wife, if that relative resides with him as housekeeper or looks after children, for whom the child allowance is given. If it is a stranger who acts as housekeeper or looks after children, it was held in the case of *MacFarlane* v. *Hubert* 19 T.C. 660 that there must be a bona fide relationship of employer and employee. It should be noted that, in accordance with *Kliman* v. *Winkworth* 17 T.C. 569, a separated or divorced person cannot obtain the allowance.

Relief of £75 may also be claimed where the claimant is unmarried and has his widowed mother or other female relative living with him to care for his brothers and sisters, for whom the child allowance is obtainable.

A man who is in receipt of the lower personal allowance of £140 is entitled to an additional allowance of £75 for a female person resident with him and maintained or employed by him to look after a child for whom he receives the child allowance. A married man may claim this relief of £75 if his wife is totally incapacitated throughout the year of assessment. A similar claim may be made by a woman who is incapacitated throughout the year or is in full-time employment and therefore unable to look after her children.

Section 17 of the Finance Act 1960 introduces a new allowance to widows and others who are entitled to claim child allowance, but who are not entitled to

    *a*) the Housekeeper allowance;

    *b*) relief to an unmarried person having a younger brother or sister;

    *c*) relief for a female person employed or maintained to take charge of children.

The amount of this new relief is £40. If, of course, a claim for the higher allowance of £75 is competent, it is advantageous for that claim to be made rather than the claim under this section. The object of this section is to give some measure of relief where the condition of residence cannot be satisfied.

## 10. Reduced Rate Relief

The first £360 of taxable income is liable to tax at rates less than the standard rate, as follows:

> On the first £60 of taxable income 1/9 in the £.
> On the next £150 of taxable income 4/3 in the £.
> On the next £150 of taxable income 6/3 in the £.

Thereafter tax at the full standard rate of 7/9 in the £ is payable.

In addition, similar relief is given against a wife's earned income after deducting the total earned income relief due on her earned income and any unabsorbed balance of her husband's allowances, other than reduced rate relief.

Thus the following figures show that a married woman may earn up to £643 per annum before tax is payable at the full standard rate:

|  |  | £ | s. | d. |  | £ | s. | d. |
|---|---|---|---|---|---|---|---|---|
| Earned Income |  |  |  |  |  | 643 | 0 | 0 |
| Deduct: |  |  |  |  |  |  |  |  |
| a) Earned Income Relief ⅔ths. of £643 = | 143 | 0 | 0 |  |  |  |  |  |
| b) Wife's Earned Income Relief (Maximum) ⅞ths. of £180 | = 140 | 0 | 0 |  |  |  |  |  |
|  |  |  |  |  |  | 283 | 0 | 0 |
|  |  |  |  |  |  | £360 | 0 | 0 |

|  | £ | s. | d. |
|---|---|---|---|
| Tax payable: |  |  |  |
| £60 @ 1/9 in the £ | 5 | 5 | 0 |
| £150 @ 4/3 in the £ | 31 | 17 | 6 |
| £150 @ 6/3 in the £ | 46 | 17 | 6 |
| £360 | £ 84 | 0 | 0 |

## 11. Life Assurance Relief

If a dentist has life assurance policies on his own life or on that of his wife, or pays premiums for a deferred annuity, there is relief due on the premium subject to certain restrictions.

1) The premium on any policy must not exceed 7 per cent. of the capital sum assured.

2) The allowable premiums must not exceed one-sixth of the total income.

3) If the policy was taken out before 22 June 1916, the relief is a deduction of tax at the following rates on the total of allowable premiums:

Where total income does not exceed £1,000—Half Standard Rate.

Where total income does not exceed £2,000—Three-quarters Standard Rate.

Where total income exceeds £2,000—Full Standard Rate.

4) For policies made after 22 June 1916, the allowance is as follows:

*a)* If the total allowable premiums do not exceed £25—£10 or the amount of the premiums, whichever is less.

*b)* If the total allowable premiums exceed £25—two-fifths of the amount of the premiums.

Receipts for the premiums should be kept in readiness to support the claims if required by the tax office.

### 3. THE TAX SCHEDULES

If a dentist is taxed by direct assessment, his income is classified according to Schedules. A very brief account of these schedules is given below and Schedules A, D and E are considered in greater detail on pages 198 to 213.

1) Schedule A relates to the income from the *ownership* of land and buildings.

2) Schedule B deals with the profits from the *occupation* of lands.

3) Schedule C relates to income from Government Stocks taxed at the source where payment is entrusted to an agent.

4) Schedule D takes charge of profits from trade or business including dental practices and any other annual profits or gains which do not come under any other schedule.

5) Schedule E covers income of all employed persons accruing as salary, fees or commission.

Before an assessment is made the dentist generally receives an Income Tax Return form. This form should be completed with every care and with reasonable expedition. Heavy penalties can be enforced if it is ignored.

If a person has income liable to tax, he must by law give notice to

ODH

the Inspector of Taxes even if no Return Form has been received. In the case of a practice the Inspector invariably asks for a copy of the Balance Sheet and Accounts to assist him in making the correct assessment, and is empowered by Section 31 of the Income Tax Act, 1952 to demand the production of such documents when that appears to the Commissioners of Inland Revenue to be necessary.

After the return form has been submitted, an assessment notice is issued to the taxpayer showing the tax due to be paid. The person assessed has the right of appeal if the assessment is not, in his opinion, correct. It is most important that as soon as the notice is received its accuracy should be checked with the details already supplied on the return form and any agreed computations based on the accounts and balance sheet. All allowances should be verified likewise. If the dentist decides to appeal against his assessment, he must give notice of his intention within thirty days from the date of his assessment notice. At the same time he must state the grounds for the appeal, which may be that the assessment is an estimate and not in accordance with the facts or that there is an overcharge. It is not sufficient for the dentist to state that he does not agree with the assessment; he must give his reasons.

On the other hand, if an Inspector finds that a taxpayer has been undercharged or that he has obtained allowances to which he is not entitled, he may make an additional assessment at any time not later than six years after the end of the year to which the assessment relates.

## A. Schedule A

Under Schedule A, tax is levied on the net annual value of lands, houses, buildings, etc., owned by a dentist in the United Kingdom. The gross annual value is based on the annual sum for which the property would be let if the landlord carried out all the repairs and the tenant paid the rates. The net annual value on which the tax is charged is arrived at by deducting from the gross annual value the Statutory Allowance for Repairs, viz:

> Lands—one eighth.
> Houses up to £40 annual value—one fourth.
> Houses of annual value £40 to £50—£10.
> Houses of annual value £50 to £100—one fifth.
> Houses of annual value over £100—£20 plus one-sixth of the excess over £100.

The tax is due in full on 1 January and is payable in the first instance by the occupier, as the net annual value is regarded as his statutory income. The occupier may then reimburse himself by deducting the tax paid from the next payment of rent. The landlord is bound to allow this deduction against the production of the official receipt. He is not compelled, however, to allow this deduction from any but the next payments of rent (*Hill* v. *Kirshenstein* (1920) 3 K.B. 556).

Where a change of occupier takes place the assessment is made on the occupier for the time being, and he may deduct the tax from the rent paid in the normal way. It should be remembered, however, that an occupier who relinquishes occupation remains liable for the Schedule A tax due for the period of his occupation so far as this tax should be ultimately paid by him.

In the event of a change in the ownership of a property, the usual custom is for the tax payable under Schedule A to be apportioned so that the person who pays the tax, or suffers it by deduction from rent, bears only the tax for his term of ownership.

Building Society interest payable is usually paid in full without tax being deducted, and the Schedule A tax otherwise payable on the property will be reduced by tax on the interest so paid. Should the interest exceed the net annual value, relief on the excess is allowable against other tax payable by the borrower.

Other mortgage interest payable on property should have tax deducted at the standard rate. Any excess of such tax over the Schedule A tax paid on the property can be set against tax paid on other income. If this is impossible, the excess has to be accounted for to the Revenue Authorities who will make an additional assessment to recover it.

Empty houses are exempt from Schedule A tax so long as no rent is being paid and all furniture removed.

If the owner of property finds that the cost of maintenance, repairs, insurance, and management of the property according to the average yearly expenditure for the five preceding years exceeds the statutory allowance, he may claim repayment of tax on the excess. The tax-payer must take the initiative and provide the inspector with vouchers and receipts to support the claim. Outside painting, interior decoration, repairs to burst water pipes and electrical wiring, the replacement of a worn-out fireplace, an accountant's charges for preparing a claim, are all allowable. Expenditure of a capital nature or expenditure made to effect an improvement is not allowed. No repayment of tax will be made in respect of any expenditure which has been otherwise allowed as a deduction in computing income for tax purposes: e.g., if the cost of repairs has been charged against practice income assessed under Schedule D; nor can the tax recoverable exceed that paid under

Schedule A in respect of the property in question. *An example will clarify the position.*

| | |
|---|---:|
| House—Gross annual value | £160 |
| Statutory repairs allowable: | |
| £20 plus ⅛th. of excess over £100 | 30 |
| Net annual value 1961–2 | £130 |
| Allowable repairs, etc.: | |
| 1956–7 | £125 |
| 1957–8 | 63 |
| 1958–9 | 10 |
| 1959–60 | 44 |
| 1960–1 | 108 |
| | 5/ 350 |
| | 70 |
| Deduct statutory allowance | 30 |
| Maintenance claim, 1961–2 | £40 |

Thus if tax has been paid on the net annual value of £130, repayment will be made of £15. 10s. (being £40 at 7/9). If, however, tax has not been paid the Schedule A assessment will be reduced to tax on £90 for 1961–2.

Where property has been recently acquired, it is the practice to allow the previous owner's figures to be brought into the average. If details of such expenditure are not available or if a maintenance claim is made for an entirely new property, the present owner may be permitted to adopt one of the following concessionary alternatives on the condition that he applies the same basis consistently year by year until a five years' average is obtained.

1) He may base his claim on a five years' average in the usual way, the excess expenditure for the years prior to ownership being treated as 'nil'; or

2) He may claim any excess of the actual expenditure over the statutory allowance each year until a five years' average is obtained. This latter method is the preferable one provided the inspector of taxes allows the concession.

Where dilapidated property has been purchased and large sums expended on repairs, the Revenue usually insist on the average basis only, the previous owners' expenditure if not known being taken as 'nil'. *The Law Shipping Case* (1923) 12 T.C. 621, is sometimes quoted as an authority for excluding from maintenance claims expenditure on property bought in a dilapidated condition, but this is open to question.

## B. Schedule E

If a dentist holds a salaried appointment or receives director's fees, he is taxed under Schedule E. It is under this schedule that assessments are made on all employees in respect of wages, salaries, bonuses, commissions and generally speaking on all remuneration arising from any employment. Pensions and annuities resulting from employment do not escape.

The following receipts, however, are not liable to tax:

1) Wound and disability pensions.
2) Pensions granted to war widows in respect of their children.
3) War gratuities.
4) Post-war credits.
5) Sick pay, strike pay, unemployment pay, etc., received from a trade union or friendly society.
6) Certain payments under the National Health Service (Super annuation) Regulations, 1961.

   *a*) Lump sum retiring allowance (Regulation 8(1) (b) and 8(2) (b).
   *b*) Injury allowance (Regulation 10(1)).
   *c*) Short service gratuity (Regulation 11).
   *d*) Death gratuity (Regulation 13).
   *e*) Gratuity payable to a widow of an officer (Regulation 10 (3)).
   (The annual allowance paid to a widow under Regulation 10 (3) is, however, subject to tax.)

Where a dentist, assessable under Schedule E, is obliged to incur expenses which are *wholly, exclusively and necessarily* disbursed in the performance of the duties of his office, he is permitted to deduct such expenses from the emoluments received from that office. A definite distinction is drawn between those expenses incurred *in* the performance of the duties and those incurred *in order* to perform them. From this it will be understood why no deduction is permissible for travelling expenses of employees from their residences to the premises of the employer. Should an employee hold an office in one town and a separate employment in another town, the costs of journeying between the two offices are not allowed. Each employment commences when the employee arrives at the place of employment (*Ricketts* v. *Colquhoun* (1926) A.C.1).

In the case of *Andrews* v. *Astley* (1924) 8 T.C. 589, it was held that even where, owing to a shortage of houses, an employee finds it necessary to live at a considerable distance from his place of employment, his travelling expenses are not allowed as a deduction.

Certain items of expenditure are dealt with specifically in the Finance Act, 1958. This Act is an important one for many professional people because it deals with the fees and subscriptions payable to professional bodies, learned societies, and other similar organizations.

Under section 16 of this Act a subscription to a professional organization is an allowable expense under Schedule E provided that the activities of that body are solely or mainly directed to the following objects:

*a*) The advancement or spreading of knowledge (whether generally or among persons belonging to the same or similar professions or occupying the same or similar positions);

*b*) the maintenance or improvement of standards of conduct and competence among the members of any profession;

*c*) the indemnification or protection of members of any profession against claims in respect of liabilities incurred by them in the exercise of their profession.

Under sub-section 3 of section 16 it is laid down that if the activities of any organization approved under this section are to any significant extent directed to objects other than those mentioned above, only part of the annual subscription may be deducted as an allowable expense. In other words, the Inspector of Taxes will not grant relief on any portion of the subscription spent on what might be termed 'trade union' activities, such as negotiations in connexion with remuneration and conditions of service unless these activities form a minor part of the association's activities. The Board of Inland Revenue may assess the extent of such activities. They have decided that in respect of the British Dental Association nine-tenths of the annual subscription will rank for Income Tax relief. This compares with eight-tenths allowed for the subscription to the British Medical Association.

The Finance Act, 1958 is also important because it deals with certain statutory registration fees which are listed in the fifth schedule. This list includes the fee payable in respect of the registration and retention of a name in the Dentists Register or in a roll or record kept for a class of ancillary dental workers.

As from 6 April 1944, the 'Pay As You Earn' system came into operation, and applied to all emoluments assessable to income tax under Schedule E. This was extended to members of H.M. Forces for 1947–8 onwards.

All employers who make payments to their employees are required to deduct the appropriate amount of tax from each payment by reference to Official Tax Tables. These are constructed to ensure that the tax deducted from payments to date from the previous 5 April corresponds with the proportion to date of the year's tax liability of the recipient, after taking into account all allowances and reliefs due.

The employer is notified by the Inspector of Taxes of the Code Number applicable to each of his employees, and, by linking up each code number with the Official Tax Tables, he knows what tax must be deducted each week or month, as the case may be, from each of his employees. Where the employee has no other employment and his rate of payment is less than £3. 15s. per week (£15. 10s. per month) no tax is deductible. If the employee has other employment this limit is reduced to £1 per week (£4 per month).

The employer must keep a tax deduction card for each employee. These cards when completed are sent to the Collector of Taxes within fourteen days after the end of the fiscal year (5 April).

The employer is required also to give each employee a certificate (Form P.60) showing the total remuneration paid and the total tax deducted therefrom during the year. For further information regarding the duties of the employer or special circumstances reference should be made to *The Employer's Guide to Pay as you Earn* which is available from the local Inspector of Taxes.

The employee, on the other hand, has certain responsibilities also. A Notice of Coding is received each year from the Inspector of Taxes. As this has to be prepared in advance of the year of assessment it is essential that the employee should notify the Inspector immediately his circumstances change, so that his code number may be rectified. The employer cannot alter the tax deduction until he is so authorized by the Inspector. When the notice of coding is received the employee should make sure that all the allowances and reliefs to which he is entitled are shown on the notice. If there are figures he does not understand he should call on or write to the Inspector about his difficulties. Once each year the employee receives a notice from the Inspector showing how his total tax liability has been calculated, and the total tax which has been deducted during the year. This statement should be compared with the Form P.60 received from the employer and mentioned above.

## C. Schedule D

The sources of income assessed under Schedule D are classified into six cases as follows:

> Case I extends to all trades.
> Case II extends to all professions or vocations.
> Case III applies to profits of an uncertain annual value.
> Case IV applies to interest arising from securities outside the United Kingdom.
> Case V applies to income arising from stocks, shares, or rents or other possessions outside the United Kingdom.
> Case VI applies to annual profits or gains not falling under the other Cases of Schedule D.

Professional profits are assessed under Case II of Schedule D and (subject to special provisions regarding new and discontinued practices) the basis of assessment is the profit of the year preceding the year of assessment. Normally the profits of the practice year ending within the preceding fiscal year are taken as being the profits of the preceding year. For example, if accounts are made up annually to 30 June, the assessment for 1961–62 will be based on the profits for the year ending 30 June 1960. If, however, the accounts are for the year ended 31 March, the 1961–62 assessment is on the profits for the year to 31 March 1961. If there is no account available for exactly twelve months, or if there is more than one account during the previous year, the Board of Inland Revenue may at their discretion decide which twelve months will be taken and they may adjust the preceding year's assessment.

The following are the special rules to be observed where a new practice is commenced:

*a*) The assessment for the first tax year will be on the proportion, for the period from the start of the practice to the following 5 April, of the profits shown by the first accounts.

*b*) In the case of the second tax year:

1) Where the first accounts are for a period of twelve months the profit shown by these accounts will be the normal basis for the second year's assessment.

2) When the first accounts are for a period of less or more than twelve months, the second year's assessment will be such a proportion of the profits or losses shown by the accounts as refers to the first twelve months of the practice.

Thus, if a practice commenced on 1 June, and the first accounts were for ten months to 31 March, the assessment for the second year would be on the profits for these ten months plus two-twelfths of the following year's profits.

*c*) The basis of assessment for the third and subsequent years will be on the profits shown by the accounts for the year ended within the preceding tax year.

*Illustration*

A practice was commenced on 1 June 1959. The accounts for the year to 31 May 1960, showed a taxable profit of £600.

Assessments:

| | |
|---|---:|
| 1959–60. Actual profits from 1 June 1959 to 5 April 1960, say ten months—(see note below) ten-twelfths of £600 | £500 |
| 1960–1. Profits for one complete year from 1 June 1959 | £600 |
| 1961–2. Profits of accounting year ended in the preceding fiscal year, i.e., year to 31 May 1960 | £600 |

*Note.* Where it is necessary to apportion the profits of a practice for Income Tax purposes, it has been laid down that the apportionment shall be made by reference to the number of months or parts of a month. Thus, the proportion of ten-twelfths used above to be strictly accurate should be $\frac{9\frac{25}{30}}{12}$.

The dentist may claim that the assessments for the second and third years shall be adjusted to the actual profits of those fiscal years. He must, however, claim for both years or not at all. The claim must be made in writing to the Inspector of Taxes within seven years after the end of the second year of assessment and can be revoked within six years after the end of the third year of assessment.

As for new practices, there are also special provisions which apply where a practice is permanently discontinued. The assessment for the last tax year is adjustable to the actual profits from 6 April to the date of cessation, whether this is more or less than an assessment based on the previous year's profits. If the assessment of the tax year preceding the year of discontinuance (i.e. the penultimate year) is less than the actual apportioned profits for that tax year, an additional assessment will be made by the Inspector for the difference. No adjustment, however, is made in favour of the dentist if the assessment exceeds the actual profits.

It will be readily appreciated that the profit and loss account of a practice, normally prepared on a commercial basis, will not usually show a profits figure which will satisfy the tax authorities. The preparation of accounts is to some extent a matter of temperament and is largely influenced by individual circumstances. For example, one dentist may decide to depreciate his equipment or furniture and fittings by writing off an unduly large amount, while another may aim at making the provision for depreciation as small as possible. Again, a single handed practitioner may charge against his practice, expenses which another would regard as personal. In order to distribute the tax burden as equitably as possible, definite rules have been made as to the calculation of profits for Income Tax purposes. Some of these rules appear to be of an arbitrary nature. There is no doubt, however, that a serious endeavour has been made to treat every taxpayer on the same basis. To appreciate this fact will be of great assistance in obtaining a proper understanding of the principles upon which these rules are founded. Very briefly, it is only revenue (as distinct from capital) profits which are assessable, while only those expenses 'wholly and exclusively laid out or expended for the purposes of the trade or profession' may be allowed.

Seldom has a phrase given the Courts as much difficulty as this quotation from the Income Tax Acts. The operative words are 'for the purposes of the trade or profession' qualified, of course, by the expression 'wholly and exclusively''. Lord Davey in *Strong & Co. of Romsey Ltd.* v. *Woodifield* (1906) A.C. 448, said, 'It is not enough that the disbursement is made in the course of, or arises out of or is connected with the trade, or is made out of the profits of the trade. It must be made for the purposes of earning the profits.' The issue in the case of Strong & Co. was whether damages and costs recovered by a guest, who was injured as a result of a chimney falling in while he was sleeping at one of the company's tied houses, could be deducted in the computation of the company's profits. The House of Lords unanimously refused to allow the deduction. Lord Davey's words were criticized in the final report of the Royal Commission on the Taxation of Profits and Income, published in June 1955. The Commission did not think that the phrase 'for the purpose of earning profits' was a good interpretation of 'for the purposes of the trade' since it suggested some limiting condition for the expenditure to which it was extremely difficult to give any concrete meaning. The Commission felt that the position might be clarified by an appropriate section in a Finance Act.

The following are a few decisions where expenditure was not allowed:

*a*) *Copeman* v. *Wm. Flood & Sons* (1940) T.R. 491—Extravagant salaries paid, particularly to members of a family.

*b*) *Allen* v. *Farquharson Bros. & Co.* (1932) 17 T.C. 59—Legal costs incurred in connexion with a tax appeal to the Commissioners.

*c*) *Spofforth & Prince* v. *Golder* (1945) 26 T.C. 310—Costs of a successful defence in connexion with a criminal charge.

*d*) *Curtis* v. *Oldfield* (1925) 9 T.C. 319—Loss arising where the director of a company died and it was found that private payments on his behalf had been made by the company.

As has been stressed already, expenditure charged must have been incurred in the earning of the profits. The adjustments necessary to bring a practitioner's accounts into line for tax purposes fall into three main categories.

1) Items which may have been charged against profits but which are not allowed as deductions for Income Tax purposes, e.g.:

*a*) Private domestic expenses.

*b*) Expenses not connected with the practice.

*c*) Capital expenditure.

*d*) Appropriations of profit.

*e*) Interest paid from which tax is deducted at the time of payment.

*f*) Interest on capital.

*g*) Legal expenses incurred in acquiring a lease, or in connexion with a partnership agreement.

*h*) Travelling expenses of a practitioner between his residence and surgery.

*i*) Any other expenses not wholly and exclusively laid out for the purpose of earning the profits.

2) Items which may have been credited to the profit and loss account, but are to be eliminated for Income Tax purposes, e.g.:

*a*) Capital profits.

*b*) Interest received from which tax has been deducted at the source.

*c*) Profits not arising out of the practice.

3) Deductions allowed for Income Tax purposes, but which have not been charged in the profit and loss account, e.g.:

*a*) Net Schedule A assessment of practice premises owned by the dentist.

Expenses allowed naturally vary from practice to practice, but as already stated all expenditure which can be proved to have been 'wholly and exclusively laid out for the purposes of the profession' will be allowed as a deduction from practice income. It is probably an appropriate time to mention here that a dentist who is on a salary basis and therefore assessed under Schedule E must prove that his expenses are 'wholly, exclusively and necessarily' disbursed. The word 'necessarily' has been excluded from the Acts for Schedule D purposes, and this certainly eases the burden considerably for the dentist in practice as compared with his colleague who receives a salary.

The following is a list of expenses which may be charged in the accounts with a view to ascertaining the net profit for tax purposes under Schedule D:

1) Salaries or payments to assistants, *locum tenens*, receptionists, chairside attendants, bookkeepers and cleaners.
Wife's salary commensurate with duties involved.

2) Purchase of materials.

3) Postages, stationery and printing.

4) Telephone and telegrams, less cost of private calls.

5) Laundry, cleaning and cleaning materials so far as the cost is attributable to professional use.

6) The cost of renewal of special garments, such as surgery coats and operating gowns, may be claimed, but not the cost of ordinary clothing.

7) Rent, rates, repairs, lighting, and heating of surgeries and waiting-rooms. If the property is owned the net annual value is allowed instead of rent. Expenses are apportioned when the premises are partly used for residence.

8) National Insurance Contributions, insurances for fire, burglary, professional risks and for loss of profits.

9) Superannuation contributions under the National Health Service rank for an allowance at the full rate of tax and may be charged either as an expense in the accounts or as a deduction from the assessment. As from 1956–7, in certain circumstances and subject to a number of restrictions, a practitioner may deduct from his 'relevant earnings' any premium paid by him in that year under an annuity contract, the main object of which is to provide him with a life annuity in old age. For this purpose 'relevant earnings' means any income arising from an office or employment other than a pensionable office or employment.

10) Periodicals and journals for waiting-rooms.

11) Renewal of professional books of reference (but not the original cost of such books).

12) Renewal and replacement of appliances and instruments. (The initial cost or the cost of additional appliances and instruments is a capital expense and disallowable.)

13) Depreciation of furniture and fittings and equipment at rates approved by the revenue authorities.

14) Bad and doubtful debts (but the Inspector may ask for details of the larger amounts).

15) Legal expenses of a revenue nature, as on debt recovery or renewing a lease.

16) Defalcations or embezzlement by employees.

17) Bank charges and commissions.

18) Bank overdraft interest.

19) Removal expenses for professional purposes.

20) Audit and accountancy fees.

21) Dilapidations are allowed on the termination of a lease of practice premises.

22) Subscriptions to Trade and Professional Associations are allowed if the Association has entered into an agreement with the Revenue Authorities to pay tax on the excess of its receipts over its allowable expenses.

Payments to the following bodies are normally allowed:

British Dental Association (see page 202).

General Dental Council.

British Medical Association.

Scientific Societies such as the:

Royal Society of Medicine;

The Odonto-chirurgical Society of Scotland, etc.

Defence Societies such as:

The Medical Defence Union, Ltd.;

The Medical Protection Society Ltd.;

The Medical and Dental Defence Union of Scotland Ltd.

23) Travelling expenses strictly incurred in the conduct of the practice, including the cost of running and maintaining a car, but not the cost of travelling between the practice and the dentist's house. Such expenses as licence, tax, insurance, petrol, oil, cleaning, garaging, repairs, renewals of tyres, etc., are all allowable. A claim may also be made for depreciation. This is calculated in two parts as follows:

*a*) An initial allowance of 30 per cent. of the cost of a new or second-hand car is given only for the year in which the expenditure was incurred.

*b*) An annual allowance of 25 per cent. calculated each year on the written down value of the car.

Where the car is partially used for pleasure and for private affairs these allowances are restricted to the proportion used for professional purposes as relevant circumstances render just and reasonable.

24) No objection is normally raised by the Inspector of Taxes to an allowance for the cost of attending refresher courses to keep one's knowledge up to date as opposed to expenditure in connexion with post-graduate study for a higher degree or special qualification. This latter expenditure is regarded as being a capital outlay and as such is disallowable.

Mention has already been made of a dentist who may decide to depreciate his equipment or furniture and fittings by writing off each year an unduly large amount, compared with his colleague who might make no provision whatsoever. This situation is counteracted by the Revenue Authorities having published fixed rates of depreciation for all the main classes of trade and items of equipment. No rates have been fixed for the dental profession, and the normal procedure is for agreement to be reached with the local Inspector of Taxes. Generally speaking the annual rates applied in dental practices are as follows:

Electrical equipment—12½ per cent. of:
*a*) in the first year; cost.
*b*) subsequently; cost less these allowances in previous years.
Non-electrical equipment—6¼ per cent. of *a*) and *b*) similarly.

When the equipment is sold, scrapped or destroyed a balancing allowance or charge will be made to ensure that the dentist is given allowances amounting in total to the difference between his capital expenditure on the equipment and what he obtains when it is sold, scrapped or destroyed.

As an alternative there is the 'renewals basis' under which the normal allowances are not given, but when equipment requires to be replaced the cost of the new equipment less the proceeds from the sale of the old equipment is allowed as a deduction. Any element of improvement, of course, requires to be excluded.

A simple tax computation may help to clarify the adjustment of profits for assessment under Schedule D.

The following is the Profit and Loss Account of A.B., for the year ended 31 December 1961, where the equipment, costing £1,200, was purchased in June 1961.

*Profit and loss account year ended 31 December 1961*

| To materials purchased | £336 | By gross income | £2,300 |
|---|---|---|---|
| „ rent and rates | 125 | „ dividends on investments | |
| „ heating and lighting | 40 | (Net) | 20 |
| „ wages and salaries | 762 | | |
| „ travelling expenses (visiting patients) | 35 | | |
| „ repairs to equipment | 5 | | |
| „ depreciation on equipment | 250 | | |
| „ bad debts | 10 | | |
| „ income tax paid | 25 | | |
| „ A.B.'s salary | 400 | | |
| „ bank interest | 10 | | |
| „ interest on A.B.'s capital | 40 | | |
| „ net profit | 282 | | |
| | £2,320 | | £2,320 |

*Income tax computation, 1962–3*

| | |
|---|---|
| Profits per above accounts | £282 |
| Add: depreciation of equipment | 250 |
| income tax | 25 |
| A.B.'s salary | 400 |
| interest on capital | 40 |
| | £997 |
| Deduct: dividends on investments | 20 |
| | £977 |
| Less: wear and tear 1962–3 | 435 |
| Assessable profits 1962–3 | £542 |

*Computation of annual wear and tear allowance*

| | | |
|---|---|---|
| Equipment purchased June 1961 | | £1,200 |
| Deduct: Initial allowance 30 per cent | £360 | |
| Annual allowance 1962–3—6¼ per cent | 75 | 435 |
| Written down value | | £765 |

*Notes:* 1) Depreciation of £250 is added back because the correct deduction allowed is £435. 2) The other items added back are in reality appropriations of profit. 3) The deduction of £20 for dividends is made because tax has already been deducted at the source.

If the equipment were sold in the following year for £725 a balancing allowance of £40 (£765 − £725) would be granted. On the other hand, if it were sold for £1,200 a balancing charge would be raised amounting to £435. (£1,200 − £765)

**Part-time Appointments**

As already mentioned, professional profits are assessable to Income Tax under Case II of Schedule D.

Over the years difficult questions have frequently arisen where practitioners held part-time appointments as consultants to Regional Hospital Boards. While remuneration from a full-time appointment is clearly assessable under Schedule E, a number of medical and dental consultants argued that a part-time appointment was merely incidental to normal professional activities the whole of which comes under Schedule D. Inspectors of Taxes were reluctant to accept this argument, insisting that income from part-time hospital appointments be assessed under Schedule E. As the expenses of travelling, etc. were not wholly, exclusively and necessarily incurred in the actual performance of the duties of the office, they were not allowable for tax purposes under Schedule E.

The uncertainty in such cases has now been removed by the House of Lords in their decision in the case of *Mitchell & Edon* v. *Ross* (38 A.T.C. 422: 39, A.T.C. 52). In this case it was established that such a part-time appointment is an 'office' within the meaning of the Income Tax Acts. It has been made clear that two distinct activities are being undertaken. There is now no doubt that while practice profits are assessed under Schedule D the emoluments from part-time appointments come under the scope of Schedule E.

The learned judge held that the tax schedules are mutually exclusive and consequently any expenses not permissible under Schedule E cannot be allowed against Schedule D earnings.

It is under Case III of Schedule D that interest received without deduction of tax is assessed. This includes untaxed interest from War Loan, Post Office Savings Bank and Trustees Savings Bank deposits, deposit account interest and discount on Treasury Bills.

Subject to special provisions where a new source of income arises or where a source of income ceases, tax under Case III is calculated in respect of the year of assessment in which the income first arises on the full amount arising within that year, and in respect of subsequent years on the full amount arising within the year preceding the year of assessment.

For 1956–7 onwards the first £15 of the total interest received in any tax year from deposits with the Post Office Savings Bank or ordinary deposits with a Trustee Savings Bank is exempt from income tax. While this exemption applies to husband and wife separately, the total interest must be entered in the Income Tax Return form. This concession does not apply for surtax purposes, when the amount in question has to be regarded as being a 'net' sum. When income tax has been added back, surtax will be charged on the gross amount. For example, with a standard rate of income tax at 7/9, £15 interest will be the equivalent of £24. 9s. 10d. and surtax will be charged on £24.

While interest from National Savings Certificates is entirely exempt from tax, certain other annual payments are assessed under Case III. In this connexion the case of *Hawkins (Inspector of Taxes)* v. *Leaky (et contra)* (1952), 2 A.E.R. 759, is of special interest to members of both the dental and medical professions. A medical practitioner had entered the National Health Service scheme and exercised the option given to him by the National Health Service (Superannuation) Regulations, 1947 under which he received 8 per cent. of his remuneration as a contribution towards the maintenance of a policy of assurance which he held. The doctor was assessed under Case II on the assumption that the payments were profits of his profession, or alternatively under Case III on the grounds that they were annual payments. It was held that:

1) the receipts did not represent profits of the doctor's profession and were not assessable under Case II;

2) the receipts represented annual payments in the nature of income and were assessable under Case III.

### 4. PARTNERSHIP ASSESSMENTS

On the principle that wherever possible tax is collected at the source, the tax levied on a partnership is computed and stated jointly and a joint assessment is made in the partnership name.

If the firm defaults in paying, the Crown has the legal right to demand the whole tax from any partner. Each partner's share of the practice income must be calculated first in order to arrive at the allowances to which he is entitled. The total allowances of both or all the partners are then deducted so that the amount of the tax payable by the partnership may be calculated. Profit-sharing on the basis agreed upon by the partners remains the same for tax purposes. If partners receive salaries or if interest on capital is credited to them, these amounts will be allocated to the individual partners before sharing the balance of profits for Income Tax purposes. For any year of assessment the partnership assessment must be divided between the partners in the same ratio as the profits *for that year* are divided. This ratio could quite easily be different from the one used for dividing the profits of the accounting year used as the basis of the assessment. In other words, it is the *arithmetical proportion* of the profits to which a partner is entitled for the year of assessment that is applied in calculating his share of the assessment.

*An example will make this clearer.*

A and B are in practice as partners and the following figures apply:

Year ended 31 December 1959
 Profits—(shared $\frac{2}{3}$ to A and $\frac{1}{3}$ to B)                                        £3,000

Year ended 31 December 1960
 Profits—(shared $\frac{2}{3}$ to A and $\frac{1}{3}$ to B)                                        £2,000

Year ended 31 December 1961
 Profits—(shared equally from 1 January 1961 onwards)                            £2,500

Assessments on firm (based on previous year's profits).
 1960–1 based on £3,000, being the profits earned in the year to 31 December 1959

Partners' allocation:

| | A | B |
|---|---|---|
| Proportion from 6/4/60 to 31/12/60 of £3,000 equals £2,250 | £1,500 ($\frac{2}{3}$) | £750 ($\frac{1}{3}$) |
| Proportion from 1/1/61 to 5/4/61 of £3,000 equals £750 | 375 ($\frac{1}{2}$) | 375 ($\frac{1}{2}$) |
| | £1,875 | £1,125 |
| Total | £3,000 | |

1961–2 based on £2,000, being the profits earned in the year to 31 December 1960.

Partners' allocation:

| | A | B |
|---|---|---|
| Proportion from 6/4/61 to 31/12/61 of £2,000 equals £1,500 | £750 ($\frac{1}{2}$) | £750 ($\frac{1}{2}$) |
| Proportion from 1/1/62 to 5/4/62 of £2,000 equals £500 | 250 ($\frac{1}{2}$) | 250 ($\frac{1}{2}$) |
| | £1,000 | £1,000 |
| Total | £2,000 | |

If any taxed charges, such as mortgage interest or an annuity to a deceased partner's widow, are paid out of the practice income, these should be added back in the Income Tax computation. Tax must be paid on these charges at the full standard rate and no deduction for earned income relief is allowed. If the practice has any taxed income, however, this can be set off against the taxed charges.

If there is any change in the practitioners comprising a partnership, from 1953–4 onwards the practice is automatically treated for Income Tax purposes as having ceased and a new partnership commenced at the date of the change. The partners engaged in the practice immediately before and immediately after the change have the right to elect, within twelve months from the date of the change, that the partnership shall not be treated as discontinued. There must, however, be one partner common to both periods and all partners must agree. Where one of the partners has died, his personal representative must act in his stead. If advantage is taken of this option, the assessment for the year of change will be apportioned by the groups of partners before and after the change 'as may be just' usually on a time basis.

In *Dickenson* v. *Gross* (1927), 11 T.C. 614, the point was made that, although there might be a partnership agreement expressed in writing, partnership does not in fact exist if the terms of the agreement remain inoperative.

Other cases where it was held that no partnership existed in fact are as follows:

*McKie* v. *Luck* (1925), 9 T.C. 511.
*I.R.* v. *Williamson* (1928), 14 T.C. 335.
*Taylor* v. *Chalkin* (1945), 26 T.C. 463.

On the other hand, a partnership may in fact exist even though there is no written agreement. The point was made in *Ayrshire Pullman Motor Services and Ritchie* v. *I.R.* (1929), 14 T.C. 754 and *Waddington* v *O'Callaghan* (1931), 16 T.C. 187, that a partnership agreement can have no retroactive effect for Income Tax purposes. Thus, if a partnership deed is subsequently prepared fixing the commencing date of the firm, it is not conclusive evidence that the partnership did in actual fact commence on that earlier date.

## 5. SURTAX

When a dentist's statutory total income (as defined on page 191) exceeds £2,000, he becomes liable to an additional tax, which was at one time known as supertax, but is now termed surtax. This is to all intents and purposes a deferred instalment of Income Tax which becomes payable on the 1 January following the end of the year of assessment. The rates of surtax are determined by Parliament, and operate on a graduated scale. The rates for 1960–1 were fixed by the Finance Act, 1961 as follows:

|  | | Rates in £ |
|---|---|---|
| On the first | £2,000 of total income | NIL |
| On the next | 500 of total income | 2/- |
| On the next | 500 of total income | 2/6 |
| On the next | 1,000 of total income | 3/6 |
| On the next | 1,000 of total income | 4/6 |
| On the next | 1,000 of total income | 5/6 |
| On the next | 2,000 of total income | 6/6 |
| On the next | 2,000 of total income | 7/6 |
| On the next | 2,000 of total income | 8/6 |
| On the next | 3,000 of total income | 9/6 |
| On the remainder of total income | | 10/- |

The income assessable to surtax for any year is the income finally agreed for Income Tax purposes for the same year after deducting:

*a*) Annual charges, including interest on a mortgage paid to a Building Society, interest paid to banks on overdrafts and loans, relief due for business losses, or in respect of a claim for repairs and maintenance of property.

*b*) The amount by which personal reliefs exceed the allowance of £140 given to a single person. The allowances which will be taken into this calculation are as follows:

1) Allowance due to a married man.
2) Child allowance.
3) Dependant relative allowance.
4) Relief for daughter's services.
5) Relief for housekeeper.
6) Allowances to widows and others in respect of children.

While the deductions under *a*) above have been allowed for many years, those falling into category *b*) require special mention. The first five items may only be deducted for 1956–7 and subsequent years. Item No. 6 is a concession dealt with in section 17 of the Finance Act, 1960 and is applicable only from 1960–1 onwards.

For the purpose of charging surtax for the year 1961–2 or any subsequent year a special allowance for earned income is given under section 14. This allowance will be calculated in two stages. The first deduction is the same as the allowance for earned income given to a taxpayer for Income Tax purposes and amounts to two-ninths of earnings up to £4,005 and one-ninth of the next £5,940 of earnings. This allowance includes the earned income allowance due in respect of the earnings of a married woman living with her husband but does not include that other additional personal allowance due to a married man which is commonly referred to as the 'wife's earned income relief'.

Where a deduction falls to be made for earned income in this way and the earned income as reduced by this amount exceeds £2,000 a further deduction will be made in respect of earned income of such excess over £2,000 up to a maximum further allowance of £2,000.

The effect of this is to exempt the first £5,000 of earned income from surtax. If a taxpayer has other income, surtax is payable on the other income even if the earned income is substantially less than £5,000. Two simple examples will make this clear.

*a*) If a single person had earned income of £5,000 and taxed dividends (unearned income) gross of £3,000 his surtax liability would be calculated as follows:

| | | |
|---|---:|---:|
| Earned income | | £5,000 |
| *Deduct:* | | |
| Earned Income Relief: | | |
| Two-ninths of £4,005 | £890 | |
| One-ninth of £995 | 110 | 1,000 |
| | | £4,000 |
| *Deduct* excess over £2,000 | | 2,000 |
| | | £2,000 |
| *Add* income from dividends (unearned) | | 3,000 |
| | | £5,000 |
| *Deduct* surtax limit | | 2,000 |
| Surtax payable on | | £3,000 |

*b*) If the earned income had been £2,700 and the dividends £3,000 gross the same result would have been achieved.

| | |
|---|---:|
| Earned Income | £2,700 |
| *Deduct:* | |
| Earned Income Relief: | |
| Two-ninths of £2,700 | 600 |
| | £2,100 |
| *Deduct* excess over £2,000 | 100 |
| | £2,000 |
| *Add* income from dividends (unearned) | 3,000 |
| | £5,000 |
| *Deduct* surtax limit | 2,000 |
| Surtax payable on | £3,000 |

These two examples show clearly the priority which the Chancellor has given to earned income as compared with other income for the purposes of calculating a person's liability to surtax.

It should be noted that the income from taxed dividends to be assessed to surtax for 1960–1 must be the actual gross amounts receivable during the year to 5 April 1961.

Building Society interest was chargeable to surtax up to 1951–2 on the amount received but thereafter at the grossed amount thereof.

While the first £15 of interest received in any year from deposits with the Post Office Savings Bank or ordinary deposits with a Trustee Savings Bank is exempt from Income Tax this concession does not apply for surtax purposes (see page 212).

Surtax payers may find it more convenient to make their surtax return to the Special Commissioners. This can be done by giving notice on or before 1 May in any year following the year of assessment, and by entering in their Income Tax returns only income which is assessable under Schedules D and E, and particulars of the allowances claimed.

In normal circumstances the income of a married woman living with her husband is deemed to be that of the husband, and the assessment on the combined incomes will be made upon the husband. If applications referring to surtax are made by either party before 6 July, separate assessments will be made on each, but the total amount of tax payable will not be altered. The procedure is for the total tax due on the combined incomes to be divided between husband and wife in proportion to their respective incomes. The application must be made in writing to the Special Commissioners and, when the arrangement is adopted, it will remain in force for all subsequent years until revoked. It should be noted that a husband cannot be assessed to surtax in respect of income received by his wife prior to her marriage.

## 6. MISCELLANEOUS MATTERS

### 1. Treatment of Losses

There may be occasions when a practitioner suffers a loss in running his practice. This can very well happen during the early years of a new practice. Where a loss is sustained relief from Income Tax may be obtained in any one of three ways:

1) A practitioner may elect to set against the income of any particular year, provided a claim is made within two years from the end of the year of assessment:

i] any loss sustained in his practice in that year;
ii] any loss so sustained in the last preceding year so far as not already relieved and provided he is still in practice.

A loss incurred on a practice in any period is to be set off against the other earned income of the claimant, then against his own unearned income and then, unless a contrary claim is made, against the earned and then the unearned income of the spouse.

2) A loss on a practice may be set off against a profit on any other distinct business, trade or profession carried on by the practitioner concerned, either by himself or in partnership. This procedure only applies in relation to an accounting period ending before 6 April 1960. Section 20 (8) of the Finance Act, 1960 terminated this privilege.

3) Any balance of the practice loss not used as stated above may be carried forward indefinitely and set off against profits of the same practice by the same practitioner.

Another point to remember is that in the case of a partnership each partner's proportion of the loss is his own personal responsibility and may be used as outlined above. Should he die or retire, his proportion of any claim for unexhausted losses cannot be utilized by his partner or partners.

## 2. Seven-Year Covenants

It is a common practice for charitable institutions to increase their annual income by persuading as many subscribers as possible to sign seven-year covenants. By this means with the standard rate of tax at 7/9 in the £, for every £1 received from covenanters, 12/8 will be recovered by the institution from the Revenue Authorities and consequently the annual income of the charity is greatly increased. In other words, a dentist, by signing a deed binding himself to pay an annual net subscription to the charity for seven years or until previous death, enables the charity to benefit by the subscription being treated as though it were the net amount after deduction of tax, and a refund of that tax is claimed by the charity. This is an ideal method for a charity to raise funds, and for a subscriber to enhance very considerably his financial support of the organization in which he is interested.

To be effective the covenant must be in proper deed form, and it is important to remember that a new deed must be executed immediately the old one expires if it is the intention to continue the arrangement. There are in addition the following most important aspects to be kept in mind:

1) When a dentist signs a seven-year covenant say for £50 per annum less income tax, he is in actual fact alienating that part of his income. He will find that this will in the first place be set against his

unearned income. Any balance will be offset against earned income, and, of course, his earned income relief will be correspondingly restricted.

2) Payments made under deeds of covenant dated after 10 April 1946, are not allowed as deductions for surtax purposes.

3) A dentist not subject to Income Tax at the full standard rate should not adopt this system. If he does, he will find that the Inspector of Taxes will keep him to the terms of the covenant under which he binds himself to pay the net amount to the charity and account for the tax to the Revenue Authorities at the full standard rate. Even if the dentist has no income and makes the payment out of capital, he is still liable to pay this tax. The Revenue Authorities will recover the tax in the normal way by taxing the dentist's income, or, if that is not possible, by raising a special assessment.

## 3. Form of Accounts

Dentists sometimes prepare their accounts on a cash basis. This means that they calculate their net profit on the cash actually received less cash actually spent during the year, and no credit has been taken for work carried out and fees earned during that period when payment therefor has not yet been received. It is contended in some quarters that this basis is equitable, because amounts owing at the end of the financial year for work done but not paid for may never be received; even if they are received later they are automatically brought into account the following year. The same principle, it is held, applies to expenses incurred in one year and paid in the following one.

The Inland Revenue, however, maintain that accounts based on a cash basis do not show the true income of the practice. This attitude was supported in the case of *E. Collins & Sons Ltd.* v. *Commissioners oʃ Inland Revenue* (1925), 12 T.C. 773, when the point was made: 'It is elementary that a profit and loss account is not an account of receipts and expenditure in cash only.' Again, Lord Morison in *Commissioners oʃ Inland Revenue* v. *Morrison* (1932), 17 T.C. 325, said that 'The word "profit" for Income Tax purposes is in general to be understood in its natural and proper meaning, and that the assessable profits are to be ascertained on the ordinary principles of commercial accounting.' No professional accountant looks with favour on accounts prepared on a cash basis only.

Again the Revenue Authorities contend that, if the practice is sold or disposed of and the outgoing dentist retains his personal book debts and fees owing, the amounts collected cannot be assessed. In *Bennett* v.

*Ogston* (1930), 15 T.C. 374, the learned judge said 'that there is no question of assessing these receipts to Income Tax'. Two main reasons are held by the Board of Inland Revenue to support their contention. Firstly, the liability of the outgoing practitioner ceases on the date on which the transfer of the practice takes place, and, secondly, that the collection of book debts is merely the realization of capital assets.

It will consequently be found that the Inland Revenue will accept accounts prepared on a cash basis, if this has been the custom in past years. They will not usually countenance the adoption of a cash basis in the case of new practices, and will insist on the submission of a proper Income and Expenditure Account. It is, however, a matter for the Commissioners ultimately to decide.

## 4. British Subjects Residing Abroad

Under section 227 of the Income Tax Act, 1952 a person who is not resident in the United Kingdom is not entitled to any Income Tax reliefs unless the Commissioners of Inland Revenue are satisfied that he or she:

*a*) Is a British subject or a citizen of the Republic of Ireland.

*b*) Is a person who is or has been employed in the service of the Crown or who is employed in the service of any missionary society or in the service of any native state under the protection of Her Majesty.

*c*) Is residing in the Isle of Man or the Channel Isles.

*d*) Has previously resided within the United Kingdom and is resident abroad for the sake of his or her health or the health of a member of his or her family residing with him or her.

*e*) Is a widow whose late husband was in the service of the Crown.

A person who comes within any of these categories is entitled to the same reliefs, such as personal, reduced rate, and life assurance allowances as a resident in the United Kingdom would receive. If he derives all his income from British taxed sources he may claim all the allowances in full. If he derives only half his income from British taxed sources his claim for relief is restricted to half those allowances and so on. If his total income from all sources (British and foreign) is below the exemption limit it is the practice to repay the whole tax charged.

Claim forms may be obtained from the Chief Inspector of Taxes, (Foreign Claims), Seafield House, Waterloo Road, Seaforth, Liverpool 21.

A right of appeal to the Special Commissioners, and if necessary to the Court, is given by section 227.

The total income from all sources including all foreign and Dominion income whether remitted to the United Kingdom or not must be stated on the claim form. The United Kingdom tax which would be payable on such income is then calculated as if the income were entirely British after deducting all appropriate allowances due. The extent of the total liability to British tax is the proportion of the amount which the part of the income assessable to British tax bears to the whole income. Any Income Tax deducted or paid beyond this will be refunded.

Where the British proportion of income is very small in comparison to the total income such claims may not be worth while unless several years claims are made together. The time limit for making claims is six years.

## 5. Penalties

Prior to the passing of the Finance Act, 1960 the penalties imposed by the Revenue Authorities on persons making incorrect or false returns or refusing or neglecting to make a return of income were harsh in the extreme.

The amount of such penalties was based not on the tax which had escaped assessment but on the full tax chargeable, whether paid or not for the year for which the penalty proceedings could be taken.

Penalties are now calculated in relation to the tax which has escaped assessment as a result of the taxpayer's irregularities. A brief outline of the principal penalties is given below.

1) Section 45 of the Finance Act, 1960 prescribes a penalty of an amount not exceeding £100 if a person chargeable to Income Tax fails to make a return of his income within one year after the end of the relevant year of assessment. The penalty under this section is not incurred by failure to make a return if the person is not liable to pay tax.

2) Where in response to a Notice a person fails 'to deliver any return, statement, declaration, list or other document . . .' or does not 'furnish any information, give any certificate or produce any document or record . . .' section 46 of the Act imposes a penalty amounting to a sum not exceeding £50. In certain cases this may be increased by the amount of the tax charged which is:

a) based on the income which should have been included in the Return and *b*) is assessed after a lapse of more than one year from the end of the year of assessment in which the Return form was issued.

In addition a penalty is increased by £10 for each day of continuation of the offence after a Declaration by the High Court or the General or Special Commissioners before whom proceedings for the penalty are taken. If no tax is chargeable the limit of a penalty is £5 in accordance with section 20 (4) Income Tax Act, 1952.

3) Section 47 (1) of the Finance Act, 1960 deals with the cases where a person fraudulently or negligently makes an incorrect return of income, makes an incorrect claim for relief, or sends to the Inspector of Taxes incorrect accounts for the purpose of ascertaining his liability to Income Tax. The amount of the penalty depends on whether this was done fraudulently or only negligently. The penalty is the total of £50 and the amount of the tax or where fraud is present twice the amount of the tax.

It should be noted that under section 47 (2) in certain special cases a penalty of £250 is imposed for negligently, or up to £500 for fraudulently, making an incorrect return or statement. For example, these increased penalties would be imposed where surtax returns are concerned or lists of investments or securities held by the taxpayer, or lists submitted by persons who are in receipt of income belonging to others.

A remedy is given to the taxpayer under sub-section 3 of section 47 of the Act to avoid a penalty by making a correct return or statement without 'unreasonable delay' provided he did not make the incorrect return or statement fraudulently or negligently. If he does not do so there is a presumption of negligence so that failing proof of fraud the Crown can take proceedings for a penalty for incorrect returns or accounts on the basis of negligence.

4) Penalties are also imposed where 'any person assists in or induces the making or delivery for any purposes of Income Tax any return, accounts, statement or declaration which he knows to be incorrect . . .' The amount of the penalty is a sum not exceeding £500 as stated in section 50 of the 1960 Act. Before the penalty applies under this section there are two conditions which must be satisfied:

*a*) The incorrect return, statement or accounts must have been sent for Income Tax purposes.

*b*) The person who assists must know that these are incorrect. It would appear that it is not essential to prove that the person who makes the return or sends the accounts knows them to be incorrect.

A good example to quote here is the case of a wife who knowingly gives false information about her income to her husband for the purpose of including this in his own return or accounts. She would be in danger of incurring a penalty, and not the husband.

## 7. CONCLUSION

It will be readily appreciated that this brief chapter on Income Tax deals with a very vast subject in a most limited way. Many matters affecting the taxpayer of necessity have been omitted. The information provided has been given in the light of the Income Tax Act, 1952 and the various Finance Acts which have been passed since then. Principles have been stated in as simple a manner as possible in an attempt to bring an understanding of certain tax problems to members of the profession.

In these days when the incidence of taxation has such crippling effects, it is suggested that much unnecessary worry and expense can be avoided by approaching a tax expert such as a chartered or incorporated accountant for advice. It should not be forgotten, however, that the taxpayer can obtain advice and help from the local Inspector of Taxes if he so desires.

# CHAPTER XV

# Superannuation for Practitioners

## INTRODUCTION

The Regulations on Superannuation are unfortunately so complicated that few practitioners will be able to discover from them their rights and their obligations under the Superannuation Scheme.

The purpose of this chapter is to set out the main provisions of the Regulations in such a form that most contributors to the scheme will be able, after simple calculations, to estimate what their benefits are likely to be.

The chapter is based on the National Health Service (Superannuation) Regulations, 1961 (S.I. 1961 No. 1441). The Ministry of Health have also published a booklet *National Health Service Superannuation Scheme* which is obtainable from the Stationery Office, Kingsway, W.C. The Ministry's booklet is, however, designed mainly for persons in salaried employment in the Health Service, and, although a short section is devoted to practitioners, it is not always a simple matter for a practitioner to apply the information given in the booklet to his own particular circumstances.

The Regulations for Scotland are substantially the same as those for England and Wales. Practitioners in Scotland are therefore safe in regarding the rules set out in this chapter as applicable to themselves. The Regulations for Scotland are the National Health Service (Scotland) (Superannuation) Regulations 1961 (S.I. 1961 No. 1398 (s. 87)). The explanatory booklet published by the Department of Health is called *National Health Service Superannuation Scheme in Scotland* and is obtainable from the Stationery Office, 13a Castle Street, Edinburgh 2.

The superannuation scheme is compulsory and all practitioners joining the service are required to contribute to it. Those who were practitioners on 5 July 1948, did have an option to remain outside the scheme on certain conditions, but the time for exercising that option expired in October 1948.

## I. CONTRIBUTIONS

Every practitioner in the scheme makes a contribution amounting to 6 per cent. of his net remuneration. This contribution is allowable as an expense for Income Tax purposes and is therefore tax free (see page 208).

## A. Net Remuneration

Net remuneration means the gross fees earned in the practice *less:*

    i] a deduction of 52 per cent. as an allowance for practice expenses; and

    ii] the amount of the remuneration paid to any assistant. This figure must be approved by the Minister, so far only as it is to be reckoned for superannuation purposes.

'Gross fees' here includes any contributions payable (whether actually paid or not) by patients towards the cost of new dentures and other treatment under the provisions of the National Health Service Acts 1951 and 1952 as amended by the 1961 Act.

The maximum net remuneration which any dental practitioner may reckon for superannuation purposes, and on which he may pay contributions, is £3,500 per annum. Any remuneration above that figure is disregarded. This maximum applies however many assistants the practice may employ. The maximum was first laid down in April 1950. Any contributions paid before that date on net remuneration in excess of £3,500 will still be credited to the practitioner's superannuation account.

## B. Assistants

Assistant practitioners are required to contribute 6 per cent. of their salary according to the figure approved by the Executive Council on behalf of the Minister. This contribution is deducted by the Executive Council from the fees paid to the employer and the employer recovers it from the assistant.

Principals should bear in mind that any assistants, whether engaged for a long or short term, are superannuable from the date they are appointed. It is therefore advisable to make the Executive Council aware, as early as possible, of the employment of any assistants so that the Council may deduct the correct contributions and make the necessary adjustments in the principal's own superannuable remuneration. Early notification to the Council will avoid the difficulties of later adjustments and the need for assistants to pay arrears of contributions.

## C. Executive Council's Contribution

The Executive Council's contribution is $9\frac{1}{2}$ per cent. of the practitioner's net remuneration. This contribution is made by the Executive Council in the case of all practitioners including assistants.

## D. Partnerships

Where two or more practitioners are in partnership they can, by giving notice in writing to the Executive Council, have their superannuation rights allocated in proportion to the size of the share which each holds in the partnership business.

### 2. AGE LIMITS

A practitioner may retire at any time after reaching sixty, if he wishes to do so, and will be entitled to any benefits for which his length of service qualifies him.

Any practitioner who resigns or retires voluntarily before reaching sixty is not entitled to any benefits under the scheme, however long his service may have been. He receives only the return of his contributions to the scheme but if he joined the Health Service before 27 July 1960 he will receive compound interest upon them at $2\frac{1}{2}$ per cent., and less Income Tax. The only exception to this rule may arise where the practitioner dies within twelve months of leaving the service when a death gratuity or widow's pension may become payable in certain circumstances (see pages 229 and 232).

When a practitioner reaches sixty-five in the service he will normally cease to pay contributions to the scheme and his service after that age will not count for the purpose of benefits under the scheme. He will not, however, draw the benefits which his service before sixty-five has earned until he actually retires—that is, until he withdraws his name from the list of the Executive Council.

If the practitioner wishes to continue to pay contributions and earn benefits after sixty-five he may do so if the Minister extends his pensionable age. Applications for the extension of pensionable age beyond sixty-five should be made to the following addresses by letter:

*England and Wales:*

> The Secretary,
>> Ministry of Health,
>>> Health Services Superannuation Division,
>>>> Government Buildings,
>>>>> Honeypot Lane,
>>>>>> Stanmore, Middx.

*Scotland:*

> The Department of Health for Scotland,
>> Health Services Superannuation Branch,
>>> Broomhouse Drive,
>>>> Saughton,
>>>>> Edinburgh, 11.

The application should specify the age to which extension is desired. No extension beyond seventy is granted. Once extension has been granted to a particular age a further extension will usually be refused.

Whether or not the practitioner's pensionable age is extended beyond sixty-five he is still entitled to remain in the service as a practitioner up to any age he likes. Service beyond sixty-five will not, however, be taken into account for the purposes of superannuation unless pensionable age has been extended.

### 3. BENEFITS

The benefits payable vary according to the length of time which the practitioner serves in the superannuation scheme. They are accordingly set out here in three sections:

> *a*) Under five years' service.
> *b*) Between five and ten years' service.
> *c*) Over ten years' service.

### A. Under Five Years' Service

A practitioner who dies before completing five years' service receives only a return of his own contributions to the scheme plus compound interest upon them at $2\frac{1}{2}$ per cent. Income Tax is payable on the total amount returned. If he resigns or retires voluntarily he is not entitled to any benefits under the scheme except for the return of his contributions (see page 227).

There is one exception. If the practitioner is forced to retire because of permanent incapacity as a result of injury sustained by him in the actual discharge of his duty, or because of disease contracted through exposure to it by the nature of his duty, he is entitled to an annual injury allowance. The amount of the allowance is fixed by the Minister in the light of the practitioner's circumstances and does not exceed two-thirds of his average annual net remuneration during his last three years of service.

If the practitioner dies as the result of one of these causes, the Minister may grant a gratuity or annual allowance to his widow. If the practitioner dies while in receipt of an injury pension, then whatever the cause of his death his widow is entitled to a pension of one-third of the amount of his pension provided that the marriage took place before the injury pension was first paid. There is no minimum period of service necessary to qualify for this type of widow's pension.

The injury pension may be allocated in the same way as a retirement pension (see page 230).

## B. Between Five and Ten Years' Service

A practitioner who completes between five and ten years' service may be eligible for the following benefits:

i] *Retiring allowance*. This is payable if the practitioner retires after completing five years' service *and* after reaching the age of sixty. The amount of the retiring allowance is equal to his contributions to the pension scheme plus compound interest upon them. No retiring allowance is payable if the practitioner retires voluntarily before reaching the age of sixty.

If this amount is less than the average annual net remuneration paid to the practitioner during the whole period of his service, the Minister may, if the practitioner makes the request in writing, increase the amount of the retiring allowance by a sum equal to the current capital value of the death gratuity to which the practitioner would be entitled. If this is done no death gratuity will subsequently be payable. (EXAMPLE I—page 238)

ii] *Death Gratuity*. This is payable if the practitioner dies either before or after retirement on age or incapacity, provided he has completed at least five years' service. A death gratuity is also payable where a practitioner who has completed at least five years' service dies within

QDH

twelve months of resigning from the Health Service, provided he has not had a return of his contributions and he has not become subject to any other superannuation scheme.

The amount of the gratuity will usually be a sum equal to the average annual net remuneration earned by the practitioner over the whole period of his service.

Where this sum is less than the practitioner's own contributions to the scheme plus compound interest upon them at $2\frac{1}{2}$ per cent., the contributions and interest will be returned in lieu of a death gratuity.

Any benefits paid to the practitioner before his death (e.g. by way of retiring allowance) are deducted from the amount of the death gratuity. (EXAMPLE I—page 238)

iii] *Short service gratuity*. If the practitioner completes more than five but less than ten years of service, and has to retire because he is incapable of carrying on his duties through permanent ill-health or infirmity, he is entitled to a short service gratuity.

The gratuity amounts to the average annual net remuneration earned by the practitioner over the whole period of his service.

(EXAMPLE 2—page 238)

iv] *Injury pension.* A practitioner completing over five years' service is eligible for an injury pension and his widow for a widow's pension in the same circumstances as a practitioner with under five years' service (see page 229).

## C. Over Ten Years' Service

i] *Pension*. A practitioner may retire on pension if:

*a*) He has completed at least ten years' service; and
*b*) He has reached the age of sixty.

If he has completed at least ten years' service and has to retire because he is incapable of carrying on his duties through permanent ill-health or infirmity he is entitled to a pension whatever his age may be.

No pension is payable to any person who retires voluntarily before reaching the age of sixty.

The pension is calculated at a sum per annum equal to $1\frac{1}{2}$ per cent. of the practitioner's net remuneration up to 1 September 1962 and $1\frac{3}{4}$ per cent. thereafter up to a maximum of forty-five years.

(EXAMPLES 3 and 4—page 239)

The pension paid on retirement because of incapacity may be larger than this in certain circumstances. If retirement through incapacity takes place before the practitioner has completed twenty years' service, the pension is calculated as if he had completed twenty years' service at the same average annual net remuneration—that is, it is calculated at $1\frac{3}{4}$ per cent. of what he would have earned in twenty years at the same rate of earning. But a practitioner who is so old that he could not have completed twenty years' service before reaching sixty-five (or such later age as the Minister may allow) has his incapacity pension calculated at $1\frac{3}{4}$ per cent. of what he would have earned at the same rate, if he had served until sixty-five (or such later date as the Minister may allow). (EXAMPLES 5 and 6—page 239)

A practitioner who retires on pension may if he wishes surrender part of the pension in order to secure a pension for his wife, or any dependent, after his death. Where a widow's pension would be payable in any case (see page 232), the effect would be to increase its amount.

The decision to allocate may be taken at the time when the practitioner retires, or when he has completed forty years' service, or when he reaches sixty-five. Not more than one-third of the pension may be surrendered in this way.

The amount of the pension gained for the beneficiary varies according to the amount surrendered and to the ages of the two parties. Booklet A.L. *Allocation of Pension—Explanatory Memorandum* (H.M. Stationery Office), gives fuller particulars of the scheme. Medical examination of the practitioner is required.

(EXAMPLE 7—page 240)

ii] *Retiring allowance*. A practitioner entitled to a pension as in i] is also entitled to a lump sum retiring allowance.

If the practitioner has not a wife eligible for a widow's pension the retiring allowance is equal to $4\frac{1}{2}$ per cent. of his net remuneration up to 1 September 1962 and $5\frac{1}{4}$ per cent. thereafter.

If the practitioner is married and his wife is eligible for a widow's pension, the allowance is $1\frac{1}{2}$ per cent. of the net remuneration up to 1 September 1962 and $1\frac{3}{4}$ per cent. thereafter. If the practitioner became a widower or divorcee, or was judicially separated during his service, the retiring allowance is calculated at $1\frac{1}{2}$ per cent. of his net remuneration during the years before his wife's death, or the divorce or separation, plus $5\frac{1}{4}$ per cent. of net remuneration thereafter. (EXAMPLES 3 and 4—page 239)

If the retiring allowance, together with the capital value of the pension, is less than the average annual net remuneration paid to the practitioner during the whole period of his service the Minister may, if the practitioner makes the request in writing, pay an additional lump sum or pension equal to the current capital or annuity value of the death gratuity and widow's pension which would otherwise be payable on his death. If this is done no death gratuity or widow's pension will subsequently be payable.

iii] *Widow's pension.* A pension is payable to the widow of a practitioner who has completed at least ten years' service before his death, if:

 *a)* He dies while still in the service; or

 *b)* He dies while in receipt of a retirement pension under the scheme; or

 *c)* He dies within twelve months of resigning from the Health Service, provided in this case that he has not had a return of his contributions and he has not become subject to any other superannuation scheme.

This benefit is calculated in these varying circumstances as follows:

 *a)* Where the practitioner dies before retirement having completed at least twenty years' service, the widow receives a pension equal to one-third of what the practitioner would have received had he retired on pension on the day before his death—that is one-third of $1\frac{1}{2}$ per cent. of his net remuneration up to 1 September 1962 and $1\frac{3}{4}$ per cent. thereafter. (EXAMPLE 8—page 240)

Where the practitioner has completed between ten and twenty years' service at the date of his death the husband's pension is first calculated as if he had served for twenty years at the same average annual net remuneration—that is $1\frac{3}{4}$ per cent. of what he would have earned in twenty years at the same rate of earning. The widow then receives one-third of that amount. (EXAMPLE 9—page 240)

But where the practitioner was too old to have completed twenty years' service before reaching sixty-five (or such later age as the Minister may allow) the widow's pension is one-third of the pension he would have received if he had served until sixty-five (or such later age as the Minister may allow).
           (EXAMPLE 10—page 240)

 *b)* Where death occurs while the practitioner is on pension the widow's pension amounts to an annual payment of one-third of the pension which her husband was receiving.

(EXAMPLES 3 and 4—page 239)

*c*) Where a widow's pension is payable in this event it is calculated in the same way as for the widow of a practitioner who dies while still in the service (see *a*) above.

A widow's pension is not payable where:

1) The marriage took place on or after the date on which the husband became entitled to a pension; or

2) The widow is entitled to a pension under the scheme in her own right. But if she has earned her pension as a practitioner she is entitled to draw both her retirement pension and the widow's pension.

If the widow marries again the pension ceases.

The widow's pension does not affect, nor is it affected in any way by, any pension payable to her under the National Insurance Act.

iv] *Injury pension.* A practitioner who has completed at least ten years' service is eligible for an injury pension under the same conditions as practitioners with less than ten year's service (see page 229). If the practitioner was also entitled to a retirement pension or other benefit, that would be taken into account by the Minister when assessing the injury pension.

v] *Death gratuity.* Where a practitioner dies either before retirement or after retiring on age or incapacity, and he has completed at least ten years' service, a death gratuity is payable except that any benefits paid to the practitioner before his death (e.g. by way of pension or retiring allowance) are deducted from the amount of the death gratuity.

The death gratuity will usually be a sum equal to the average annual net remuneration earned by the practitioner over the whole period of his service. But where a widow's pension becomes payable the gratuity is $1\frac{1}{2}$ per cent. of net remuneration up to 1 September 1962 and $1\frac{3}{4}$ per cent. thereafter.

(EXAMPLES 8, 9 and 10—page 240)

Where no widow's pension is payable and the death gratuity is less than the practitioner's own contributions to the scheme plus compound interest at $2\frac{1}{2}$ per cent., the contributions with interest are returned in lieu of a death gratuity.

#### 4. EFFECT OF NATIONAL INSURANCE SCHEME

Under the National Insurance Scheme contributors become eligible for a pension at the age of sixty-five (sixty for a woman) subject to certain conditions.

The Health Service Superannuation Scheme takes this into account and for most practitioners the superannuation contribution is reduced, and the superannuation retirement pension reduced too when the pensioner becomes entitled to his National Insurance retirement pension.

The contribution is reduced by 2s. 4d. a week (2s. 6d. for a woman). The superannuation retirement pension is reduced by £1. 14s. a year for each year of service during which the reduced contribution has been paid. (EXAMPLE 11—page 241)

The retirement pension is the only benefit affected in this way. Any widow's pension is payable in full without reduction.

All practitioners are affected by this rule except:

1) Those who were in the Health Service on 5 July 1948. They continue to pay full contributions and will receive their pension in full unless they exercise an option to reduce both.

2) Men who were over fifty-five and women who were over fifty on 5 July 1948, and who were not contributors under the national schemes before that date.

3) Those who on 5 July 1948 were on war or National Service and who joined the Health Service within six months of ceasing their war or National Service.

#### 5. EFFECT OF NATIONAL INSURANCE GRADUATED PENSION SCHEME

Practitioners working as principals and part-time specialists engaged for less than six sessions a week are not affected by the National Insurance Pension Scheme introduced on 3 April 1961.

Practitioners who are employed persons for National Insurance purposes and who can complete ten years' contributing service or its equivalent in the Health Service by sixty-five (sixty for a woman), are contracted out of the graduated pension scheme.

Where a practitioner leaves the Health Service before becoming entitled to a pension and either takes a return of his contributions or a lump sum benefit, or does not within twelve months either resume superannuable employment in the Health Service or transfer to contracted-out employment, the benefits or return of contributions to which he is thus entitled will be reduced by an amount equal to one-half of the payment in lieu of contributions to the National Insurance Fund.

## 6. CHANGES OF EMPLOYMENT—BENEFIT OF PAST SERVICE

Where a person changes his employment in the Health Service (where for example a general dental practitioner becomes a public dental officer or full time hospital officer, or either of the latter becomes a practitioner), he may carry with him his past service to reckon in the scheme if there has not been a break of more than twelve months between the two posts. If he wishes to do this he must give notice in writing to his new employing authority within three months of taking up his new post. He must also repay any sum already paid to him by way of return of contributions, together with any sum which was deducted in respect of Income Tax when the refund was made.

There are arrangements whereby on transfer to and from a number of other employments outside the Health Service continuity of superannuation may be maintained, e.g. the Colonial Service; employment by universities; the armed forces; the civil service. Further information on this point can be obtained from the appropriate Government department. A practitioner who is thinking of changing to another employment would be well advised to inquire how his superannuation will be affected by the change. In any case care should be taken to raise the matter immediately the change of employment takes place in order that any time limits prescribed by the Regulations may be complied with.

## 7. BREAKS IN SERVICE

A practitioner who leaves the Health Service without taking other employment to which he can transfer his superannuation rights and subsequently rejoins the service, loses the benefit of his first period in the Health Service if he has been out of it for more than twelve months. If he wishes, however, he has the right to 'buy back' that previous service by making additional contributions. The amount of the contributions varies according to the age of the practitioner and there is provision for payment in instalments. Notice of intention to 'buy back' must be given in writing to the new employer within three months of re-entering the service.

(EXAMPLE 12—page 241)

### 8. MIXED SERVICE — CALCULATION FOR BENEFITS

If a practitioner is engaged also in part-time service in some other branch of the Health Service, his remuneration from that employment is added to his remuneration as a practitioner, and his superannuation benefits are calculated on the one total.

A practitioner who served for ten years or less as a whole-time salaried officer before becoming a practitioner has his remuneration as a salaried officer added to his remuneration as a practitioner, and his superannuation benefits are calculated on the one total.

(EXAMPLE 13—page 241)

A practitioner who served for more than ten years as a salaried officer before becoming a practitioner, or a practitioner who has had a period of salaried service after becoming a practitioner, has his benefits calculated differently. His benefits in respect of his practitioner service are calculated in the usual way, on $1\frac{3}{4}$ per cent. or $5\frac{1}{4}$ per cent. of total net remuneration. His benefits in respect of his salaried service are calculated on the basis of 1/80th or 3/80ths of his average remuneration during his last three years of salaried service, in respect of each year of such service. The two sums are then added together.

(EXAMPLES 14 and 15—page 242)

### 9. RE-EMPLOYMENT OF PENSIONERS

In general a practitioner who has retired and started to draw a pension under the scheme, and who subsequently takes any employment paid out of public funds, cannot draw both his pension and his pay in full. So long as he continues being re-employed his pension is reduced or suspended so that his pay plus his pension does not exceed his average annual net remuneration during the last three years of his previous service.

This reduction does not apply to any practitioner who first drew his pension at sixty-five or after, and who is re-employed as a practitioner between the ages of sixty-five and seventy. Such a practitioner is entitled to draw both his pension and remuneration in full, but his further service cannot go towards increasing his pension if he has already elected to take it on his first retirement.

Pensioners who are re-employed in the Health Service and who have their pensions reduced have a choice how to treat their further service in the superannuation scheme. If they wish they may apply to have the further service added to their previous service, and their benefits recalculated on that basis. If they do not apply for this method of treatment their further service will be dealt with entirely separately and benefits calculated upon it in the usual way. In the case of the latter alternative the service on which the first pension and allowance were calculated is taken into account only for determining the length of service on which his additional benefits are ultimately calculated, and not for determining their amount.

A pensioner who takes up employment paid out of public funds is required to notify:

1) H.M. Paymaster-General.
2) The Health Services Superannuation Division.
3) His new employer.

A person drawing a retirement pension from public funds but from outside the Health Service Superannuation Scheme, who takes employment as a practitioner, does not pay any contributions or earn any benefits under the Health Service scheme unless his pension is subject to reduction because of his re-employment.

### 10. MISCELLANEOUS

### A. Lump Sum in lieu of Pension

In general a pension under the scheme must be taken as a pension and cannot be compounded for a lump sum. Where, however, the pension does not exceed £26 per annum a lump sum payment may be made in discharge of the liability.

### B. Forfeiture of Superannuation Rights

The Minister has power to forfeit all superannuation rights in the case of any person who is dismissed or resigns after a fraudulent offence or grave misconduct in connexion with the duties of his employment.

### C. Illness of Practitioner

Where a practitioner's remuneration is reduced because of absence from his employment owing to illness or injury, his remuneration, for superannuation purposes only, is regarded as continuing during his absence at its previous annual rate. That is, he pays contributions on his reduced remuneration but earns benefits as if he were still working. This arrangement is, however, limited to a period of twelve months.

## D. Small Benefits

In any case where the benefits payable under the scheme are less than the amount of the contributions which the practitioner has made, plus compound interest, the latter amount is payable.

## E. Income Tax on Benefits

Benefits paid by way of a lump sum, i.e. retiring allowance, short service gratuity, and death gratuity, are not subject to Income Tax.

Benefits paid by way of pension are all subject to Income Tax except for the injury pension payable to a practitioner (pages 229, 230 and 233).

### II. EXAMPLES

For the sake of simplicity no allowance is made, except in Example II, for the effect of the National Insurance Scheme on contributions or benefits (see page 234).

*Example:*

1) Entered service at 58.
Retired at 64 with six complete years' service.
Died at 67.
Total net remuneration—£9,000.

*Benefits* (Whether married or single):
a) Retiring allowance—6 per cent. of £9,000 plus interest—say £600.
b) Death gratuity = average annual net remuneration over whole period of service—say £1,500 less retiring allowance already paid—£600 = £900.
No pension or widow's pension is payable because he did not complete ten years' service.

The practitioner may in certain circumstances ask the Minister to add the current capital value of the death gratuity to the retiring allowance and pay him the total sum on retirement (see page 229).

2) Entered service at 35.
Retired at 43 because of permanent incapacity through ill-health.
Completed eight years' service.
Died at 49.

*Benefits* (whether married or single):
Short service gratuity = average annual net remuneration over the whole period of service = say, £1,500.
No pension or widow's pension is payable because he did not complete ten years' service.
No death gratuity is paid because benefits already paid at the time of his death exceed the amount of the death gratuity otherwise payable.

3) Entered service at 57. Pensionable age extended to 68.
Retired at 68 with ten complete years' service.
Died at 72.
Total net remuneration—£15,000.

*Benefits:*
    *a)* (Whether married or single.) Retirement pension=$1\frac{3}{4}$ per cent. × £15,000= £262. 10s. per annum.
    *b)* (If single.) Retiring allowance=$5\frac{1}{4}$ per cent. × £15,000= £787. 10s.
    *c)* (If married.) Retiring allowance=$1\frac{3}{4}$ per cent. × £15,000= £262. 10s.
    *d)* (If married.) Widow's pension=$\frac{1}{3}$ of £262. 10s.= £87. 10s. per annum.
No death gratuity is paid because benefits already paid at the time of his death exceed the amount of the death gratuity otherwise payable.

4) Entered service at 27.
Retired at 60 with thirty-three complete years' service.
Died at 65.
Total net remuneration—£49,500.

*Benefits:*
    *a)* (Whether married or single.) Retirement pension=$1\frac{3}{4}$ per cent. × £49,500= £886. 5s. per annum.
    *b)* (If single.) Retiring allowance=$5\frac{1}{4}$ per cent. × £49,500= £2,598. 15s.
    *c)* (If married.) Retiring allowance=$1\frac{3}{4}$ per cent. × £49,500= £866. 5s.
    *d)* (If married.) Widow's pension=$\frac{1}{3}$ of £866. 5s.= £288. 15s.
No death gratuity is paid because benefits already paid at the time of his death exceed the amount of the death gratuity otherwise payable.

5) Entered service at 37.
Retired at 50 because of permanent incapacity through ill-health, having completed thirteen years' service.
Died at 59.
Total net remuneration—£19,500.

*Benefits:*
    *a)* (Whether married or single.) Pension is calculated as if he had worked for twenty years in the service at the same average rate of remuneration. It equals—$1\frac{3}{4}$ per cent. × £1,500 × 20= £525 per annum.
    *b)* (If single.) Retiring allowance=$5\frac{1}{4}$ per cent. × £19,500= £1,023. 15s.
    *c)* (If married.) Retiring allowance=$1\frac{3}{4}$ per cent. × £19,500= £341. 5s.
    *d)* (If married.) Widow's pension=$\frac{1}{3}$ of £525= £175 per annum.
No death gratuity is paid because benefits already paid at the time of his death exceed the amount of the death gratuity otherwise payable.

6) Entered service at 48.
Retired at 59 because of permanent incapacity through ill-health, having completed eleven years' service.
Died at 62.
Total net remuneration—£16,500.

*Benefits:*
    *a)* (Whether married or single.) Pension is calculated as if he had worked

until 65 (for sixteen complete years) at the same average rate of remuneration. It equals $1\frac{3}{4}$ per cent. $\times$ £1,500 $\times$ 16 = £420 per annum.

  *b*) (If single.) Retiring allowance = $5\frac{1}{4}$ per cent. $\times$ £16,500 = £866. 5*s*.
  *c*) (If married.) Retiring allowance = $1\frac{3}{4}$ per cent. $\times$ £16,500 = £288. 15*s*.
  *d*) (If married.) Widow's pension = $\frac{1}{3}$ of £420 = £140 per annum.
  No death gratuity is paid because benefits already paid at the time of his death exceed the amount of the death gratuity otherwise payable.

7) Retired at 65 with a retirement pension of £700 per annum.
On his death the widow would normally draw a pension of $\frac{1}{3}$ of £700 = £233. 6*s*. 8*d*. per annum.
By surrendering £100 per annum of his own pension the practitioner can if his wife is aged 61 increase her pension by £200 per annum.
Thus, if he 'allocated' in this way, his pension would be £600 per annum and his widow's pension would be £433. 6*s*. 8*d*. per annum.

8) Entered service at 35.
Died in the service at 57 with twenty-two complete years' service.
Total net remuneration—£33,000.

*Benefits:*

  *a*) (If single.) A death gratuity would amount to the average annual net remuneration earned by the practitioner over the whole period of his service = say £1,500. But this is less than the practitioner has contributed to the scheme over twenty-two years namely £1,980. His contributions are therefore returned with interest upon them at $2\frac{1}{2}$ per cent.
  *b*) (If married.) Death gratuity = $1\frac{3}{4}$ per cent. $\times$ £33,000 = £577. 10*s*.
  *c*) (If married.) Widow's pension = $\frac{1}{3}$ of £577. 10*s*. = £192. 10*s*. per annum.

9) Entered service at 35.
Died in service at 52 with seventeen complete years' service.
Total net remuneration—£25,500.

*Benefits:*

  *a*) (If single.) A death gratuity would amount to the average annual net remuneration earned by the practitioner over the whole period of his service = say £1,500. But this is less than the practitioner has contributed to the scheme over seventeen years namely £1,530. His contributions are therefore returned with interest upon them at $2\frac{1}{2}$ per cent.
  *b*) (If married.) Death gratuity = $1\frac{3}{4}$ per cent. $\times$ £25,500 = £446. 5*s*.
  *c*) (If married.) Widow's pension is calculated as if he had worked for twenty years in the service at the same average rate of remuneration. It equals: $\frac{1}{3} \times 1\frac{3}{4}$ per cent. $\times$ £1,500 $\times$ 20 = £175 per annum.

10) Entered service at 50.
Died in the service at 61 with eleven complete year's service.
Total net remuneration—£16,500.

*Benefits:*

  *a*) (If single.) Death gratuity = average annual net remuneration earned by the practitioner over the whole period of his service = say £1,500.
  *b*) (If married.) Death gratuity = $1\frac{3}{4}$ per cent. $\times$ £16,500 = £288. 15*s*.

*c*) (If married.) Widow's pension is calculated as if he had worked until 65 (i.e. for fourteen complete years). It equals: $\frac{1}{3} \times 1\frac{3}{4}$ per cent. $\times$ £1,500 $\times$ 14 = £122. 10s. per annum.

11) Entered Health Service at 32.
Retired at 62 after thirty complete year's service.
Total net remuneration—£45,000.
Assuming his remuneration was a steady £1,500 net per annum he would have contributed to the scheme each year 6 per cent. $\times$ £1,500

$$= £90 \quad 0 \quad 0 \text{ per annum,}$$

*less 2s. 4d.* per week National Insurance modification = 6    1    4

$$\overline{£83 \quad 18 \quad 8}$$

*Benefits:*
   *a*) His pension would be calculated as follows:
     From 62–65 : $1\frac{3}{4}$ per cent. $\times$ £45,000 = £787. 10s. per annum. After 65 (when he becomes eligible for a National Insurance pension): $1\frac{3}{4}$ per cent. $\times$ £45,000

$$= £787 \quad 10 \quad 0$$

     *less* £1. 14s. $\times$ 30

$$= \quad 51 \quad 0 \quad 0$$

$$\overline{£736 \quad 10 \quad 0 \text{ per annum.}}$$

   *b*) The widow's pension, whether he dies before or after 65 = $\frac{1}{3}$ of £787. 10s. = £262. 10s. per annum.

12) Entered service at 40.
Resigned at 45 taking a refund of his contributions.
Re-entered at 48.
The five years' service between 40 and 45 is reckoned for superannuation purposes only if he 'buys it back'.

Assuming that his net annual remuneration from 40 to 45 is £1,500, the total payments he would have to make in order to 'buy back' his five years would be approximately £600. The contributions refunded to him when he resigned at 45 would have been £450 (plus interest if he joined the Health Service before 27 July, 1960).

13) Entered hospital service at 26.
After eight years' service became a practitioner.
Retired at 63.
Total net remuneration:

| | |
|---|---|
| As hospital officer | £ 8,000 |
| As practitioner | £43,500 |
| Total | £51,500 |

His pension and other benefits are calculated on £51,500 as if the whole of it had been earned as a practitioner.

14) Entered hospital service at 26.
After twelve years' service became a practitioner.
Retired at 63.
Died at 70.

Total net remuneration:

As hospital officer (with an average annual remuneration
during last three years of £1,200) ................................. £12,000

As practitioner ................................................................. 37,500

His pension and other benefits are calculated in two parts.
Thus, if he is married, he is entitled to:

*a)* Pension = $1\frac{3}{4}$ per cent. × £37,500      =    £656   5

    *Plus* 1/80th × £1,200 × 12      =    180   0

                                              £836   5

*b)* Retiring allowance =

    $1\frac{3}{4}$ per cent. × £37,500      =    £656   5

    *Plus* 1/80th × £1,200 × 12      =    £180   0

                                                £836   5

*c)* Widow's pension = $\frac{1}{3}$ of £836. 5s. = £278. 15s.

15) Entered service as practitioner at 25.
Transferred to hospital service at 30, and became a practitioner again at 35.
Retired at 65.
Died at 67.

Total net remuneration:

As practitioner ................................................................. £52,500

As hospital officer (with an average annual remuneration
    during the last three years of £1,500) ..................... 7,500

His pension and other benefits are calculated in two parts.
Thus, if he is married, he is entitled to:               £    s.

*a)* Pension = $1\frac{3}{4}$ per cent. × £52,500      =    £918   15

    *Plus* 1/80th × £1,500 × 5      =    93   15

                                               £1,012   10

*b)* Retiring allowance =

    $1\frac{3}{4}$ per cent. × £52,500      =    £918   15

    *Plus* 1/80th × £1,500 × 5      =    93   15

                                               £1,012   10

*c)* Widow's pension = $\frac{1}{3}$ of £1,012. 10s. = £337. 10s.

*Appendix*

# APPENDIX I

[NOTE—*This Act replaces the Dentists Acts of* 1878, 1921, 1923 *and* 1956.]

# Dentists Act, 1957

## 5 & 6 ELIZ. 2 CH. 28

## ARRANGEMENT OF SECTIONS

### Part I

#### THE GENERAL DENTAL COUNCIL

### Part II

#### THE DENTAL PROFESSION

##### *Qualification for registration*

##### *Qualifying examinations*

##### *Dental education*

RDH

## Part III

## Part IV

### ANCILLARY DENTAL WORKERS

## Part V

### SUPPLEMENTAL

An Act to consolidate the enactments relating to dentists and other dental workers with corrections and improvements authorized under the Consolidation of Enactments (Procedure) Act, 1949.

[6th June, 1957]

B E it enacted by the Queen's most Excellent Majesty, by and with the advice and consent of the Lords Spiritual and Temporal, and Commons, in this present Parliament assembled, and by the authority of the same, as follows:

## Part I

### THE GENERAL DENTAL COUNCIL

## 1. Constitution and general duties of Council

(1) There shall continue to be a body called the General Dental Council whose general concern it shall be to promote high standards of professional education and professional conduct among dentists, and who shall in particular perform the functions assigned to them by this Act.

(2) Part I of the First Schedule to this Act shall have effect with respect to the General Dental Council.

## Part II

### THE DENTAL PROFESSION

## 2. Qualification for registration

(1) A person who is a graduate or licentiate in dentistry of one of the dental authorities shall be entitled to be registered in the dentists register in accordance with the provisions of this Act.

(2) A degree or licence in dentistry granted by a dental authority shall not confer any right or title to be registered under the Medical Act, 1956, nor to assume any name, title or designation implying that the holder of the degree or licence is by law recognized as a practitioner or licentiate in medicine or general surgery.

(3) For the purposes of this Act the expression 'dental authority' means any medical authority within the meaning of the following provisions of this section who grant diplomas in dentistry.

(4) For the purposes of this section the expression 'medical authority' means, subject to the next following subsection, any of the universities

or other bodies who choose appointed members of the General Medical Council.

(5) If a new university is at any time hereafter created in the Republic of Ireland and any of their examinations become qualifying examinations in medicine, surgery and midwifery for the purposes of the Medical Act, 1956, the expression 'medical authority' in this Act shall include that university.

## 3. Qualifying examinations

(1) Any medical authority within the meaning of the last foregoing section who have power for the time being to grant surgical degrees may, notwithstanding anything in any Act of Parliament, charter or other document, hold examinations in dentistry and grant licences certifying the fitness of the holders to practise dentistry; and the holders' names shall be entered on a list of licentiates in dentistry to be kept by the medical authority.

(2) The foregoing subsection shall be without prejudice to any power to grant a degree or licence in dentistry which a medical authority may possess apart from the provisions of this Act.

## 4. Conduct of examinations for degrees and licences

(1) For the purpose of any examinations to qualify for a degree or licence in dentistry held by—

(a) any university in England or Wales, Scotland or Ireland,

(b) the Royal College of Surgeons of Edinburgh,

(c) the Royal Faculty of Physicians and Surgeons of Glasgow, or

(d) the Royal College of Surgeons in Ireland,

the Council or other governing body of the university, college or faculty may appoint a board of examiners.

(2) Each of the said boards shall be called the Board of Examiners in Dental Surgery or Dentistry, and shall consist of not less than six members, one half of whom at least shall be registered dentists, and nothing in any Act of Parliament, charter or other document shall make it necessary for them to possess any other qualification.

(3) Persons appointed under this section shall continue in office for such period, and shall conduct the examinations in such manner, as the governing body appointing them may by byelaws or regulations respectively direct.

(4) A casual vacancy in any such board of examiners may be filled by the governing body which appointed the board and the person so appointed—

(*a*) shall be a registered dentist if the person in whose place he is appointed was a registered dentist, and

(*b*) shall hold office for such time only as that other person would have held office.

(5) Such reasonable fees shall be paid for a degree or licence awarded after examination by a board of examiners under this section as the governing body by whom they were appointed may by byelaws or regulations direct and the degrees or licences awarded after examination by the board of examiners shall be in such form as that governing body may so direct.

(6) All byelaws and regulations made by a dental authority under the authority of this section, and any further byelaws or regulations altering or revoking them, shall be made in such manner, and subject to such approval or confirmation, if any, as in the case of other byelaws or regulations made by that dental authority.

## 5. Granting of licences by Royal College of Surgeons of England

The Royal College of Surgeons of England shall continue to hold examinations, and to appoint a board of examiners in dentistry, and to grant licences certifying the fitness of the holders to practise, subject to and in accordance with the provisions of their charter dated the eighth day of September, eighteen hundred and fifty-nine, and the byelaws made in pursuance of that charter; and the name of the holder of any licence so granted shall be entered on a list of licentiates in dentistry to be kept by the said college.

## 6. Admission of candidates to examinations

A dental authority shall admit to the examinations held by them to qualify for a degree or licence in dentistry any person desirous of being examined who has attained the age of twenty-one years, and has complied with the regulations in force (if any) as to education laid down by the dental authority.

## 7. Supervision of examinations

(1) Every dental authority shall from time to time when required by the General Dental Council furnish them with such information as the Council may require as to the course of study and examinations to be gone through in order to obtain a degree or licence in dentistry and generally as to the conditions laid down for obtaining such a degree or licence.

(2) Any member of the General Dental Council or any person appointed by the Council may be present at any such examinations and the General Dental Council shall have power to remunerate members of the Council, as well as non-members, for being present at the examinations.

## 8. Dental education

The General Dental Council shall refer to their Education Committee for advice on all matters relating to dental education and examinations and that Committee shall be constituted in accordance with paragraph 10 of Part II of the First Schedule to this Act.

## 9. Attendance of visitors at dental schools

(1) The General Dental Council may appoint persons to visit, subject to any directions which the Privy Council may deem it expedient to give and to compliance with any conditions specified in those directions, places where instruction is given to dental students under the direction of a dental authority.

(2) It shall be the duty of visitors appointed under this section to report to the General Dental Council as to the sufficiency of the instruction given in the places which they visit and as to any other matters relating to the instruction which may be specified by the Council either generally or in any particular case; but no visitor shall interfere with the giving of any instruction.

(3) On the receipt of a report of a visitor under this section, the Council shall send a copy of the report to the dental authority in question, and on the receipt of the copy a dental authority may, within such period (not being less than one month) as the Council may have specified at the time they sent the copy of the report, make to the Council observations on the report or objections thereto.

(4) As soon as may be after the expiration of the period specified under the last foregoing subsection the Council shall send a copy of any such report as is therein referred to and of any observations thereon or objections thereto duly made, together with the Council's comments on the report and on any such observations and objections, to the Privy Council.

(5) The Council shall have power to remunerate members of the Council, as well as non-members, for acting as visitors under this section and the remuneration shall be at such rates as the Privy Council may approve.

## 10. Remedy where qualifying courses of study or examinations are inadequate

(1) Where it appears to the General Dental Council that the course of study and examinations to qualify for a degree or licence in dentistry granted by a dental authority are not such as to secure the possession by the graduates or licentiates of the requisite knowledge and skill for the efficient practice of dentistry, the General Dental Council may make a representation to that effect to the Privy Council and on any such representation the Privy Council may, if they think fit, order that any degree or licence in dentistry granted by the dental authority after a time specified in the order shall not confer any right to be registered under this Act.

(2) If an order is made under this section, no person shall be entitled to be registered under this Act in respect of a degree or licence in dentistry granted by the dental authority after the time mentioned in the order.

(3) The Privy Council may, if it appears to them on a further representation from the General Dental Council or otherwise that the dental authority in question has made effectual provision to the satisfaction of the General Dental Council for the improvement of the course of study or examinations, revoke an order made under this section, but the revocation shall not entitle a person to be registered in respect of a degree or licence in dentistry granted before the revocation.

(4) Any order of the Privy Council under this section may be made conditionally or unconditionally, and may contain such terms and directions as appear to the Privy Council to be just.

## 11. Candidates not to be required to adopt or reject particular theories of dentistry

(1) If it appears to the General Dental Council that a dental authority has attempted to impose on any candidate offering himself for examination an obligation to adopt, or to refrain from adopting, the practice of any particular theory of dentistry as a test or condition of admitting him to examination or of granting a degree or licence in dentistry, the General Dental Council may make a representation to that effect to the Privy Council.

(2) On any such representation the Privy Council may direct the authority to desist from attempting to impose any such obligation and if the authority does not comply with the direction the Privy Council

may order that the authority shall cease to have power to grant degrees or licences in dentistry so long as they continue to attempt to impose any such obligation.

(3) Any order of the Privy Council under this section may be made conditionally or unconditionally, and may contain such terms and directions as appear to the Privy Council to be just.

## 12. Qualification for registration as a Commonwealth or foreign practitioner

(1) A person who shows to the satisfaction of the registrar—
   (a) that he is of good character,
   (b) that he holds a Commonwealth or a foreign diploma, and
   (c) that he has satisfied the General Dental Council that he has the requisite knowledge and skill,

shall be entitled to be registered in the dentists register in accordance with the provisions of this Act.

(2) Except in a case falling within the next following subsection, the Council shall for the purpose of satisfying themselves that a person has the requisite knowledge and skill, and in addition to such other requirements as they may impose on him, require him to sit for examinations held by a dental authority, or a group of dental authorities, under arrangements made by the Council.

(3) If the diploma held by the said person is of a kind recognised for the time being by the Council as furnishing such guarantees of that person's possessing the requisite knowledge and skill as warrant dispensing with further inquiry, that person shall be taken to have satisfied the Council that he has the requisite knowledge and skill.

(4) The Council may make regulations as to the examinations to be held for the purposes of this section and may include in the regulations provisions for withdrawing the right to sit for any such examinations from a person who has not first paid the fee prescribed by the regulations for sitting for the examinations or from a person who has previously failed to pass such examinations on such number of occasions as may be prescribed by the regulations.

Regulations under this subsection shall not come into force until approved by order of the Privy Council.

(5) The Council may direct that for the purposes of this section a particular person who has passed the examinations required to obtain a foreign diploma shall be treated as a person holding a foreign diploma.

### 13. Temporary registration

(1) Where the General Dental Council, with a view to permitting any person holding a Commonwealth or foreign diploma temporarily to practise dentistry in a hospital or other institution, give a direction that he be registered as respects practice in that hospital or institution for such period as may be specified in the direction, that person shall, without showing that any requirements under the last foregoing section are fulfilled in his case, be entitled to be registered in the dentists register in accordance with the provisions of this Act subject to the entry against his name of the restrictions specified in the direction.

(2) Registration under this section shall not make it lawful for a person to practise dentistry otherwise than subject to the said restrictions nor constitute him a registered dentist for the purposes of the First Schedule to this Act.

(3) The Council may direct that for the purposes of this section a particular person who has passed the examinations required to obtain a foreign diploma shall be treated as a person holding a foreign diploma.

### 14. Meaning of "Commonwealth diploma" and "foreign diploma"

In this Act, "Commonwealth or foreign diploma" means a diploma granted in a country overseas and recognised for the time being by the General Dental Council for the purposes of this Act, and the diploma shall be a Commonwealth or a foreign diploma according as the country in which it is granted is or is not within the Commonwealth.

### 15. Use by registered dentists of titles and descriptions

(1) A registered dentist shall by virtue of being registered be entitled to take and use the description of dentist, dental surgeon or dental practitioner.

(2) A registered dentist shall not take or use or affix to or use in connection with his premises any title or description reasonably calculated to suggest that he possesses any professional status or qualification other than a professional status or qualification which he in fact possesses and which is indicated by particulars entered in the register in respect of him and a person contravening this subsection shall be liable on summary conviction to a fine not exceeding fifty pounds.

(3) If the General Dental Council are of opinion that any special branch of dentistry has become so distinctive that it would be for the convenience of the public or of the dental profession that registered dentists qualified to practise, or practising, in that branch of dentistry

should use a distinctive title, they may by regulations prescribe appropriate titles and conditions under which they may be used; and the use of a prescribed title under the prescribed conditions shall not constitute a contravention of the last foregoing subsection.

(4) If an abbreviated form of a diploma granted in a country overseas is under section nineteen of this Act entered against a person's name in the dentists register, that person shall not take or use, or affix to or use in connection with his premises, any other abbreviation of that diploma and a person contravening this subsection shall be liable on summary conviction to a fine not exceeding fifty pounds.

## 16. The dentists register and the procedure for registration

(1) There shall continue to be a register known as the dentists register which shall contain three separate alphabetical lists—

(a) one of persons registered as graduates or licentiates of a dental authority,

(b) one, to be called the Commonwealth list, of persons registered as holding some Commonwealth diploma,

(c) one, to be called the foreign list, of persons registered as holding some foreign diploma.

(2) The register shall be kept by the registrar who shall perform such duties in connection with the dentists register as the General Dental Council may direct and in the execution of his duties he shall act on such evidence as in each case appears sufficient.

(3) The register shall be deemed to be in proper custody when in the custody of the registrar, and shall be of such a public nature as to be admissible as evidence of all matters therein on its mere production from that custody.

(4) A certificate purporting to be a certificate under the hand of the registrar stating that any person is, or was at any date, or is not, or was not at any date, duly registered in the register or stating that any particulars are, or were at any date, or are not, or were not at any date, contained in the register with respect to any person, shall be *prima facie* evidence in all courts of law of the facts stated in the certificate.

(5) Any appointment to the office of registrar shall be made by the General Dental Council and any person appointed shall hold office for such period and shall receive such salary as may be fixed by the Council.

(6) The General Dental Council may appoint a person to act as assistant registrar who shall be paid such salary or remuneration as the Council may from time to time determine.

(7) A registrar who wilfully makes, or causes to be made, any

falsification in a matter relating to the dentists register shall be guilty of a misdemeanour and on conviction thereof shall be liable to imprisonment for a term not exceeding twelve months.

## 17. Procedure for registration

(1) Subject to the provisions of subsection (3) of this section and of section thirteen of this Act, any right to registration shall be conditional on the making of an application supported by such evidence as is required by subsection (2) of this section.

(2) A person applying to be registered shall produce or send to the registrar the document conferring or evidencing his licence or other qualification with a statement of his name and address and the other particulars, if any, required for registration.

(3) Any dental authority may from time to time transmit to the registrar certified lists of the persons who are graduates or licentiates of that body in dentistry, stating the qualifications and places of residence of the persons included in the lists and the registrar on receipt of any such lists shall duly register those persons.

## 18. Power to make regulations with respect to the register

(1) The General Dental Council may make regulations with respect to the form and keeping of the register and the making of entries and erasures therein and, in particular—

(a) prescribing a fee to be charged on the entry of a name in the register or on the restoration of any entry to the register,

(b) prescribing a fee to be charged in respect of the retention in the register of the name of a person first registered after the twenty-eighth day of July, nineteen hundred and twenty-one, in any year subsequent to the year in which that person was first registered,

(c) providing for the registration in and removal from the register of additional diplomas of prescribed kinds held by a registered dentist and prescribing a fee to be charged in respect of the registration,

d) authorising the registrar notwithstanding anything in this Act to refuse to make in or restore to the register any entry until a fee prescribed by regulations under this section has been paid.

(2) Regulations under this section may authorise the registrar to erase from the register the name of a person who, after such notices and warnings as may be prescribed by the regulations, fails to pay a fee prescribed under paragraph (b) of the foregoing subsection and, where

a person's name is so erased, that name may be restored to the register on that person's application.

(3) Regulations under this section prescribing fees may provide for the charging of different fees in different classes of cases.

(4) Regulations under this section shall provide that persons registered in the Commonwealth list or the foreign list under section thirteen of this Act shall appear in a separate sub-division of the list in question.

(5) Regulations under this section prescribing fees or authorising the registrar to erase a person's name for non-payment of a fee shall not come into force until approved by order of the Privy Council; and the Privy Council shall not approve any regulations under this section prescribing a fee of an amount exceeding five pounds unless in their opinion a fee of that amount is justified by changes in circumstances which have taken place since the passing of the Dentists Act, 1956.

### 19. Selection of proper abbreviations of diplomas granted in countries overseas

Where a person's name is entered in the Commonwealth list or the foreign list, or an additional diploma granted in a country overseas is entered against a person's name in any part of the register, the registrar shall enter the diploma by virtue of which that person is registered or, as the case may be, the additional diploma in such abbreviated form as the registrar after consultation with the president of the General Dental Council may select as being convenient but not capable of being mistaken for the abbreviated form of any other diploma.

### 20. Publication of the register

(1) The General Dental Council shall cause a correct copy of the register to be at least once a year printed under their direction, published and sold, and subject to the provisions of this section such a copy shall be admissible in evidence.

(2) Regulations under section eighteen of this Act may provide for the inclusion in such a copy of the register of honours or distinctions accorded to a person in the register but it shall not be admissible as evidence of those honours or distinctions and regulations so made shall require an indication to be given in the copy of the register that the honours or distinctions do not form part of the register itself.

### 21. Erasure of names of deceased persons and of those who have ceased to practise

(1) The registrar shall erase from the register the name of every

deceased person and on registering the death of a registered dentist a registrar of births and deaths shall, without charge to the recipient, send forthwith by post to the registrar of the dentists register a copy certified under his hand of the entry in the register of deaths relating to the death.

(2) If a registered dentist has ceased to practise, the registrar may with his consent erase his name from the register.

(3) The registrar may send by post to a registered dentist a notice inquiring whether he has ceased to practise or has changed his residence and if no answer is received to the inquiry within six months from the posting of the notice, he may erase the dentist's name from the register.

(4) Where a person's name has been erased from the register under the last foregoing subsection or at his request, the name may be restored to the register on his application unless the original entry of his name was incorrectly or fraudulently made.

### 22. Erasure on grounds of fraud or error

(1) It shall be the duty of the General Dental Council to cause to be erased from the register any entry which has been incorrectly or fraudulently made but where a question arises whether an entry is fraudulent it shall be referred to and determined by the Disciplinary Committee.

(2) Where a person's name has been erased on the ground that it was entered fraudulently that name shall not again be entered in the register except on an application in that behalf to the General Dental Council and on any such application the General Dental Council may, if they think fit, direct that the person shall not be registered, or shall not be registered until the expiration of such period as may be specified in the direction.

(3) The General Dental Council shall refer any application under the last foregoing subsection to the Disciplinary Committee for determination by them.

### 23. Alteration of names and addresses

The registrar shall from time to time insert in the register any alteration which may come to his knowledge in the name or address of any registered person.

### 24. Transfer from Commonwealth or foreign list to main list

(1) If the registrar learns that a person registered in the Commonwealth or foreign list is entitled to be registered as being a graduate or

licentiate of a dental authority he shall serve a notice on that person informing him that upon the expiration of a period specified in the notice (being a period of not less than three months from the time of the notice) he proposes to strike that person's name out of the Commonwealth or, as the case may be, the foreign list and also informing that person of his right to be registered as a graduate or licentiate.

(2) On the expiration of the said period, the registrar shall strike that person's name out of the Commonwealth or foreign list in accordance with the notice and shall register that person in the list of dentists registered as being such graduates or licentiates as aforesaid with the entries appearing against his name in the other list when the name was struck out.

(3) Regulations under this Act relating to the register shall not be made so as to require the payment of a fee for the making of an entry under this section.

(4) A notice to be served under this section may be served by post in a registered letter addressed to the dentist at his address in the register, or at his last known address if that address differs from his address in the register and it appears to the registrar that such service will be more effective.

## 25. Disciplinary cases

(1) A registered dentist who either before or after registration—
  (a) has been convicted either in Her Majesty's dominions or elsewhere of an offence which, if committed in England, would be a felony or misdemeanour, or
  (b) has been guilty of any infamous or disgraceful conduct in a professional respect,
shall be liable to have his name erased from the register.

(2) A person's name shall not be erased under this section—
  (a) on account of conviction for an offence which does not, either from the trivial nature of the offence or from the circumstances under which it was committed, disqualify a person for practising dentistry, or
  (b) on account of a conviction for a political offence outside the British Isles and the Commonwealth, or
  (c) on account of his adopting or refraining from adopting any particular theory of dentistry.

(3) In an inquiry under this Act whether a person has been guilty of any infamous or disgraceful conduct in a professional respect, a finding of fact which is shown to have been made in any matrimonial

proceedings in the United Kingdom or the Republic of Ireland, being proceedings in the High Court or the Court of Session or on appeal from a decision in such proceedings, shall be conclusive evidence of the fact found.

(4) Where a dental authority in exercise of a power conferred by law strike the name of a person who is a registered dentist off a list of their graduates or licentiates in dentistry and notify to the General Dental Council the fact of the striking off—

(a) the registrar shall make a note of the fact in the register, and

(b) if the dental authority notify to the Council the findings of fact on which the decision to strike off the name was based, then for the purpose of any such inquiry as is mentioned in subsection (3) of this section the findings may, if the body holding the inquiry think fit, be treated as conclusive of the facts found.

(5) Any case of a person alleged to be liable to have his name erased from the register under this section is hereafter in this Act referred to as a "disciplinary case."

### 26. Committees of Council entrusted with disciplinary cases

(1) There shall continue to be committees of the General Dental Council known as the Preliminary Proceedings Committee and the Disciplinary Committee which shall be respectively constituted in accordance with paragraph 11 and paragraph 12 of Part II of the First Schedule to this Act.

(2) It shall be the function of the Preliminary Proceedings Committee to decide whether a disciplinary case ought to be referred to the Disciplinary Committee to be dealt with by them in accordance with the following provisions of this section.

(3) If after the Preliminary Proceedings Committee have referred a disciplinary case to the Disciplinary Committee, but before the Disciplinary Committee have opened their enquiry into the case, it appears to the Disciplinary Committee that the question whether an enquiry should be held needs further consideration, they may refer the disciplinary case back to the Preliminary Proceedings Committee for consideration of that question but, subject to that, it shall be the duty of the Disciplinary Committee to hold an enquiry into any disciplinary case referred to them under this section and the Disciplinary Committee, if satisfied as to the facts rendering the person in question liable to have his name erased, may determine that the name of that person shall be erased from the register.

(4) Where the Disciplinary Committee determine that a person's

name shall be erased from the register, the registrar shall serve on him a notification of the determination of the Committee which notification may be served by post in a registered letter addressed to that person at his address in the register, or at his last known address if that address differs from his address in the register and it appears to the registrar that such service will be more effective.

## 27. Proceedings in disciplinary cases

(1) Subject to the provisions of this section, the General Dental Council shall make rules as to the procedure to be followed and rules of evidence to be observed in proceedings before the Disciplinary Committee under the last foregoing section and in particular—

(*a*) for securing that notice that the proceedings are to be brought shall be given, at such time and in such manner as may be specified in the rules, to the person to whose registration the proceedings relate;

(*b*) for securing that any party to the proceedings shall, if he so requires, be entitled to be heard by the Committee;

(*c*) for enabling any party to the proceedings to be represented by counsel or solicitor, or (if the rules so provide and the party so elects) by a person of such other description as may be specified in the rules;

(*d*) for requiring proceedings before the Committee to be held in public except in so far as may be provided by the rules;

(*e*) for requiring, in cases where it is alleged that a registered dentist has been guilty of infamous or disgraceful conduct in a professional respect, that where the Committee judge that the allegation has not been proved they shall record a finding that the dentist is not guilty of such conduct in respect of the matters to which the allegation relates.

(2) Before making rules under this section the Council shall consult such bodies of persons representing dentists as appear to the Council requisite to be consulted.

(3) Rules under this section shall not come into force until approved by order of the Privy Council contained in a statutory instrument, and the Privy Council may approve such rules either as submitted to them or subject to such modifications as appear to them requisite:

Provided that where the Privy Council propose to approve any rules subject to modifications they shall notify to the General Dental Council the modifications they propose to make and consider any observations of the General Dental Council thereon.

## 28. Assessor in disciplinary cases

(1) For the purpose of advising the Disciplinary Committee on questions of law arising in proceedings before them in disciplinary cases there shall in all such proceedings be an assessor to the Committee who shall be a barrister, advocate or solicitor of not less than ten years standing.

(2) The power of appointing assessors under this section shall be exercisable by the General Dental Council but if no assessor appointed by them is available to act at any particular proceedings the Disciplinary Committee may appoint an assessor under this section to act at those proceedings.

(3) The Lord Chancellor may by statutory instrument make rules as to the functions of assessors appointed under this section, and, in particular, rules under this subsection may contain such provisions for securing—

(a) that where an assessor advises the Committee on any question of law as to evidence, procedure or any other matters specified in the rules, he shall do so in the presence of every party, or person representing a party, to the proceedings who appears thereat or, if the advice is tendered after the Committee have begun to deliberate as to their findings, that every such party or person as aforesaid shall be informed what advice the assessor has tendered;

(b) that every such party or person as aforesaid shall be informed if in any case the Committee do not accept the advice of the assessor on any such question as aforesaid,

and such incidental and supplementary provisions, as appear to the Lord Chancellor expedient.

(4) Subject to the provisions of this section, an assessor under this section may be appointed either generally or for any particular proceedings or class of proceedings, and shall hold and vacate office in accordance with the terms of the instrument under which he is appointed.

(5) Any remuneration paid by the General Dental Council to persons appointed to act as assessors shall be at such rates as the Privy Council may approve.

## 29. Appeals in disciplinary cases

(1) At any time within twenty-eight days from the service of a notification that the Disciplinary Committee have determined under the

foregoing provisions of this Act that the name of a person shall be erased from the register, that person may, in accordance with such rules as Her Majesty in Council may by Order provide for the purposes of this section, appeal to Her Majesty in Council; and the Judicial Committee Act, 1833, shall apply in relation to the Disciplinary Committee as it applies to such courts as are mentioned in section three of that Act (which provides for the reference to the Judicial Committee of the Privy Council of appeals to Her Majesty in Council).

(2) The General Dental Council may appear as respondent on any such appeal; and for the purpose of enabling directions to be given as to the costs of any such appeal the Council shall be deemed to be a party thereto, whether they appear on the hearing of the appeal or not.

(3) Where no appeal is brought against the determination or where such an appeal is brought but withdrawn or struck out for want of prosecution, the determination shall take effect on the expiration of the time for appealing, or, as the case may be, on the withdrawal or striking out of the appeal.

(4) Subject as aforesaid, where an appeal is brought against the determination the determination shall take effect if and when the appeal is dismissed and not otherwise.

## 30. Restoration of name erased in a disciplinary case

(1) Where a person's name has been erased from the register in consequence of a decision in a disciplinary case, the name of that person shall not again be entered in the register except by direction of the General Dental Council, but the Council may direct that the name of that person shall be restored to the register:

Provided that an application for the restoration of a name to the register shall not be made to the Council—

(a) within ten months from the date of erasure; or

(b) within ten months from a previous application.

(2) The General Dental Council shall refer any application under this section to the Disciplinary Committee for determination by them.

## 31. Co-operation with Dental Board of Republic of Ireland

(1) With a view to preventing the holding of simultaneous inquiries—

(a) the General Dental Council shall report to the Dental Board of the Republic of Ireland every case in which it is proposed, in connection with the exercise of the disciplinary powers of the Council or of the Council's committees, to hold an inquiry into the conduct in the United Kingdom of a person registered in the dental register of the Republic of Ireland;

(*b*) where the General Dental Council receives a report from the Dental Board of the Republic of Ireland as to a proposal to hold an inquiry in connection with the exercise of the disciplinary powers of that Board, the Council and the Council's committees shall have regard to the desirability of postponing inquiry by them into the matter to which the report relates until the inquiry by the Dental Board of the Republic of Ireland is completed.

(2) The General Dental Council shall report to the Dental Board of the Republic of Ireland every case in which disciplinary action resulting in erasure from the register is taken against a person registered in the dental register of the Republic of Ireland.

## 32. Exemption from jury service and certain other duties

(1) A registered dentist shall, if he so wishes, be exempt from serving on all juries and inquests whatsoever, and from serving in any corporate, parochial, ward, hundred or township office and the name of such a person shall not be returned in any list of persons liable to serve in any such office as aforesaid.

(2) Nothing in this section shall affect subsection (1) of section two of the Juries Act, 1922 (which provides that persons named in the jurors book shall be liable to serve as jurors notwithstanding that they might have claimed exemption).

## Part III

RESTRICTIONS ON PRACTICE OF DENTISTRY AND CARRYING ON BUSINESS OF DENTISTRY

## 33. The practice of dentistry

(1) For the purposes of this Act, the practice of dentistry shall be deemed to include the performance of any such operation and the giving of any such treatment, advice or attendance as is usually performed or given by dentists, and any person who performs any operation or gives any treatment, advice or attendance on or to any person as preparatory to or for the purpose of or in connection with the fitting insertion or fixing of dentures, artificial teeth or other dental appliances shall be deemed to have practised dentistry within the meaning of this Act.

(2) Dental work shall not be treated for the purposes of this Act as amounting to the practice of dentistry if it is undertaken—

(*a*) by a person recognised by a dental authority as a student of dentistry, or by a person recognised by a medical authority as a medical student, as part of a course of instruction approved by that authority for students of that kind, or as part of an examination so approved, or

(*b*) by any person as part of a course of instruction which he is following in order to qualify for membership of a class of ancillary dental workers or as part of examinations which must be passed in order to qualify for membership of a class of ancillary dental workers,

but subject to the foregoing provisions of this subsection a person who undertakes dental work in the course of his studies shall be treated for the purposes of this Act as practising dentistry if he would have been treated for those purposes as practising dentistry if he had undertaken that work in the course of earning his livelihood.

(3) In this section the expression "medical authority" means one of the universities and other bodies who choose appointed members of the General Medical Council.

## 34. Prohibition on practice of dentistry by laymen

(1) A person who is not a registered dentist or a registered medical practitioner shall not practise or hold himself out, whether directly or by implication, as practising or as being prepared to practise dentistry and a person who acts in contravention of this subsection shall be liable—

(*a*) on conviction on indictment to a fine not exceeding five hundred pounds, and

(*b*) on summary conviction to a fine not exceeding one hundred pounds.

(2) Nothing in this section shall operate to prevent—

(*a*) the extraction of a tooth by a duly registered pharmaceutical chemist where the case is urgent and no registered medical practitioner or registered dentist is available and the operation is performed without the application of any general or local anaesthetic, or

(*b*) the performance in any public dental service of minor dental work by any person under the personal supervision of a registered dentist and in accordance with conditions approved by the Minister of Health after consultation with the General Dental Council or (in the case of conditions laid down before the setting up of the General Dental Council) with the Dental Board.

(3) Summary proceedings for an offence under this section may, notwithstanding anything in section one hundred and four of the Magistrates' Courts Act, 1952, or any corresponding enactment forming part of the law of Scotland or Northern Ireland be instituted at any time within one year from the commission of the offence.

(4) In the application of this section to Scotland a reference to the Secretary of State shall be substituted for the reference to the Minister of Health and in the application of this section to Northern Ireland a reference to the Ministry of Health and Local Government in Northern Ireland shall be substituted for the like reference and the reference to a registered chemist shall include a reference to a registered druggist and to a licentiate apothecary.

## 35. Prohibition on use of practitioners' titles by laymen

(1) A person who is not a registered dentist or a registered medical practitioner shall not take or use the title of dentist, dental surgeon or dental practitioner, either alone or in combination with any other word, and no person shall take or use any title or description implying that he is a registered dentist unless he is a registered dentist.

(2) A person who acts in contravention of the provisions of this section shall be liable—

(a) on conviction on indictment to a fine not exceeding five hundred pounds, and

(b) on summary conviction to a fine not exceeding one hundred pounds.

## 36. Restrictions on carrying on the business of dentistry

(1) For the purposes of this Act a person shall be treated as carrying on the business of dentistry if, and only if, he or a partnership of which he is a member receives payment for services rendered in the course of the practice of dentistry by him or by a partner of his, or by an employee of his or of all or any of the partners.

(2) Notwithstanding the foregoing subsection neither the receipt of payments—

(a) by an authority providing national and local authority health services, or

(b) by a person providing dental treatment for his employees without a view to profit, or

(c) by a person providing dental treatment without a view to profit under conditions approved by the Minister of Health or the Secretary of State or the Ministry of Health and Local Government for Northern Ireland,

nor in the receipt of payment in respect of any such operations as is mentioned in paragraph (*a*) of subsection (2) of section thirty-four of this Act shall constitute the carrying on of the business of dentistry for the said purposes.

## 37. Restriction on individuals

(1) Subject to the provisions of this section, an individual who is not a registered dentist or a registered medical practitioner shall not carry on the business of dentistry unless he was engaged in carrying on the business of dentistry on the twenty-first day of July, nineteen hundred and fifty-five, and an individual who contravenes this section shall be liable—

    (*a*) on conviction on indictment to a fine not exceeding five hundred pounds, and

    (*b*) on summary conviction to a fine not exceeding one hundred pounds.

(2) Where a registered dentist or registered medical practitioner who died on or after the fourth day of July, nineteen hundred and fifty-six, was at his death carrying on a business or practice constituting the business of dentistry, this section shall not operate to prevent his personal representatives or his widow or any of his children, or trustees on behalf of his widow or any of his children, from carrying on the business of dentistry in continuance of that business or practice during the three years beginning with his death.

(3) Where a registered dentist or a registered medical practitioner who died before the fourth day of July, nineteen hundred and fifty-six, was at his death carrying on a business or practice constituting the business of dentistry, this section shall not operate to prevent—

    (*a*) his personal representatives or any of his children or trustees on behalf of any of his children from carrying on the business of dentistry in continuance of that business or practice at any time before the fourth day of July, nineteen hundred and fifty-nine, or

    (*b*) his widow or trustees on behalf of his widow from carrying on the business of dentistry in continuance of that business or practice at any time during her life.

(4) Where a registered dentist or registered medical practitioner becomes bankrupt at a time when he is carrying on a business or practice

constituting the business of dentistry, this section shall not operate to prevent his trustee in bankruptcy, or in Northern Ireland, the official assignee, from carrying on the business of dentistry in continuance of that business or practice during the three years beginning with the bankruptcy or, if he became bankrupt before the fourth day of July, nineteen hundred and fifty-six, at any time before the fourth day of July, nineteen hundred and fifty-nine.

### 38. Restrictions on bodies corporate

(1) It shall be unlawful for a body corporate, other than one exempted under the next following section, to carry on the business of dentistry and a body contravening this section shall be liable on summary conviction to a fine not exceeding one hundred pounds.

(2) Where a body corporate is convicted of an offence under this section, every director and manager thereof shall, unless he proves that the offence was committed without his knowledge, be guilty of the like offence.

### 39. Bodies corporate entitled to carry on business of dentistry

(1) A body corporate may, subject to the following provisions of this Act, carry on the business of dentistry—

    (a) if it were carrying on the business of dentistry on the twenty-first day of July, nineteen hundred and fifty-five, and

    (b) if it carries on no business other than dentistry or some business ancillary to the business of dentistry, and

    (c) if a majority of the directors are registered dentists, and

    (d) if all its operating staff are either registered dentists or ancillary dental workers:

Provided that paragraph (a) of this subsection shall not apply—

    (i) to a society registered under the Industrial and Provident Societies Acts, 1893 to 1954, or the Industrial and Provident Societies Acts (Northern Ireland), 1893 to 1955, or

    (ii) to a body corporate coming into existence on the reconstruction of a body corporate carrying on business on the said day or on the amalgamation of two or more such bodies.

(2) Paragraph (b) of the foregoing subsection shall not apply to a body corporate which was carrying on the business of dentistry before the twenty-eighth day of July, nineteen hundred and twenty-one, so as to prevent it from carrying on any business which that body was at that date lawfully entitled to carry on.

(3) Every body corporate carrying on the business of dentistry shall

in every year transmit to the registrar a statement in the prescribed form containing the names and addresses of all persons who are its directors or managers or who perform dental operations in connection with its business and if any such body corporate fails to do so, it shall be deemed to be carrying on the business of dentistry in contravention of the provisions of the last foregoing section.

(4) Nothing in this section shall prevent a body corporate from carrying on the business of dentistry in the circumstances mentioned in sub-sections (2), (3) and (4) of section thirty-seven of this Act, and the last foregoing subsection shall not apply in those circumstances.

(5) In this section 'prescribed' means prescribed by regulations made by the General Dental Council.

## 40. Withdrawal of privilege from body corporate

(1) Where—

    (a) a body corporate is convicted of an offence under section thirty-eight of this Act, or

    (b) the name of a director of a body corporate is erased from the register under section twenty-five of this Act, or

    (c) a director of a body corporate is convicted under section thirty-four or section thirty-seven of this Act,

the Disciplinary Committee may direct that the exemption conferred by the last foregoing section shall cease to extend to that body corporate as from such date as the Committee may specify:

Provided that the Committee shall not take a case into consideration while proceedings by way of appeal are pending which may result in this subsection being rendered inapplicable in that case nor during the period within which any such proceedings as aforesaid may be brought.

(2) Where—

    (a) the name of a member of the operating staff of a body corporate is erased from the register under section twenty-five of this Act, and

    (b) in the opinion of the Disciplinary Committee the act or omission constituting the offence or infamous or disgraceful conduct on account of which his name was erased was instigated or connived at by a director of the body corporate, or, if the act or omission was a continuing act or omission, a director of the body corporate had, or reasonably ought to have had, knowledge of the continuance thereof,

the Committee may direct that the exemption conferred by the last foregoing section shall cease to extend to that body corporate as from such date as the Committee may specify:

Provided that the Committee shall not take a case into consideration while proceedings by way of appeal are pending which may result in this subsection being rendered inapplicable in that case nor during the period in which any such proceedings as aforesaid may be brought.

(3) Where the Disciplinary Committee determine under either of the foregoing subsections that the exemption conferred by the last foregoing section shall cease to extend to a body corporate, the Committee shall notify the body corporate of their determination and the body corporate may, within twenty-eight days of the notification, in accordance with such rules as Her Majesty in Council may by Order provide for the purposes of this section, appeal to Her Majesty in Council—

(*a*) in the case of a determination under subsection (1) of this section on the ground that, notwithstanding the conviction or, as the case may be, the erasure of the name, the Disciplinary Committee's decision was unjustified; and

(*b*) in the case of a determination under subsection (2) of this section, on the ground that the opinion of the Disciplinary Committee as to the matters referred to in paragraph (*b*) of the said subsection (2) was incorrect or that, although that opinion was correct, the Committee's decision was unjustified.

(4) The provisions of section twenty-nine of this Act shall apply for the purposes of the last foregoing subsection as they apply in relation to an appeal under that section.

(5) A body corporate shall not be liable under this section to be deprived of the right to carry on the business of dentistry in consequence of the erasure of the name of a director or member of the operating staff or in consequence of a conviction of the body corporate or of a director if the erasure or conviction took place before the fourth day of July, nineteen hundred and fifty-six.

## Part IV

### ANCILLARY DENTAL WORKERS

### 41. Power of Council to create classes of ancillary dental workers

(1) Subject to the provisions of this and the next following section the General Dental Council may by statutory instrument make regulations for the establishment of classes of ancillary dental workers to

undertake dental work of kinds prescribed by the regulations, being dental work amounting to the practice of dentistry (as defined in this Act).

(2) Regulations under this section may in particular make provision as respects any class so established—

> (a) for prescribing the qualifications for becoming a member of that class;
>
> (b) for prescribing the dental work which a member of that class may undertake and the conditions, if any, under which he may undertake it;
>
> (c) for the establishment of a roll or record for that class.

(3) The regulations shall be so framed as to secure that provisions in the regulations as to the arrangements to be made for training persons to become members of a class of ancilliary dental workers do not materially impair the facilities for the training of dental students.

(4) Regulations under this section may authorise members of a class of ancilliary dental workers established by the regulations to use a title indicating their membership, and a person who wilfully uses that title when he is not authorised under the regulations to use that title shall, on summary conviction, be liable to a fine not exceeding fifty pounds.

(5) If a member of a class of ancillary dental workers uses any title or description reasonably calculated to suggest that he possesses any status or qualification connected with dentistry other than a status or qualification which he in fact possesses and which is indicated by particulars entered in the roll or record of the class in respect of him, he shall be liable on summary conviction to a fine not exceeding fifty pounds:

Provided that where the regulations do not provide for a roll or record of the class in which particulars of status and qualifications may be entered, this subsection shall have effect as if the words "and which is indicated by particulars entered in the roll or record of the class in respect of him" were omitted.

(6) If after regulations have been made under this section establishing a class of ancillary dental workers the General Dental Council proposes to make further regulations varying the provisions relating to that class or abolishing that class, the further regulations shall be so framed as to secure that a person belonging to that class at the time when the further regulations are made is still permitted to do any dental work of a kind which he was previously permitted to do:

Provided that the Council need not comply with this subsection in framing the regulations if they are satisfied that reasonable steps have been taken to give to each of the persons belonging to the class in question particulars of their proposals with an opportunity of raising objections and none of those persons has maintained any objection to those proposals.

(7) Where a roll or record is established for a class of ancillary dental workers, regulations under this section may, in particular, provide for—

(a) prescribing a fee to be charged when a person's name is entered in the roll or record,

(b) prescribing a fee to be charged in respect of the retention of a person's name in the roll or record in any year subsequent to the year in which that person's name was first recorded, and

(c) authorising the person in charge of the roll or record to erase from the roll or record the name of a person who, after such notices and warnings as may be prescribed by the regulations, fails to pay a fee prescribed under the last foregoing paragraph.

(8) Section thirty-four of this Act shall not operate to prevent a person doing anything which he is permitted to do by regulations under this section, and the prohibition contained in that section on a person holding himself out as practising or being prepared to practise dentistry shall not apply to a person for the time being permitted by regulations under this section to practise dentistry of any particular kind.

(9) The General Dental Council shall not make any regulations under this section unless a draft of those regulations which has been approved by the Privy Council has been laid before Parliament and has been approved by a resolution of each House of Parliament, and the Privy Council shall not approve a draft of regulations prescribing—

(a) a fee under paragraph (a) of subsection (7) of this section of an amount exceeding two pounds, or

(b) a fee under paragraph (b) of that subsection of an amount exceeding one pound

unless in their opinion a fee of that amount is justified by changes in circumstances which have taken place since the passing of the Dentists Act, 1956.

## 42. Restrictions on employment of ancillary dental workers

(1) Regulations under the last foregoing section shall not permit an ancillary dental worker of any class to undertake—

(a) the extraction of teeth other than deciduous teeth, or

(b) except in the course of the provision of national and local authority health services, the filling of teeth or the extraction of deciduous teeth, or

(c) the fitting, insertion or fixing of dentures or artificial teeth.

(2) Regulations under the last foregoing section shall be so framed as to secure that dental work amounting to the practice of dentistry carried out by an ancillary dental worker in the course of the provision of national and local authority health services is carried out under the direction of a registered dentist, and it shall be the duty of the General Dental Council to secure, either by provision in the said regulations or otherwise, that, so long as they think it advisable, such work is only carried out after the registered dentist has examined the patient and has indicated to the ancillary dental worker the course of treatment to be provided for the patient.

(3) Regulations under the last foregoing section shall be so framed as to secure that dental work amounting to the practice of dentistry carried out by an ancillary dental worker otherwise than in the course of providing national and local authority health services is carried out under the direct personal supervision of a registered dentist.

(4) References in this section and in any other provision of this Act to the provision of national and local authority health services shall be construed as references to the provision—

(a) of hospital and specialist services under Part II of the National Health Service Act, 1946, Part II of the National Health Service (Scotland) Act, 1947, or Part III of the Health Services Act (Northern Ireland), 1948, or

(b) of services at health centres under section twenty-one of the National Health Service Act, 1946, section fifteen of the National Health Service (Scotland) Act, 1947, or section seventeen of the Health Services Act (Northern Ireland), 1948, or

(c) of services for mothers and young children under section twenty-two of the National Health Service Act, 1946, section twenty-two of the National Health Service (Scotland) Act, 1947, or section thirty-eight of the Health Services Act (Northern Ireland), 1948, or

(d) of medical inspection and treatment of pupils under section forty-eight or seventy-eight of the Education Act, 1944, section four of the Education (Miscellaneous Provisions) Act, 1953, section fifty-one of the Education (Scotland) Act, 1946, section six of the Education (Scotland) Act, 1956, or section forty-two or subsection 2) of section seventy-four of the Education Act (Northern Ireland), 1947.

## 43. Duty to make arrangements for experimental scheme

(1) If the Privy Council, after consulting the General Dental Council,

are of opinion that, in order that the value to the community of the existence of a class of ancillary dental workers—

(*a*) permitted to undertake the filling of teeth and the extraction of deciduous teeth, and

(*b*) employed to do work of that kind in the course of the provision of national and local authority health services,

may be judged, the experiment provided for by the following subsections of this section should be carried out, they may require the General Dental Council to comply with the following subsections of this section; and those subsections shall not come into operation unless the Privy Council make that requirement.

(2) The General Dental Council shall make arrangements for encouraging and helping a number of persons to undergo training approved by the General Dental Council for the purposes of this section and arrangements for making available to such of those persons as, in the opinion of the General Dental Council, attain the necessary standards of proficiency, employment in the course of the provision of national and local authority health services.

(3) The General Dental Council shall ensure that the number of persons selected to undergo training under the arrangements is adequate having regard to the conclusions which will be drawn from the experiment under this section.

(4) The General Dental Council shall delegate their functions under subsections (2) and (3) of this section to a committee constituted in accordance with paragraph 13 of Part II of the First Schedule to this Act and that committee shall carry out those functions subject to the general control of the Council.

(5) The General Dental Council may by regulations contained in a statutory instrument prescribe the kinds of dental work which persons designated by the regulations, being persons to whom employment is made available under the arrangements, may undertake in the course of the provision of national and local authority health services and the conditions subject to which they may undertake work of that kind and subsection (8) of section forty-one of this Act shall apply in relation to regulations under this subsection as it applies in relation to regulations under that section.

(6) The General Dental Council shall exercise the power conferred by the last foregoing subsection so as to secure that—

(*a*) while the arrangements are in force, persons to whom employment is made available under the arrangements are not permitted to practise dentistry except in accordance with the arrangements; and

(b) when the arrangements have been terminated, the persons who have in the opinion of the General Dental Council attained the necessary standards of proficiency under the arrangements shall, unless they infringe disciplinary provisions laid down by the regulations, or unless they become qualified to become members of such a class as is referred to in subsection (1) of this section, continue to have an opportunity to earn their livelihood by doing work of the kind for which they have been trained under the arrangements.

(7) The General Dental Council shall, not later than three years after the arrangements are set in train, make to the Privy Council an interim report on the progress of the experiment under this section, and the Privy Council shall lay the said report before Parliament.

(8) The Minister of Health and the Secretary of State shall have power with the consent of the Treasury to contribute out of moneys provided by Parliament towards defraying expenses incurred by the General Dental Council in connection with the making of arrangements under this section.

## 44. Termination of experimental scheme

(1) The Privy Council may, when, after consulting the General Dental Council, it appears to them that they are in a position to judge the results of the arrangements under the last foregoing section, require the General Dental Council to terminate the arrangements; and the General Dental Council shall have regard to the desirability of not admitting persons for training under the arrangements under such circumstances that they are unlikely to have completed their training before the arrangements are terminated.

(2) The General Dental Council on being required by the Privy Council to terminate the arrangements shall make to them a final report on the results of the experiment and the Privy Council shall lay the report before Parliament.

(3) After the termination of the arrangements the Privy Council, unless in the light of the said reports they conclude that the existence of such a class of ancillary dental workers as is referred to in subsection (1) of the last foregoing section would not be of value to the community, may require the General Dental Council to make regulations under section forty-one of this Act for the establishment of such a class as aforesaid; and the General Dental Council shall comply with the requirement.

This subsection shall be without prejudice to the power of the Council to make such regulations without any requirement.

## 45. Establishment of Ancillary Dental Workers Committee

(1) The General Dental Council shall set up an Ancillary Dental Workers Committee and shall refer to the Committee all matters connected with ancillary dental services.

(2) Paragraph 14 of Part II of the First Schedule to this Act shall have effect as respects the Ancillary Dental Workers Committee.

(3) Regulations under section forty-one of this Act may provide for entrusting to the Ancillary Dental Workers Committee the duty of enforcing standards of conduct among ancillary dental workers and for enabling that Committee to withdraw from a person not conforming to those standards the right to undertake dental work as an ancillary dental worker of all or any classes.

### Part V

SUPPLEMENTAL

## 46. Provisions as to proceedings before Disciplinary Committee

(1) For the purposes of any proceedings under this Act before the Disciplinary Committee relating to the removal of a person's name from the register, or its restoration to the register, or relating to the withdrawal from a body corporate of the right to carry on the business of dentistry, the Committee may administer oaths, and any party to the proceedings may sue out writs of subpoena ad testificandum and duces tecum, but no person shall be compelled under any such writ to produce any document which he could not be compelled to produce on the trial of an action.

(2) Section forty-nine of the Supreme Court of Judicature (Consolidation) Act, 1925 (which provides a special procedure for the issue of such writs so as to be in force throughout the United Kingdom), shall apply in relation to any such proceedings as aforesaid as it applies in relation to causes or matters in the High Court.

(3) In relation to proceedings before the Disciplinary Committee, the expression "party" means, unless the context otherwise requires—

    (a) in a case relating to the removal of a person's name from the register or its restoration to the register, that person, and

    (b) in a case relating to the withdrawal from a body corporate of a right to carry on the business of dentistry, that body corporate and any director of that body corporate, and

(c) in any case, any person on whose complaint the proceedings are brought or any solicitor appointed by the General Dental Council to represent them at the proceedings.

## 47. Exercise of powers conferred on Privy Council

The powers conferred by this Act on the Privy Council (other than the power of hearing appeals against determinations to erase names from the register or determinations to withdraw from bodies corporate the right to carry on the business of dentistry) shall be exercisable by any two or more members of the Privy Council.

## 48. Rules, regulations, orders and other instruments

(1) The Statutory Instruments Act, 1946, shall apply to a statutory instrument containing regulations made by the General Dental Council under this Act in like manner as if the regulations had been made by a Minister of the Crown.

(2) Prima facie evidence of any document issued by the General Dental Council or the Dental Board (that is to say the Board dissolved in pursuance of the Dentist Act, 1956, and replaced by the General Dental Council) may be given in all legal proceedings by the production of a copy or extract purporting to be certified to be a true copy or extract by the registrar or some other officer of the General Dental Council authorised to give a certificate for the purposes of this sub-section.

(3) No proof shall be required of the hand-writing or official position or authority of any person certifying in pursuance of this section to the truth of any copy of or extract from any regulations or other document.

## 49. Transitional provisions as respects employees prejudiced by dissolution of Dental Board

The Privy Council may by statutory instrument make regulations for compensating, out of the funds of the General Dental Council, such of the employees of the Dental Board as have suffered loss of employment or loss or diminution of emoluments attributable to the dissolution of the Dental Board and the other consequences of the passing of the Dentists Act, 1956.

## 50. Interpretation

(1) In this Act—

"dental authority" has the meaning assigned to it by section two of this Act;

TDH

"diploma" means any diploma, degree, fellowship, membership, licence, authority to practise, letters testimonial, certificate or other status or document granted by any university, corporation, college or other body or by any department of, or persons acting under the authority of, the government of any country or place within or without Her Majesty's dominions;

"Commonwealth diploma" and "foreign diploma" have the meanings assigned to them by section fourteen of this Act;

"disciplinary case" has the meaning assigned to it by section twenty-five of this Act;

"practice of dentistry" has the meaning assigned to it by section thirty-three of this Act.

(2) References in this Act to the provision of national and local authority health services shall be construed in accordance with the provisions of section forty-two of this Act.

(3) Any reference in this Act to any provision of any other Act shall, unless the context otherwise requires, be construed as including a reference to that provision as amended by any other Act, including any Act of the Parliament of Northern Ireland.

## 51. Repeal and savings

(1) The enactments set out in the Second Schedule to this Act shall be repealed to the extent specified in the third column of that Schedule.

(2) Nothing in the repeals made by this section shall affect any bye-law, rule, regulation, order or other instrument made under an enactment repealed by this section, or any appointment, election, nomination, application, authority, direction, notice, registration or other thing so made, given or done and every such instrument or other thing which at the commencement of this Act has effect or is continued in force under an enactment so repealed shall continue in force and, so far as it could have been made, given or done under the corresponding provision of this Act, shall have effect as if made, given or done under that provision.

(3) Without prejudice to subsection (2) of this section, the said repeals shall not affect the continued registration in the dentists register of persons duly admitted to the register under any enactment nor reproduced in this Act.

(4) A reference in any Act to colonial dentists or to registration as a colonial dentist shall, unless the context otherwise requires, be construed as a reference to dentists registered in the Commonwealth list and to registration as a Commonwealth dentist.

(5) Any enactment or other document whatsoever referring to any enactment repealed by this Act shall be construed as referring to the corresponding enactment in this Act.

(6) The mention of particular matters in this section shall not be held to prejudice or affect the general application of section thirty-eight of the Interpretation Act, 1889, with regard to the effect of repeals.

## 52. Application to Northern Ireland

It is hereby declared that this Act extends to Northern Ireland and for the purposes of section six of the Government of Ireland Act, 1920 (which precludes the Parliament of Northern Ireland from amending Acts of Parliament of the United Kingdom passed after the day appointed under that Act) this Act shall be treated as passed before that day.

## 53. Short title and commencement

(1) This Act may be cited as the Dentists Act, 1957.

(2) This Act shall come into operation at the expiration of a period of three months beginning with the date on which it is passed.

# SCHEDULES

## FIRST SCHEDULE: The General Dental Council and its Committees

### Part I

#### CONSTITUTION, ETC., OF COUNCIL

1. The General Dental Council shall be a body corporate, shall have a common seal, and shall have power to acquire and hold land without licence in mortmain.

2.—(1) The General Dental Council shall consist of eighteen members, together with the members to be nominated under this Part of this Schedule by the authorities who are for the time being dental authorities.

(2) Of the members of the Council—

    (a) eleven shall be elected by registered dentists from among themselves;

    (b) three, who shall be registered dentists, shall be nominated by Her Majesty on the advice of Her Privy Council;

    (c) three, who shall not be registered dentists, and of whom two shall be chosen for England and Wales and one for Scotland, shall be nominated by Her Majesty on the advice of Her Privy Council;

    (d) one, who shall not be a registered dentist, shall be nominated by the Governor of Northern Ireland;

and of the remaining members, all of whom shall be registered dentists, the University of London (so long as it is a dental authority) shall nominate two, and every other authority which is for the time being a dental authority shall nominate one.

(3) In addition there shall be six persons nominated by the General Medical Council from among members of that Council who shall act and vote as members of the General Dental Council in connexion with dental education and examinations, but who, save as otherwise expressly provided by this sub-paragraph or any other provision of this Act, shall not be treated as members of the General Dental Council for the purposes of this Act:

Provided that no proceedings of the General Dental Council shall be invalid by reason of any member nominated by the General Medical Council having acted or voted in a manner not permitted by this sub-paragraph.

3.—(1) The term of office of those elected as members of the General Dental Council on its establishment shall end at the expiration of five years from the fourth day of July, nineteen hundred and fifty-six, and on that date in the year nineteen hundred and sixty-one, and at the expiration of each succeeding period of five years, all the persons who are then elected members of the Council shall retire together; and elections shall be held accordingly before the end of the said periods.

(2) An election shall be held to fill a casual vacancy among the elected members if, and only if, the vacancy occurs more than twelve months before the beginning of the next five-year period.

(3) Of the eleven elected members—

    (*a*) seven shall be elected by the dentists whose addresses in the register are in England, the Isle of Man or the Channel Islands;

    (*b*) one shall be elected by the dentists whose addresses in the register are in Wales;

    (*c*) two shall be elected by the dentists whose addresses in the register are in Scotland;

    (*d*) one shall be elected by the dentists whose addresses in the register are in Ireland.

(4) Elections under this paragraph shall be conducted in accordance with rules made by the General Dental Council which shall include provision—

    (*a*) for nominations being made by registered dentists;

    (*b*) for the use of voting papers and for voting by post.

(5) This paragraph shall apply in relation to Monmouthshire as if it were part of Wales and not part of England and references to England and Wales shall be construed accordingly.

4.—(1) The term of office of those nominated as members of the Council shall end at the expiration of three years from the fourth day of July, nineteen hundred and fifty-six, and on that date in the year nineteen hundred and fifty-nine, and at the expiration of each succeeding period of five years, all the persons who are then nominated members of the Council shall retire together; and nominations shall be made accordingly before the end of the said three-year period and of each five-year period.

(2) A nomination shall be made to fill a casual vacancy among the nominated members whenever it occurs.

(3) In this paragraph references to nominated members include references to members nominated by the General Medical Council for the limited purposes set out in sub-paragraphs (3) of paragraph 2 of this Part of this Schedule.

(4) Where in the course of the said period of three years or one of the said periods of five years an authority becomes for the first time a dental authority, the right of that authority to nominate a member of the General Dental Council shall be postponed until the end of that period.

5.—(1) The General Dental Council shall elect a registered dentist as President from among the members of the Council.

(2) The President shall hold office until he next retires from membership of the Council.

6. A person shall not be disqualified for being elected or nominated as a member of the Council or for being elected as President of the Council by reason of having already served as a member or, as the case may be, as President.

## General powers of Council

7.—(1) Subject to the following provisions of this Part of this Schdeule, the Council shall have power to do any thing which in their opinion is calculated to facilitate the proper discharge of their functions.

(2) The Council shall, in particular, have power to pay to its members, including the members nominated by the General Medical Council, fees for

attendances at meetings of the Council or its committees and travelling and subsistence allowances while attending such meetings or while on any other business of the Council but, save as expressly provided by this paragraph or any other provision of this Act, the Council shall not have power to pay to its members any remuneration for doing the business of the Council and shall not have power to pay the said fees for attendance to a member of the Council who is also a member of the House of Commons or a member of the Senate or House of Commons of Northern Ireland.

(3) The powers of the Council and of any of the Council's committees may be exercised notwithstanding any vacancy, and no proceedings of the Council or of any of the Council's committees shall be invalidated by any defect in the appointment of a member.

8.—(1) The Council may, after paying their expenses, including the payment authorized under this Schedule to be made to their members and the salaries or remuneration of their officers, allocate any money received by them whether by way of fees or otherwise to purposes connected with dental education and research or any other public purposes connected with the profession of dentistry in such manner as they may think fit.

(2) The Council shall keep accounts of all sums received or paid by them under this Act and the accounts shall be audited in manner prescribed by regulations made by the Privy Council and shall be published annually and laid before Parliament.

9.—(1) The Council may make rules for regulating the proceedings (including quorum) of the Council and for delegating, subject to the provisions of this Act, to committees, including the committees referred to in Part II of this Schedule, functions of the Council and, subject as aforesaid, for appointing the members and regulating the proceedings (including quorum) of any committees referred to in Part II of this Schedule and any sub-committees.

(2) The power conferred by the foregoing sub-paragraph shall include power to make rules as to the procedure to be followed and rules of evidence to be observed in proceedings before the Disciplinary Committee (other than proceedings in disciplinary cases) but rules under this sub-paragraph shall not come into force until approved by order of the Privy Council contained in a statutory instrument:

Provided that before making any rules under this sub-paragraph the Council shall consult with such bodies of persons representing dentists as appear to the Council requisite to be consulted.

(3) Nothing in this paragraph shall authorize the Council to delegate any power of making rules or regulations under any other provision of this Act or the power of appointing assessors in inquiries in disciplinary cases.

## Part II

### COMMITTEES OF THE COUNCIL

### The Education Committee

10.—(1) The Education Committee shall consist of the President and eight other members of the Council (who shall all be registered dentists) and those persons who are only members of the Council for the limited purposes set out in sub-paragraph (3) of paragraph 2 of Part I of this Schedule.

(2) The Committee shall appoint a registered dentist to be chairman from among the members of the Committee.

## The Preliminary Proceedings Committee

11. The Preliminary Proceedings Committee shall consist of the President and five other members of the Council of whom one shall be a person who is not a registered dentist:

Provided that the President may appoint for the consideration of any particular case one or two members of the Council to be additional members of the Committee notwithstanding that the membership of the Committee is thereby raised to seven or eight.

## The Disciplinary Committee

12.—(1) The Disciplinary Committee shall consist of the President and ten other members of the Council of whom at least four shall be elected members of the Council and at least two shall be neither such elected members nor registered dentists.

(2) A member of the Preliminary Proceedings Committee other than the President of the Council shall not at the same time be a member of the Disciplinary Committee.

(3) At any meeting of the Disciplinary Committee the President of the Council or, in his absence, such member of the Committee as the Committee may choose shall be chairman.

(4) All acts of the Disciplinary Committee shall be decided by a majority of the members present at any meeting.

(5) The quorum for a meeting of the Disciplinary Committee shall be five, of whom at least one shall be an elected member of the Council.

## The committee entrusted with carrying out the experimental scheme for training ancillary dental workers

13.—(1) The committee entrusted with carrying out the experimental scheme for training ancillary dental workers shall consist of the President and eight other members of the Council and four persons who need not be members of the Council.

(2) Not less than three of the said eight members of the committee shall be members of the Council appointed by the dental authorities and not less than two of the said eight members of the committee shall be members of the Council elected by registered dentists.

(3) The four members of the committee who need not be members of the Council shall be appointed by the Privy Council, and of those four members of the committee two shall be registered dentists who are employed in the course of the provision of national and local authority health services and one shall be a person who is not a registered dentist.

(4) The committee shall appoint a registered dentist to be chairman from among the members of the committee.

## The Ancillary Dental Workers Committee

14.—(1) The Ancillary Dental Workers Committee shall consist of the

President and eight other members of the Council and six persons who are not members of the Council.

(2) Not more than six members of the Committee (excluding the President) shall be both members of the Council and registered dentists.

(3) Three of the six members of the Committee who are not members of the Council shall be appointed by the Minister of Health, the Secretary of State and the Minister of Health and Local Government for Northern Ireland acting jointly and two of the said three so appointed shall be registered dentists who are or have been employed in the course of the provision of national and local authority health services.

The said three members appointed by the said Ministers shall be appointed in the first instance to take office at the same time and they and their successors shall retire together at the end of successive three year periods, and an appointment made in the course of one of the said periods to fill a casual vacancy shall be for the remainder of that period.

(4) The other three of the six members of the Committee who are not members of the Council shall not be appointed until regulations have been made under this Act establishing a class of ancillary dental workers and shall then, in the first instance, be appointed by the Council from among members of the class so established.

(5) The said three persons appointed by the Council in the first instance shall retire on such date as the Council may fix and the persons to fill their vacancies shall be elected by members of all the classes of ancillary dental workers established by regulations under this Act in such manner and at such intervals as may be provided by rules made by the Council.

(6) The Council shall pay to members of the Committee who are not members of the Council allowances and fees at the same rates as in the case of those who are members of the Council and shall, as respects any member who is also a member of the House of Commons, or of the Senate or House of Commons of Northern Ireland, follow the same rule as to not paying him any fees for attendance.

(7) The chairman of the Committee shall be chosen by the Committee from among the members of the Committee who are registered dentists.

(8) The Committee may appoint a sub-committee to deal with disciplinary questions connected with members of a class of ancillary dental workers. The said sub-committee shall consist of not more than nine members.

## SECOND SCHEDULE: **Enactments Repealed**

| Session and Chapter | Short Title | Extent of Repeal |
|---|---|---|
| 41 & 42 Vict. c. 33. | The Dentists Act, 1878 | Section two. Section five so far as it applies in the United Kingdom. Sections six to forty and the Schedule. |
| 11 & 12 Geo. 5 c. 21. | The Dentists Act, 1921 | The whole Act. |
| 13 & 14 Geo. 5. c. 36 | The Dentists Act, 1923 | The whole Act. |
| 17 & 18 Geo. 5. c. 39. | The Medical and Dentists Acts Amendment Act, 1927. | In section two, in subsection (1) the words from 'and so far as' to the end of the subsection and subsection (2). In section three, subsection (3). |
| 4 & 5 Eliz. 2. c. 29. | The Dentists Act, 1956 | The whole Act except subsection (9) of section sixteen and in subsection (1) of section thirty-seven the short title. |

# Notice—for the Guidance of Registered Dental Practitioners concerning the Disciplinary Jurisdiction of the Council

*Issued by the General Dental Council*

### I. STATUTORY JURISDICTION OF THE COUNCIL

Under the Dentists Act, 1957,[1] the General Dental Council have a general responsibility to promote high standards of conduct among dentists. Section twenty-five of the Act provides that a dentist shall be liable to have his name erased from the dentists register if, either before or after he is registered, he has *a*) been convicted or an offence or *b*) been guilty of infamous or disgraceful conduct in a professional respect.

This Notice is issued for the information and guidance of registered dentists to indicate the nature of the criminal and professional offences which have in the past led to erasure from the register. It does not purport to give a complete list of offences which may lead to erasure. Any conviction or allegation of infamous or disgraceful conduct may be the subject of an inquiry by the Disciplinary Committee who must consider and judge, upon the facts brought before them, whether the name of the practitioner concerned shall be erased.

A registered dentist will be summoned to attend any inquiry concerning him but if he fails to attend the Disciplinary Committee may hold the inquiry and reach a determination in his absence.

A registered dentist is not outside the jurisdiction of the Council solely by reason of the fact that he is not in practice.

A registered dentist may be required to answer a charge of infamous or disgraceful conduct before the Disciplinary Committee in respect of facts which have already been the subject of an inquiry by a Dental Service Committee or Tribunal.

[1] Where reference is made in this Notice to the Dentists Act details and qualifying provisions are often omitted for the sake of simplicity. Accordingly whenever it is necessary to know the full meaning of the Act, recourse should be had to the text.

## II. CONVICTIONS

In considering a conviction reported to the Council the Disciplinary Committee have to determine whether the gravity of the offence which the dental practitioner has committed, or the cumulative gravity of offences committed by him on more than one occasion, makes it necessary in the public interest to erase his name from the register. Convictions for trivial offences are not normally referred to the Disciplinary Committee. The circumstances of the offence need not be directly connected with his profession or practice to render him liable to have his name erased from the register, but the Council are particularly concerned with offences which affect the practitioner's fitness to practise.

In considering convictions, the Committee accept the findings of the court on matters of fact as evidence of the facts proved. It is therefore unwise for a practitioner to plead guilty in a court of law to a charge to which he believes he has a defence, since such a plea will be regarded by the court, and subsequently by the Disciplinary Committee, as a confession that the charge made against him was well-founded.

Erasure from the register has been directed in consequence of convictions for the following offences among others not particularized in this Notice:

*a*) Driving, or being in charge of, a motor vehicle when under the influence of drink or drugs, or being found drunk, or being drunk and disorderly or incapable;

*b*) Forgery, fraud, larceny, embezzlement and cognate offences;

*c*) Bigamy;

*d*) Offences involving indecency.

## III. UNPROFESSIONAL CONDUCT

**1. Covering:** Under section thirty-four of the Dentists Act, 1957, it is unlawful for anyone to give, or even to suggest that he is prepared to give, any treatment or advice (including any treatment or advice in connexion with the fitting, insertion or fixing of dentures, artificial teeth or other dental appliances) such as is normally given by a dentist, unless he is registered either in the dentists register or under the Medical Acts, or is an enrolled dental hygienist practising dentistry to the limited extent permitted by the Ancillary Dental Workers Regulations, 1957. A registered dentist who employs the services of any person to practise dentistry has a duty to satisfy himself that that person is permitted by law to do so; and a registered dentist who, either knowingly or through neglect of this duty, enables a person to do dental work which that person is not permitted by law to do is liable to have his name erased from the register.

**2. Dangerous Drugs:** A registered dentist who commits an offence under the Dangerous Drugs Acts or Regulations involving an abuse of the privileges conferred upon registered dentists under those Acts is liable to have his name erased from the register, whether or not his offence has been the subject of criminal proceedings.

**3. Abuse of Professional Relationship:** A registered dentist who commits any act of immorality, indecency or dishonesty or any other act involving abuse of the professional relationship in which he stands to a patient is liable to have his name erased from the register.

**4. Improper Statements or Certificates:** A registered dentist who makes any statement or declaration or signs, or authorizes any person to sign on his behalf by means of a rubber stamp or otherwise, any certificate or other document (including any document required by Regulations made under the National Health Service Acts), or who induces or permits a patient to sign any certificate or document, which he knows, or ought to know, to be untrue, misleading or otherwise improper, is liable to have his name erased from the register.

**5. Use of Titles and Descriptions:** Under section fifteen of the Dentists Act, 1957, a registered dentist is prohibited from using any title or description, other than dentist, dental practitioner or dental surgeon, reasonably calculated to suggest that he possesses any professional status or qualification other than one which he in fact possesses and which is indicated by particulars entered against his name in the register. Under this section is included not only the use of titles as a form of address, but also the use of words or letters on a professional plate or sign or on stationery, forms or documents such as are reasonably calculated to suggest a professional status or qualification which does not appear against the practitioner's name in the dentists register (even though he possesses it in fact). A registered dentist who contravenes the provisions of this section is liable on summary conviction to a fine not exceeding fifty pounds and is liable to have his name erased from the register.

**6. Misleading Announcements:** In general the Council consider that any act or omission by a registered dentist in connexion with his practice which is calculated to mislead the public may be held to constitute infamous or disgraceful conduct. Consequently they disapprove of a registered dentist carrying on a dental practice in a name other than the name in which he appears in the dentists register. In the case of a body corporate or partnership carrying on the business of dentistry the name of every registered dentist regularly attending patients should be shown at the premises where he practices and given normal prominence. The Council disapprove of any announcements or signs which state or imply that a particular dentist is in regular attendance at a practice when this is not a fact. Therefore the Council consider that a registered dentist should only retain the professional plate of his predecessor in the practice, in addition to his own professional plate, if the name of the predecessor is plainly preceded by the word 'late' or 'formerly'.

**7. Advertising, Canvassing, etc.:** It is in the opinion of the Council contrary to the public interest and discreditable to the profession of dentistry for any registered dentist to advertise or canvass, whether directly or indirectly, for the purpose of obtaining patients or promoting his own professional advantage. Accordingly, a registered dentist who advertises or canvasses for any such purpose or who employs or is professionally associated with any one who does so, or who procures or acquiesces in the publication of notices commending or drawing attention to his own professional skill, knowledge, qualifications or services or depreciating those of others, is liable to have his name erased from the register.

In determining whether or not any particular course of conduct constitutes advertising or canvassing in accordance with the foregoing paragraph, the Council will take into consideration the circumstances in which it was pursued. Nevertheless they believe that the following observations concerning certain practices which, among others, may be held to constitute such advertising and canvassing will serve as a guide to registered dentists seeking information on the subject.

*a)* Signs:

The Council disapprove of the exhibition in connexion with a dental practice of any sign which, by its nature, position, size or wording, exceeds what is reasonably necessary to indicate to those who are seeking the practice the location of, and entrance to, the premises at which it is carried on.

For example, the Council consider that when a practice is carried on in a private house nothing more is normally required than the usual professional plate, although exceptionally a small lamp, either plain or with the number or name of the house, may be necessary where there is some special risk of confusion or accident. Where a practice is carried on at business premises in a shopping thoroughfare, it may be necessary to add lettering on not more than two windows or, alternatively, where such signs are common, a hanging sign or illuminated box sign, with the words 'Dentist', 'Dental Surgeon' or 'Dental Surgery'. Neither lettering nor sign should, however, be more conspicuous than is necessary for the purpose of enabling persons seeking the practice to find it. No other type of sign is necessary or permissible and the Council wish to warn practitioners specifically against the use of daylight, flashing or neon signs, show cases and garishly coloured shop fronts; against inadequately screened surgery windows and against the exhibition of any sign elsewhere than on the premises at which the practice to which it refers is carried on. The use of signs indicating participation in or abstention from the National Health Service or otherwise describing the nature of the treatment provided, or giving the names of persons, other than registered dentists, employed in the practice is not permissible.

*b*) Announcements, circulars, etc.:

Publication by a registered dentist in a newspaper, broadcast or notice, or by any other means of any announcement, article, correspondence or other matter may be held to be advertisement within the meaning of this Notice if it includes both *a*) the name or professional address of a registered dentist and *b*) any indication of his profession or that he is in practice. A registered dentist who gives an interview to a representative of a newspaper or periodical should take steps to ensure that these views are respected. This does not, however, apply to books on scientific or professional subjects or to articles or correspondence in professional journals or to entries in normal type in a street or telephone directory,

Advertisements of staff vacancies inserted in the appropriate columns of newspapers may include the telephone number of the practice as well as either the name and address of the practitioner or an indication of the profession (but not both). Such advertisements should be in normal type and should be restricted to a statement of the essential facts.

The Council disapprove of a registered dentist sending, or causing to be sent, through the post an open card or envelope bearing both *a*) his name or professional address and *b*) any indication of his profession or that he is in practice. A registered dentist who finds it necessary to inform the patients of his practice of a modification in the circumstances of the practice should do so by means of a circular letter or card, enclosed in an envelope and restricted to a statement of the modification which has taken place without any addition such as might be held to draw attention to the professional skill of any practitioner or to constitute an invitation to consult or visit any practitioner. The sender of such a letter or card is responsible for ensuring that it is sent only to persons whom he is reasonably entitled to assume to be patients of his practice. Cards notifying patients of the time which has elapsed since their previous appointments should only be sent with the prior agreement of the persons to whom they are addressed.

*c*) Canvassing, etc.:

The Council do not consider it permissible for a registered dentist to call upon or communicate with any person who is not already a patient of his practice with a view to providing advice or treatment unless expressly requested to do so by that person or by some other person duly authorized to act on his behalf. They do not object to a registered dentist, upon acquiring the goodwill of a practice, notifying the fact to persons whom he is reasonably entitled to assume to be patients of that practice in accordance with the procedure described in the subsection above.

In particular the Council wish to point out that a practitioner may be held to have canvassed i] if he enters into or connives at any arrangement by which persons are referred to a registered dentist for professional attendance to those who carry on, or are employed in, the business of a denture repair shop or dental mechanics; ii] if he pays commission or allows discount to any person or organization; iii] if he attempts to induce persons whom he has treated as patients of a practice in which he is or has been employed by some other person to attend him for treatment or advice in any other practice. It is the duty of a registered dentist who ceases to be employed, whether as assistant or principal, by some other person to ensure that arrangements are made for the completion of any treatment which he has commenced to provide under the terms of the National Health Service Acts and that the local Executive Council are informed accordingly but a registered dentist who makes such arrangements without the consent of the lawful owner of the practice may be held to have canvassed for the purpose of obtaining patients or promoting his own professional advantage. Where the consent of the owner of the practice is withheld, the dentist should request the local Executive Council to make the necessary arrangements.

**8. Responsibility of Partners and Directors:** By sections thirty-six to forty of the Dentists Act, 1957, it is in general unlawful for an individual who is not registered in the dentists register or under the Medical Acts or for a body corporate to carry on the business of dentistry unless that business was being carried on by the individual or body corporate on 21 July 1955.[1] For the purposes of the Act, a person shall be treated as carrying on the business of dentistry if he, or a partnership of which he is a member, receives payment for services rendered in the course of the practice of dentistry by him or by a partner of his, or by an employee of his or his partners.

Accordingly, any registered dentist who enters into partnership with, or is employed by, an individual who unlawfully carries on the business of dentistry, or any registered dentist who becomes a director of a body corporate which unlawfully carries on the business of dentistry, is liable to have his name erased from the register.

Moreover, the Council wish it to be understood that a registered dentist who enters into a partnership or becomes a director of a body corporate carrying on the business of dentistry as recognized by the Act thereby accepts responsibility for the maintenance of a high standard of professional conduct in that business and may be required to answer to the Council for any act or omission in the conduct of that business which appears to the Council to constitute infamous or disgraceful conduct in a professional respect.

By order of the General Dental Council,

DAVID HINDLEY-SMITH,

*November,* 1959. *Registrar.*

[1] Special provision is, however, made in the Act for a widow to carry on her late husband's practice.

# Guidance for Professional Conduct

*Issued by the British Dental Association*

The following statement has been approved by the Representative Board.

The Association, in this statement, aims at guiding members on questions which are not dealt with by the General Dental Council. It is the duty of this statutory body to deal with conduct which is regarded as 'infamous or disgraceful' in a professional respect.

## ESTABLISHMENT IN PRACTICE

*a*) **In General Practice.**—A dentist is free to practise where he chooses and may obtain assistance in his choice from advertisements in the dental press and from dental trade houses. He should not take advantage of information obtained during negotiations for a practice or a partnership where these negotiations have broken down, nor should he commence practice where he has acted as assistant or locum tenens for the practitioner in that locality without the written consent of the established practitioner.

*b*) **In Specialist Practice.**—A dentist seeking to practise as a specialist in some branch of dentistry may indicate his intention by:

i] Calling upon dentists in general practice in the area;
ii] Writing to general dental practitioners, provided he does not refer to himself in too laudatory terms;
iii] Sending reports of his published work to those dental practitioners who might be interested;
iv] Reading papers at Association or Branch meetings.

It is desirable that he should inform the British Dental Association of his intention to specialize.

## PROFESSIONAL ANNOUNCEMENTS

**Standard.**—Nameplates, signs, lamps, etc., should conform to the standards laid down by the Association. A copy of the recommendations may be obtained from the Secretary.

**Misdirection.**—Nothing by way of initials or otherwise which may

misdirect the public must be used. For example the letters M.B.D.A.,
indicating membership of the Association, must not be used.

## ADVERTISING

### Advertising in any Form is Unethical

**Articles in the Lay Press.**—Articles written for the lay press should
not appear to laud the writer. His photograph, qualifications, or address
should not be published along with the article.

**Lectures to Lay Audiences.**—While there is no objection to a
dentist delivering lectures to lay audiences, he should take all reasonable steps to see that in any preliminary announcement or subsequent
press report of the lecture, his professional qualifications and/or ability
(as distinct from the subject-matter of the lecture) are not made the
subject of laudatory references

**Directories.**—The dental practitioner's name must never appear in
extra large type, nor may he pay to have his name or telephone number
inserted in any directory, except in the case of an extra entry, e.g.
partner, in the Post Office Directory.

**Post Cards and Envelopes.**—No qualification or professional description may appear on any post card or on the outside of any envelope
sent through the post.

### CHANGES IN PRACTICE ARRANGEMENTS

**Change of Address.**—Where a practice is moved to a new address,
or a new branch is opened, notification may be sent to all patients on
the books of the practice. This notification should not, however, be
sent to patients who the practitioner knows have had treatment elsewhere since their last visit to his practice; nor should it go to those
who, to judge from the lapse of time since their last visit, have almost
certainly changed their dentist.

**Changes in Ownership.**—On the sale of a practice, a notice may
be circulated to all patients on the books, as in the case of change of
address. It is desirable that this notice should be circulated by the vendor dentist, or at least in his name and with his consent.

Changes in partnership may also be notified to patients in the same
way.

Notices sent through the post which bear any indication of the dentist's profession or the nature of his practice should always be sent under
cover of an envelope.

**Notices in the Press.**—In the case of a change in the practice address only, it is permissible to insert an announcement in the press. The announcement should give no indication that it refers to a dentist or his practice and three insertions should be the maximum.

### NEW PATIENTS—PROCEDURE TO BE ADOPTED

It is understood that all patients have a right to choose or change their dentist, but the following general rules of procedure should be observed:

1) When a dentist, in whatever form of practice, has reason to believe that a patient who requests him to give advice or treatment is not under the care of another practitioner, he is at liberty to accede to the request, unless he had previously seen the patient in consultation with a colleague or when acting as deputy for a colleague. In either of the latter two events, while dealing with any emergency that may exist, he should forthwith explain the position to his colleague and should not accept the patient for further treatment without his colleague's consent.

2) When a dentist is consulted by a patient who he has reason to believe is normally attended by another practitioner, he should ascertain if the reason for the consultation is the wish of the patient to change his dentist; if so he is entitled to accept the patient.

3) When a dentist is consulted by a patient who normally attends another dentist, the reason for the consultation may be either to seek advice or treatment on some special condition—in this case the usual practitioner should be communicated with—or to obtain advice or treatment owing to the usual practitioner being prevented from giving it, by absence or illness—in this case only such work as is immediately necessary should be undertaken before communicating with the patient's usual dentist.

In either of the above cases no attempt should be made by the dentist consulted to secure for himself the permanent care of the patient, nor should a dental practitioner supersede another during the course of treatment.

4) When a dentist is consulted by a patient who has been previously treated by a colleague, it is his duty to avoid, as far as possible, any word or action which might disturb the confidence of the patient in the previous dentist.

In the National Health Service this rule may give rise to difficulty where a patient has already received treatment elsewhere (such as the provision of dentures), which in the opinion of the second dentist is so unsatisfactory that it must be carried out again. Because of the central recording of treatment by the Dental Estimates Board, an estimate under the Health Service for a repetition of treatment recently given by another dentist may well lead to an official enquiry.

It is, therefore, essential for the second dentist to satisfy himself beyond doubt that the treatment already given is so unsatisfactory that his professional duty to his patient compels him to remedy it. When making up his mind on this point, the practitioner should constantly remember that there is considerable room in dentistry for genuine differences of clinical opinion, and that treatment is not necessarily inadequate or unsatisfactory because it is not the treatment which he himself would have given.

If, however, the dentist is satisfied on this point, he should first suggest to the patient that he return to the dentist who gave the treatment. At the same time, if he has no reason to suppose that such an approach would be unsuccessful, the second dentist should approach the first dentist and advise him of the circumstances.

If these steps do not result in the return of the patient to his first dentist, the second practitioner may proceed to give the treatment he considers necessary without breach of any ethical obligation to his colleague; and if he is obliged to do so he is free to say either to the patient or to the authorities that he took action because he considered that the work was unsatisfactory.

### CONSULTATIONS—RULES GOVERNING

## Dentists Needing Medical Opinion

1) Where the dentist considers medical advice to be necessary he should advise the patient to consult his usual doctor; and, subject to the patient's consent, he should communicate to the doctor any relevant information or opinion which he considers should be available to him.

2) Where the patient has no doctor, the dentist should advise the patient to seek medical opinion, and should further advise the patient to inform the doctor selected that the dentist will be glad to communicate with him regarding the case. On the specific request of the patient the dentist may, with propriety, indicate the name of a doctor known to him who might be consulted.

3) The doctor should communicate to the dentist his opinion of the case.

4) If the dentist desires a further medical opinion, he should inform the patient's doctor and the procedure should be governed by the rules laid down in the subsequent paragraphs.

### Medical Practitioner Needing Dental Opinion

Normally the dentist consulted should ascertain if the patient has a dentist and should satisfy himself that the latter is cognisant and willing that the consultation should take place. The dentist consulted should subsequently notify the patient's dentist as well as the doctor or medical consultant regarding—

  i] His general opinion of the case;

  ii] Any urgent treatment carried out or to be carried out by him, i.e. the dentist consulted;

  iii] His recommendations regarding further treatment; normally this further treatment should be carried out by the patient's usual dentist or by the dentist consulted in co-operation with the former. Prosthetic and conservative work should normally be carried out by the patient's usual dentist.

### Dentist Needing Further Dental Opinion

1) It is desirable that the patient's dentist, if not to be present during the examination of the patient, should communicate all relevant information concerning the condition upon which advice is sought to the dentist consulted, who should reply giving his conclusions. The dentist consulted may give to the patient such information as he judges appropriate to the occasion.

2) The dentist consulted should not attempt to secure for himself the care of the patient sent in consultation, nor should he treat the patient then or subsequently, except with the consent of the dentist who referred the patient.

### Rules for Treatment in Hospital

1) In the case of an in-patient in a general hospital, the dental officer to the institution should carry out any dental treatment demanded by the patient's general condition. If further dental treatment is necessary, nothing should be done to influence the patient's free choice of dentist.

2) In the case of a patient attending the out-patient department of a general hospital, the dental officer to the institution should advise concerning any dental treatment necessitated by the patient's general condition; if treatment is necessary, nothing should be done to influence the patient's free choice of dentist.

3) It is unethical for a hospital dental officer to use his position to influence patients to consult him in his private capacity whether for dentures or otherwise.

## ANÆSTHETICS

When an anæsthetic is advised by the dentist, it is competent for him to select the anæsthetist, but if such anæsthetist is not the patient's doctor, no objection should be taken to the patient inviting his doctor to be present. Where the operation proposed is a major one, or if it is known to the dentist that the patient is under medical care, the dentist should inform the patient's doctor of the operation proposed and should invite him to be present if the patient so desires.

On the completion of any dental operation, and especially if there is any reason to think that post-operative complications may ensue, the patient should be advised to consult the dentist immediately if such complications arise and the dentist should take all reasonable steps to facilitate such consultation.

## RADIOGRAPHY

Where the patient is sent to a radiologist, whether medical or dental, for radiographic examination the report and/or radiographs should be sent direct to the doctor or dentist. Clinical advice should not be given to the patient by the radiologist.

## PROFESSIONAL CHARGES

A dental practitioner is free to make whatever charges he thinks reasonable. He should, however, inform his patients at their first visit what the fee is likely to be, especially if so requested by the patient. If it is the practitioner's custom to charge for broken appointments, he should notify his patients to this effect. Omission to do so may lead to the failure of any subsequent action he may take in regard to recovery of such fees for broken appointments.

**Dichotomy.**—An arrangement between two practitioners whereby, unknown to the patient, one practitioner, either medical or dental, receives part of the fee due to the other practitioner, is highly detrimental to the honour of the professions.

## THE NATIONAL HEALTH SERVICE

A contravention of the practitioner's terms of service in the General Dental Services may lead to inquiry into his conduct by the General Dental Council or by the Association if the action complained of was in any way disgraceful or unethical. Not every breach of the terms of services is likely to lead to inquiry of this kind, but cases where the dentist has 'contracted out', i.e. demanded a private fee for work which is wholly paid for under the National Health Service, have been investigated by the General Dental Council in the past. A false declaration by the dentist on Form E.C.17 that he has examined the patient or that he has completed all the treatment shown on the form, might also be regarded as disgraceful or unethical.

In cases where the patient pays part of the cost of treatment, it is undesirable from the professional point of view for the dentist to accept from the patient anything less than the full amount of his contribution.

### PROFESSIONAL ASSISTANTS

When an assistant is engaged, terms of engagement should be drawn up and agreed between the parties. The principal may reasonably include a clause prohibiting the assistant from practising on his own account within a certain radius of the practice. If such an agreement has not been drawn up at the outset, no attempt should be made to impose such a condition when the assistant has left the practice.

### EMPLOYEES

A dental practitioner should do nothing to entice any employee from a fellow practitioner's employment. If, in reply to a press advertisement, a technician or receptionist employed by a dentist practising in the same town seeks to enter the advertiser's employ, the advertiser should inform that dentist before agreeing to employ the person.

**Wages.**—Wages paid to dental technicians should not be less than the scale agreed for the time being by the National Joint Council for the Craft of Dental Technicians. A copy of the scale can be obtained from the Secretary of the Association.

### DENTURE REPAIR SHOPS

It is not in the general interest that dental practitioners should have mechanical work performed by a repair shop or by a mechanic to the profession who is associated with a repair shop.

# British Dental Association—
# Professional Announcements

1) Advertising by means of plates, lamps and signs, which is customary in certain parts of the country, is considered to be degrading to the profession.

2) The justification frequently offered for such exhibits is 'the existing custom of the neighbourhood.'

3) The adoption of recognized standards in respect of Lamps and Signs is essential.

4) Positive standards, as set forth in the attached schedule, are suggested as maxima, the criterion in each case being a sufficiency of information to enable the patient easily to find the situation of, and entrance to, the surgery.

5) Surgeries shall be classified either as:

 *a*) Residential houses;

 *b*) Shops or business premises.

As a rule the neighbourhood shall be classified according to the nature of the premises adjacent, or in the case of upper-floor surgeries, the premises below.

6) The professional announcements under review are those exhibited on or external to or visible through the door of the surgery premises which is normally opened to admit patients, including those affixed to walls, posts, fences, doors, gates, etc., and those to be seen from outside through windows.

## SCHEDULE

**A. RESIDENTIAL HOUSES**

The chief means of indicating the premises shall be the professional plate. Lamps which may only be allowed for the purpose of giving light in dark places shall be of uncoloured, plain or opal glass.

**Plates.** *Number and Size*:

| | |
|---|---|
| *a*) for practitioners working on their own account whether employing assistants or not. | One plate not exceeding 18 in. × 12 in., OR not more than three plates having a maximum aggregate area of 18 in. × 12 in. |
| *b*) for practitioners in partnership. | One plate not exceeding 18 in. × 12 in., OR not more than three plates having a maximum aggregate area of 24 in. × 18 in. |

Where in the case of a partnership or other practice with two or more dentists, each practitioner has a separate plate the aggregate area of such plates shall not exceed 24 in. × 18 in.

### Lettering

Each plate may exhibit the practitioner's name, titles, descriptions, qualifications, and consulting hours. Lettering shall not exceed 2 in. in height, and shall not be of any luminous material.

### Lamps

Where it is difficult to see the entrance of, or approach to, the surgery premises, a lamp may be allowed, which must then conform to the following specification:

*Size:* The overall diameter should not exceed 10 in.

*Nature:* Plain or opal glass, uncoloured. The use of neon or intermittent lamps is prohibited.

*Lettering* (if any): Only the name or number of the house may appear. The size of the lettering must not exceed 2 in. in height.

B. SHOPS OR BUSINESS PREMISES

The chief indication shall be the professional plate, or plates. In certain circumstances:

a Lamp;
a Hanging Sign; *or*
a Window Sign.
    may appear.

**Lettering.** As in (A).

**Lamps.** As in (A).

**Plates.** *Number and Size:*

i] Where the entrance to the premises is direct from the main thoroughfare. } As in (A).

ii] Where the entrance to the premises is not direct from the main thoroughfare, e.g. up an entry, or in a block of offices. } In addition to plates as in A (*above*) which may be visible from the thoroughfare the practitioner may be permitted to exhibit, within the entry or premises an additional plate or plates, not exceeding in area the dimensions laid down for (A) (*above*). Such additional plate or plates shall not be visible from the thoroughfare.

**Window Signs.** These include all signs painted on, or visible through, windows, fanlights, or doors.

*Number and size:*
Letting may be exhibited on not more than two windows or fanlights or be visibly exhibited through not more than two windows, doors or fanlights. Such lettering shall not exceed 2 in. in height on the ground floor level, or not more than 6 in. in height on any higher floor level.

*Nature:*
The lettering must be backed with an opaque substance so as not to act as an illuminated sign.

*Lettering:*
Each window may exhibit the name and qualifications of the practitioner, OR the word 'Dentist,' OR 'Dental Surgeon' whichever is applicable.

**Hanging Signs.** If desired, a hanging sign may be used INSTEAD of the window sign, or signs.

*Number and size:* One only, not exceeding 24 in. × 18 in.
*Nature:* Illuminated, flashing or 'daylight' reflecting signs shall not be used.
*Lettering:* As allowed on windows.

**Special Considerations:**

*Office Blocks:* In office blocks where it is customary for all tenants to be listed on a common notice-board in the vestibule, the exhibit shall in this case be in conformity with those of other tenants, even if the above sizes cannot be strictly adhered to.

*Converted Shops:* If shop premises are converted to professional use the shop front or window shall be obscured to a height of not less than 7 feet.

## In General:

Converted shop windows shall not be painted in any unduly bright colour.

No plates, signs, window lettering, etc., shall be of such design or colour as to be unprofessionally ostentatious.

# Forms in Use in the General Dental Service in England and Wales

*Part 1*

**NATIONAL HEALTH SERVICE** Dental Estimate Form **E.C. 17**

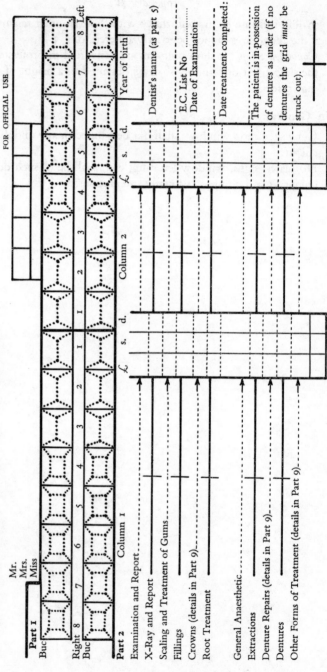
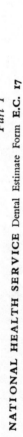

FOR OFFICIAL USE

Mr.
Mrs.
Miss

Part I

Buc
Right 8 7 6 5 4 3 2 I I 2 3 4 5 6 7 8 Left
Buc

Year of birth

**Part 2**

| | Column 1 | | | | Column 2 | | | |
| --- | --- | --- | --- | --- | --- | --- | --- | --- |
| | £ | s. | d. | | £ | s. | d. | |
| Examination and Report | | | | | | | | |
| X-Ray and Report | | | | | | | | |
| Scaling and Treatment of Gums | | | | | | | | |
| Fillings | | | | | | | | |
| Crowns (details in Part 9) | | | | | | | | |
| Root Treatment | | | | | | | | |
| General Anaesthetic | | | | | | | | |
| Extractions | | | | | | | | |
| Denture Repairs (details in Part 9) | | | | | | | | |
| Dentures | | | | | | | | |
| Other Forms of Treatment (details in Part 9) | | | | | | | | |

Dentist's name (as part 5)

E.C. List No ..............
Date of Examination ..............

Date treatment completed:

The patient is in possession of dentures as under (if no dentures the grid *must* be struck out).

**Part 3.** To be completed by the DENTIST.

PATIENT'S Mr.
SURNAME Mrs.
Miss...........................................................
(Block Letters)
CHRISTIAN
NAMES..........................................................
ADDRESS........................................................

Nat. Health
Service No...................................................

**Part 5.**
DENTIST'S NAME AND ADDRESS AT
WHICH TREATMENT IS TO BE GIVEN ⟶
(Rubber stamp or block letters)

**Part 6.** To the DENTIST

Your estimate as detailed in Part 2 is approved at £ : :
which includes the payment by the patient of the sum of £ : :

**Part 7.** To be completed by the DENTIST
I certify that, having examined this patient, I have carried out treatment as detailed in Part 2
*(a) in accordance with the clinical condition indicated in Part I *and I certify that in my opinion the patient is now dentally fit.*
*(b) as emergency treatment of a casual patient
(c) and that a general anaesthetic has been administered by ....................................
a doctor or another dentist, on ..............occasions.
No part of the treatment in respect of which I claim fees has been carried out as part of the Hospital and Specialist Services

Total cost of treatment is
£ s. d.

I claim the balance of fees due
* Delete as necessary (see explanatory note).                    Signature .........................

**Part 8.** To be signed by the DENTIST and retained by the PATIENT
I am prepared to accept Mr.
Mrs.
Miss ..................................................... as a patient under the
National Health Service for *treatment as detailed by me/or *emergency treatment on .......................
E.C. List No...........................
                                              Signature .........................
* Delete as necessary.

**Part 4.** To be completed by the DENTIST only in prior
approval cases.

To the DENTAL ESTIMATES BOARD
I have examined this patient and have entered in Part I
the clinical condition and in Part 2 details of the treat-
ment which I consider necessary to secure dental fitness.
The Board's approval of my estimate is requested.
Signature ..................................

Date ..................  Dentist's E.C. List No.

For Official Use

For Official Use

I have received, or am claiming,
from the patient the sum of
£ s. d.

Date .........................  19.....

305

**Part 9.**　　　　DENTIST'S OBSERVATIONS　　　FOR OFFICIAL USE　This form is the property of the Ministry of Health

FOR OFFICIAL USE

Enclosures:

**Part 10.**　To be signed by the PATIENT

I desire treatment under the National Health Service and understand that it is a condition of receiving treatment under the Service that I shall if required, submit myself for examination by a Dental Officer of the Ministry of Health. I am not at present being treated by another dentist.

(a) **Undertaking to be completed so far as applicable**

I undertake to pay the dentist towards the cost of treatment (including any denture or bridge) the sum required under the National Health Service Act, 1951, and the National Health Service Act, 1952, as varied by the National Health Service Act, 1961, or regulations made thereunder, £　　: 　: 　and I understand that the dentist may require me to pay the whole or part of this sum before proceeding with my treatment.

Any payment by the National Assistance Board on my behalf shall be in relief of the whole or part of my undertaking.

(b) **Declaration to be completed, so far as applicable, by persons claiming exemption from charges**

I declare that I am:—

(i) an expectant mother and expect my confinement on or about ......... (i.e. within twelve months of the date below) and undertake to ......... **OR** the mother of a child born on ......... 
provide such documentary evidence of this as may be required.

(ii) aged under 16/21† years at last birthday and was born on ......... School at ......... (Town)

(iii) attending full-time
(applies only if aged 16 or over and claiming exemption from charges for dentures, addition to or relining of dentures, or bridges).

†Delete which of these is not applicable

* Signature ......... Date .........

Persons knowingly making a false declaration under (b) above may be liable to a fine not exceeding £100 or to imprisonment for a term not exceeding three months or to both.

**Part 11.**　To be signed by the PATIENT when treatment is completed.

I certify that to the best of my belief treatment has been completed.

* Signature ......... Date .........

*Where the patient is under the age of 16 or is an invalid the parent, guardian or other authorised person should sign for the patient in Parts 10 and 11, indicating after his signature his relationship to the patient.

NOTE TO PATIENT

Patients should give their dentist as much notice as possible if for any reason they are likely to be unable to keep an appointment. Failure to do so may result in treatment being delayed and in the patient having to pay the dentist for the broken appointment.
If patients wish to change their dentist they must at once give notice of the fact to the dentist they wish to leave.
Patients who lose or damage their dentures may have to pay the full cost of their replacement.

National Health
Service

# NATIONAL HEALTH SERVICE

Mr.

Mrs...............................

Miss

Address...........................

As required by the National Health Service Acts,

Mr./Mrs./Miss..........................................................................

Address.....................................................................................

.................................................................................................

..........................................

has paid the sum of

£    :    :

has paid me the sum of
towards the cost of dental treatment   £    :    :

Signature   ...........................................................................

Date ......................................

E.C. List No........................................   Date.........................

### To be completed by the Dentist and retained by the Patient

**Form E.C.64**

## Part 3

# NATIONAL HEALTH SERVICE
### SPECIAL TREATMENT AND APPLIANCES
### INVOLVING PAYMENT BY THE PATIENT

This form is to be completed in addition to and submitted with the Dental Estimates form in respect of any more expensive form of treatment or appliance to be provided at the request of the patient.

In the appropriate space below ENTER ONLY THE AMOUNT TO BE PAID BY THE PATIENT.

| Patient's Name | Dentist's Name |
|---|---|
| Nat. Reg. Identity No. | Dentist's E.C. List No. |

### DETAILS OF TREATMENT AND ADDITIONAL CHARGES

|  | £ | s. | d. |
|---|---|---|---|
| Fillings ................................. | | | |
| Dentures.............................. | | | |
| Other Treatment........................................... | | | |
| ................................................................ | | | |

### TO BE SIGNED BY THE PATIENT*

I desire the treatment as detailed above and understand that I am responsible for payment to the dentist of the charges set out above, or such other charges as may be approved by the Dental Estimates Board.

Signed   ...............................................................   Date ....................................

* In the case of a child or invalid, the parent, guardian or other authorised person should sign for patient.

**E.C. 18**

*Part 4* (left)

## ASSISTANCE WITH CHARGES FOR DENTURES
## AND DENTAL TREATMENT*

1. Any person getting a weekly allowance from the National Assistance Board can get help with charges he has to pay for dentures and dental treatment for himself or his dependants. Apply as in paragraph 3.

2. Other persons over the age of 16 (whether or not in fulltime work) to whom the charge would be a hardship by national assistance standards can also apply. The Board's officer assesses each case according to individual circumstances which he records at a personal interview, normally in your own home. Broadly speaking assistance may be given with the charge if after paying your rent and rates (or the equivalent outgoings of an owner-occupier) out of your normal weekly income including family allowances and any other income of a wife or husband, the amount left is not much above the following (which are the standard national assistance rates at April, 1961)—

| | |
|---|---|
| A single person living alone | 53s. 6d. |
| Other single persons, e.g. living with relatives | 49s. 6d. |
| A married couple living alone | 90s. 0d. |
| —with one child under five | 107s. 0d. |
| —for each additional dependent child 17s. (or more according to age) is added. | |

A grant may be payable if you have more than this where there are extra expenses (e.g. because of sickness or disability) or if part of your income comes from disability or disablement pension, superannuation, sick pay, charitable payments or earnings; on the other hand if you have savings of more than £100 or so, you may be regarded as in a position to pay the charge yourself. (Further information about the Board's standards and the amounts of income disregarded is given in leaflet A.L.18 available at the Post Office.)

3. *If you wish to apply* ask the dentist to complete Part I of this form, complete Part II yourself, then fold the form as directed and post it unstamped to the Board's Area Office. The address can be obtained at your local Post Office or Pensions and National Insurance Office, or from the telephone directory.

**\*NOTE.** For replacement of dentures consult your dentist as assistance may be obtainable under arrangements other than those described above.

*Part 4* (right)

# NATIONAL ASSISTANCE BOARD

## APPLICATION FOR A GRANT TOWARDS THE COST OF DENTURES OR DENTAL TREATMENT PROVIDED UNDER THE NATIONAL HEALTH SERVICE

(For official use)

C.P. No.

---

PART I (*to be completed by the dentist*)      The amount payable by:—

Full name and postal address

M.................................................................

..................................................................

..................................................................

for dental treatment to be provided under the National Health Service will be:—

  (i) the sum of £    :    :    for dentures
  (ii) the sum of £    :    :    for treatment

TOTAL £    :    :

Signature of dentist ...........................................................
Address
(*rubber stamp or block letters*)

---

←—PLEASE READ NOTE AT SIDE

PART II (*to be completed by the patient*)

  1. Are you a member of the Hospital Saving Association?................................
        (*Please answer YES or NO*)

  2. Are you a member of any other hospital contributory scheme?..................
        (*Please answer YES or NO*)

    If so, please state its name and how much you expect to receive under that

    scheme towards the above charge.........................................................

..................................................................

I apply for a grant and declare that these statements are true.

SIGN HERE.............................................................     DATE............................................

F.I.D (Rev.)

TDH        **309**

*Part 5*

# DENTAL RECORD—NATIONAL HEALTH SERVICE

SURNAME............................................................... ADDRESS.............................................

CHRISTIAN NAMES ...................................... ............................................................

N.H.S. NUMBER.............................................. ............................................................

DATE OF BIRTH................................................ ............................................................

TELEPHONE NO............................................... ............................................................

CLINICAL NOTES

| DATE | TREATMENT | DATE | TREATMENT |
|------|-----------|------|-----------|
|      |           |      |           |
|      |           |      |           |
|      |           |      |           |
|      |           |      |           |
|      |           |      |           |
|      |           |      |           |
|      |           |      |           |
|      |           |      |           |
|      |           |      |           |
|      |           |      |           |
|      |           |      |           |
|      |           |      |           |
|      |           |      |           |
|      |           |      |           |
|      |           |      |           |

ENCLOSURES:

DENTIST'S NAME ............................................... E.C. LIST NO. ....................

(To be used if desired)

**FORM E.C.25 (Rev.)**

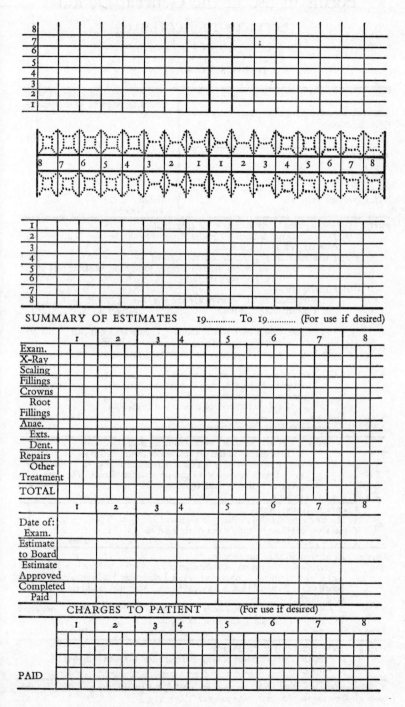

|  | 8 | 7 | 6 | 5 | 4 | 3 | 2 | 1 | 1 | 2 | 3 | 4 | 5 | 6 | 7 | 8 |

SUMMARY OF ESTIMATES    19............ To 19............ (For use if desired)

|  | 1 | 2 | 3 | 4 | 5 | 6 | 7 | 8 |
|---|---|---|---|---|---|---|---|---|
| Exam. | | | | | | | | |
| X-Ray | | | | | | | | |
| Scaling | | | | | | | | |
| Fillings | | | | | | | | |
| Crowns | | | | | | | | |
| Root Fillings | | | | | | | | |
| Anae. | | | | | | | | |
| Exts. | | | | | | | | |
| Dent. | | | | | | | | |
| Repairs | | | | | | | | |
| Other Treatment | | | | | | | | |
| TOTAL | | | | | | | | |

|  | 1 | 2 | 3 | 4 | 5 | 6 | 7 | 8 |
|---|---|---|---|---|---|---|---|---|
| Date of: Exam. | | | | | | | | |
| Estimate to Board | | | | | | | | |
| Estimate Approved | | | | | | | | |
| Completed | | | | | | | | |
| Paid | | | | | | | | |

CHARGES TO PATIENT    (For use if desired)

|  | 1 | 2 | 3 | 4 | 5 | 6 | 7 | 8 |
|---|---|---|---|---|---|---|---|---|
| | | | | | | | | |
| | | | | | | | | |
| PAID | | | | | | | | |

# Forms in use in the General Dental Services in Scotland

*Part 1*

## SUMMARY OF ESTIMATES
## CHARGES TO PATIENT

| Patient's Surname (Mr./Mrs./Miss) (block letters) | Dentist's name and address at which treatment is to be given (rubber stamp) |
|---|---|
| Christian Names | |
| Address | |
| Nat. H.S. Number | Dentist's E.C. List Number |

**Part 1.** To be completed by the Patient so far as applicable.

(a) I desire dental treatment under the National Health Service. I am not under contract with another dentist.

(b) I undertake to pay the dentist the sum of £ : : and I understand that the dentist may require me to pay the whole or part of this sum before proceeding with the work.

(c) I declare that:—

(i) I am under 16/21† years of age and was born on ...................................

(ii) I am attending full-time ............................... School at ...............................
(town)
(applies only if over 16 and claiming exemption from charges for dentures, additions to and relining of dentures, or bridges.)

(iii) I am an expectant mother and expect my confinement on or about........

...................................

(iv) I am the mother of a child born on...................................
I undertake to provide such documentary evidence as may be required in support of my statement at (iii) or (iv) above.

†Delete whichever of these is not applicable.

★*Patient's Signature*................................................................ Date...................

Persons making a false declaration will be liable to a penalty.

**Prior Approval Cases Only**

**Part 2.** To the Scottish Dental Estimates Board.
I have examined this patient, whose dentition is as shown in Part 6, and I propose to carry out the treatment detailed in Part 7 which is in my opinion necessary to promote dental fitness. The patient is prepared to undergo this treatment.
*Dentist's Signature*................................................ Date...................

**Part 3.** To the Dentist.
The treatment detailed in Part 7 is approved at £ : : .
including payment by the Patient of the sum of £ : : .
*Signed for the Board*................................................ Date...................

**Part 4.** To be completed by the Dentist.
I certify that the treatment as detailed in Part 7 has now been completed. No part of the treatment in respect of which I claim fees has been carried out on behalf of the National Health Service Hospital Authority, and I claim payment accordingly.
A general anaesthetic has been administered in this case on occasions by..................................................................

*Dentist's Signature*................................................ Date...................

**Part 5.** To be completed by the Patient.
I certify that to the best of my belief treatment has been completed.
★*Patient's Signature*................................................ Date...................

★ If the patient is a child under 16 or is an invalid, the parent, the guardian, or other authorised person should sign for the patient.

**Form E.C. 17**

**Part 6.** To be completed by the Dentist.     Year of Birth

Strike out from this chart the figures corresponding to any teeth missing from the mouth.

|   |   | E | D | C | B | A |   | A | B | C | D | E |   |   |   |   |
|---|---|---|---|---|---|---|---|---|---|---|---|---|---|---|---|---|
| 8 | 7 | 6 | 5 | 4 | 3 | 2 | 1 | 1 | 2 | 3 | 4 | 5 | 6 | 7 | 8 |

R.————————————————————————————L

|   |   |   |   |   |   |   |   |   |   |   |   |   |   |   |   |
|---|---|---|---|---|---|---|---|---|---|---|---|---|---|---|---|
| 8 | 7 | 6 | 5 | 4 | 3 | 2 | 1 | 1 | 2 | 3 | 4 | 5 | 6 | 7 | 8 |
|   |   | E | D | C | B | A |   | A | B | C | D | E |   |   |   |

Board's
Serial   Number

Date of Examination:

---

**Part 7.**                                    £   s.   d.

Examination and Advice and Report... ...  ... .....|....|....

X-Ray and Report ————|———— ....|....|....

Scaling and treatment of gums... ... ... ... .....|....|....

Fillings ————|———— ....|....|....

Root Treatment ————|———— ....|....|....

Extractions ————|———— ....|....|....

General Anaesthetic... ... ... ... ... ... ... .....|....|....

Crowns:  Type
           Material ————|———— ....|....|....

Inlays: Material ————|————
Dentures: Material ———|———— ....|....|....

Denture Repairs ... ... ... ... ... ... ... . ....|....|....

Special Treatment required on clinical grounds .....|....|....

The patient is in possession of dentures as under

—————|—————

Material:
Condition:

For use by Board

For use by Board

---

**Part 8.**   Dentist's observations

Payment Authorised
          £    s.    d.
T.
D.

**Enclosures:** No.                    **Description**

Patient's Contribution
          £    s.    d.
T.
D.

**Form E.C. 17 (reverse)**

# EMERGENCY TREATMENT CASUAL PATIENTS

| Patient's Surname (Mr., Mrs., Miss) (block letters) | Dentist's name and address at which treatment has been given (rubber stamp or block letters) |
|---|---|
| ................................................. | |
| **Christian Names** | |
| ................................................. | |
| **Address** | |
| ................................................. | ................................................. |
| **Nat. Health Service Number** | **Dentists' E.C. List Number** |

**Part 1.**  To be completed by the Patient so far as applicable.

(a) I desire emergency dental treatment under the National Health Service.

(b) I undertake to pay the dentist the sum of £ : : : and I understand that the dentist may require me to pay the whole or part of this sum before proceeding with the work.

(c) I declare that:

I am under 21 years of age.  I was born on.................................................

I am an expectant mother and expect my confinement on or about ................

I am the mother of a child born on ................................................

★ *Patient's Signature*................................................. Date........................

Persons making a false declaration will be liable to a penalty.

---

**Part 2.**  To be completed by the Dentist.

I certify that emergency treatment as detailed in Part 4 has been completed, and I claim payment accordingly.

*Dentist's Signature*................................................. Date................

---

**Part 3.**  To be completed by the Patient.

I certify that to the best of my belief emergency treatment has been completed.

★ *Patient's Signature*................................................. Date...................

---

★ In the case of a child under 16 or an invalid, the parent, guardian or other authorised person should sign.

---

**Part 4.**  Particulars of treatment given:

Extractions

General Anaesthetic (Anaesthetist's
                     name where applicable).................................

Dressings

X-Ray

Dentist's observations:

| £ | s. | d. |
|---|---|---|
| | | |
| | | |
| | | |

**For**

**Official**                    Patient's Contribution                    £  s.  d.

**Use**

**Form E.C. 17B (Scotland)**

## EXPLANATORY NOTE

This Form is to be used only for casual patients urgently seeking treatment for the relief of pain or other casual treatment of the kinds set out below:

The Treatment which may be the subject of this Form is as follows:

1.  Not more than two extractions.

2.  General Anaesthetic.

3.  Dressings.

4.  A single radiological examination involving one intra-oral or extra-oral film in connection with Items 1 or 3 above.

**This Form must not be used except for treatment of the kinds specified above and then only in case of urgency.   In all other cases the Dental Estimate Form E.C.17 (Scotland) must be used.**

**Form E.C. 17B (SCOTLAND (reverse)**

*Part 3*

## SPECIAL TREATMENT AND APPLIANCES
## INVOLVING PAYMENT BY THE PATIENT

This form is to be completed in addition to and submitted with the Dental Estimate Form in respect of any more expensive form of treatment or appliance to be provided at the request of the patient.

In the appropriate space below ENTER ONLY THE AMOUNT PROPOSED TO BE PAID BY THE PATIENT.

| Patient's Name | Dentist's Name |
|---|---|
| Nat. Reg. Identity No. | Dentist's E.C. List No. |

### DETAILS OF TREATMENT AND ADDITIONAL CHARGES

| | £ | s. | d. |
|---|---|---|---|
| Fillings............................................. | | | |
| Dentures ......................................... | | | |
| Other Treatment ........................................ | | | |
| ................................................................................................ | | | |

### TO BE SIGNED BY THE PATIENT*

I desire the treatment as detailed above and understand that I am responsible for payment to the dentist of such charges as may be fixed by the Scottish Dental Estimates' Board, not exceeding the amount shown above.

Signed*................................................................................................ Date...................................

\* In the case of a child or invalid, the parent, guardian, or other authorised person should sign for the patient.

**Form E.C. 18 (Scotland)**

*Part 4*

| National Health Service | NATIONAL HEALTH SERVICE |
|---|---|
| Mr. | As required by the National Health Service Acts. |
| Mrs................................. | Mr./Mrs./Miss............................................. |
| Miss | |
| Address................................. | Address................................................................ |
| ................................................. | ................................................................................ |
| ................................................. | has paid me the sum of |
| has paid the sum of | towards the cost of dental treatment   £  :  : |
| £   :   : | Signature ................................................... |
| Date................................. | E.C. List No................................ Date.................. |

*To be completed by the Dentist and retained by the Patient*

**Form E.C. 17D (Scotland) (Revised)**

# Index

# Table of Cases Cited

★ Income Tax decisions